Science
Milestones

The story of the epic scientific achievements
and the men who made them possible

Windsor Press Chicago • New York

Acknowledgments

CHRISTOPHER COLUMBUS: Condensed from the article, "Greatest Seafaring Yarn in History," by Walter Monfried, in the June 3, 1951, issue of *The Milwaukee Journal.*

PARACELSUS: Condensed from a General Electric Science Forum broadcast by Dr. Gordon R. Fonda.

EDWARD JENNER: From *The Laboratory,* Vol. 19, No. 1; published by the Fisher Scientific Company.

DANIEL BERNOULLI: Published by special permission of *Current Science and Aviation,* the high school science periodical, 400 South Front Street, Columbus, Ohio.

JAMES WATT: From *Life Stories of the Great Inventors,* by Henry and Dana Lee Thomas. Copyright, 1948, Garden City Publishing Company, Inc.

LUIGI GALVANI: *Exploring Electricity; Man's Unfinished Quest,* by Hugh Hildreth Skilling. Copyright 1948 by The Ronald Press Company.

ELI WHITNEY: *The World of Eli Whitney,* copyright 1952 by Jeannette Mirsky and Allan Nevins and published by The Macmillan Company.

ROBERT FULTON: *From Life Stories of the Great Inventors,* by Henry and Dana Lee Thomas. Copyright 1948 by Garden City Publishing Company, Inc.

JOSEPH HENRY: From a General Electric Science Forum broadcast by Thomas Coulson.

FRIEDRICH WOEHLER: *Man, the Chemical Machine,* copyright 1952 and published by the Columbia University Press.

PAUL EMILE BOTTA: Reprinted from *Gods, Graves and Scholars,* by C. W. Ceram, by permission of Alfred A. Knopf, Inc. Copyright 1951 by Alfred A. Knopf, Inc.

LOUIS BRAILLE: *Light Bearer to the World of Darkness,* by Helen Keller, reprinted by permission of the author and Doubleday & Company, Inc.

ABBOT MENDEL: From *Human Fertility: The Modern Dilemma,* by Robert C. Cook; copyright 1951 by Robert C. Cook. Reprinted with permission of William Sloane Associates, Inc., New York, N. Y.

ERNST MACH: From the article, "Ernst Mach and His Number," by Bill Bullock in the January, 1952, issue of *Flying.* Copyright 1952 by the Ziff-Davis Publishing Company, 336 Madison Avenue, New York, New York.

GEORGE WESTINGHOUSE: Condensed from an article in *Railway Progress* by Dorothy Rickard. Copyright 1954 and published by the Federation for Railway Progress.

J. J. THOMSON: From J. J. Thomson's *Recollections and Reflections,* published in London by George Bell and Sons, Ltd., in 1936.

ROBERT E. PEARY: Reprinted from *The North Pole: Its Discovery in 1909 Under the Auspices of the Peary Arctic Club,* by Robert E. Peary. Copyright, 1910, 1938, by Robert E. Peary. Published by permission of J. B. Lippincott Company.

RUDOLF C. DIESEL: From *Life Stories of the Great Inventors,* by Henry and Dana Lee Thomas. Copyright, 1948, Garden City Publishing Company.

WRIGHT BROTHERS: Condensed and reprinted from *Flight Into History: The Wright Brothers and the Air Age,* by Elsbeth E. Freudenthal, by permission of the publisher and copyright owner, the University of Oklahoma Press, 1949.

GUGLIELMO MARCONI: Condensed from an article by Edwin H. Armstrong in the *Midwest Engineer.*

ALBERT EINSTEIN: Reprinted from an article in *Science Service* by Dr. Edwin E. Slosson. Copyright, 1949, by Science Service.

IRVING LANGMUIR: Condensed from an article by John Pfeiffer in the January 28, 1951, issue of *The New York Times Magazine.*

ALEXANDER FLEMING: *Milestones of Medicine,* reprinted by permission of Random House, Inc. Copyright 1950 by Ruth Fox.

ROBERT H. GODDARD: "The Persistent Man" in condensed form from *The Coming Age of Rocket Power* by G. Edward Pendray. Copyright 1945 by Harper & Brothers.

By permission of *Science Digest,* the chapters on: Hippocrates, Archimedes, Eratosthenes, Vitruvius, Leonardo da Vinci, Copernicus, Benvenuto Cellini, Vesalius, William Gilbert, Francis Bacon, Galileo, William Harvey, Robert Boyle, Christian Huygens, Anton van Leeuwenhoek, Isaac Newton, Edmund Halley, Benjamin Franklin, Joseph Priestley, Antoine Lavoisier, William Smith, Rene Laennec, Michael Faraday, Charles Darwin, William Morton, Louis Pasteur, Joseph Lister, Robert Koch, Wilhelm Roentgen, Thomas A. Edison, Alexander Graham Bell, William Osler, Paul Ehrlich, Sigmund Freud, Hall and Héroult, Marie Curie, Ernest Rutherford.

Foreword

THIS BOOK will be of considerable interest to our fellow scientists; but its greatest value will be to the millions of our lay citizens whose education was largely confined to the traditional "3 Rs," reading, writing and arithmetic. Without some understanding of what science has now added to our factual understanding of man and nature, the citizens are unfortunately strangers in our modern world. Even under the most general education, the factual understanding of the nature of man and the nature of the universe is not achieved at the end of the senior year in the high school, or even at the end of the senior year in college. That education must continue throughout the life of every sane citizen.

The understanding of man and of nature achieved by science is very recent. During the hundreds of thousands of years of man's past his social behavior was largely determined by direct experience, ignorance, and traditions based partly on ignorance. We now have some indications that the voluntary behavior of all sane citizens can be directed toward the best interest of mankind through the understanding and acceptance of the nature of man and the universe, as revealed by modern science. The special social responsibility of scientists is to promote this understanding on the part of all people of all nations.

I have been an investigator and a teacher of science, that is, I have tried to teach for fifty years. I think that we teachers underestimate the mental capacity of our fellow citizens. They can learn, they can understand, they can even reason, if we the teachers can really teach by word, by demonstration, by example. But we must rekindle the suppressed natural curiosity, a curiosity largely supported by education through dictation, in the home, in the church, in the public schools, and sometimes even in our colleges and universities. Education by dictation depends on memory, faith, and tradition rather than on understanding of man and nature. We cannot defeat ideas with guns or bombs or mere say so.

Bad ideas can be defeated with better ideas based on better evidence. That is, we should apply the scientific method to our education at all levels.

This book reports the striking achievements of individual first-class scientists throughout the ages, and how they erected their individual milestones. This will give the attentive laymen some basic information of the scientific method of penetrating the realm of ignorance as to the nature of man and the nature of the universe. Some of these milestones have added years to our life, as well as more life to our years. But there is still much important research to be done in both of these fields, if we are to do full justice to the human forebrain, which is clearly superior to the forebrain of all other animal species.

The editors have made a fair selection of the milestones in basic discoveries, and in the practical application of some of these basic discoveries. More of the milestones erected in both of these fields during the last fifty years could have been added, of course, had space permitted.

This book will aid all our fellow citizens in understanding the necessity and the supreme value of supporting the factual education and the scientific research which will produce more and more essential milestones on the difficult road towards better days for the human race.

ANTON J. CARLSON

Frank P. Hixon Distinguished
Service Professor Emeritus
of Physiology, University of
Chicago

Contents

MJ

part two   1641—1821
*In which some applications
are made*

continued on following page

contents continued

Introduction

IT IS THE PURPOSE of this book to review in words and pictures the lives and accomplishments of some of the inspired men of science and invention who have supplied the building blocks for our present-day science and technology.

This is not a history of science, although in the ensuing pages there is much of scientific history. It is not, in fact, a book about the "greatest" scientists, although many of the scientific craftsmen and philosophers portrayed herein are surely among the giants in their chosen fields.

This book is, above all else, a looking back at certain *Science Milestones* that have marked man's advancement along the road of human knowledge and progress.

There are milestones of science written, for example, in the test tube of an Ehrlich working in a Frankfort laboratory, inscribed on the walls of a Mendel's monastery garden, emblazoned on the wings of a strange contrivance which, as fashioned by the brothers Wright, rose from the sands at Kitty Hawk and flew under its own power.

In the vast and fascinating fields of science, invention and technology, our milestones range from the great Greek physician Hippocrates, whose observations of some diseases are valid even today, to the contemporary Fleming and his discovery of penicillin; from Bacon, who more than 300 years ago set forth the inductive method of modern science, to Einstein, whose intellectual acumen has changed our conception of matter and energy; from that grand genius of the Renaissance, Da Vinci, who laid the foundation for the modern air age, to Diesel, who produced the engine of the "greatest thermal efficiency" in the history of science.

These scientific signposts we call milestones are many indeed. The often slow, but sometimes frighteningly fast, developments of centuries past, have led to the founding of the modern sciences as we know them. To the pure scientists, who laid down the rules, and to the applied scientists who made something practical of them, we are indebted for a way of life that is perhaps better than anything that has gone before. The hydrogen bomb notwithstanding, the milestones of scientific progress are weighted on the side of human development as against human destruction.

But science never stands still. Out of the laboratories and workshops, out of the theories and speculations of the 20th century, will come, and are coming daily, new bits of knowledge about nature which will further enhance and change our lives and our world. It is enough, however, for the purposes of this book, to look back on some of the many striking discoveries and developments that are already a part of our scientific heritage.

They are not *all* here within these pages—not all of those gifted and dedicated men of science who have contributed to human welfare and to man's comfort, to his peaceful occupations, to his better understanding of the universe, and also to his warmaking. The editors of this book recognize that no anthology is ever complete, much less one dealing as this one does with a subject as broad as that of scientific achievement. The editors make no apologies for the omissions. They hope that what the reader *does* find here will be more than sufficient to give him a feeling for the scientific adventure, an insight into the never-ceasing scientific struggle to wrest facts from nature and make them of benefit to man.

All of the stories that comprise this book have previously appeared in SCIENCE DIGEST magazine, now in its 18th year of publication.

The same criteria, namely *interest* and *importance*, that governed SCIENCE DIGEST editors in their selection of the original material, have determined what shall go into this book. It is possible that some day—and the editors are not prescient enough to name that day—the gaps in the *Milestones* series will have been filled, the material brought completely up to date, providing a full and connected story of the scientific adventure. Meanwhile, it is hoped that the reader will find in this not-too-slim anthology much of "interest" and of "importance."

GEORGE B. CLEMENTSON
Managing Editor, SCIENCE DIGEST

HIPPOCRATES, the son of Heraclides, a physician-priest, was born on the Island of Cos around 460 B.C. He practiced on the Island of Thasos, and is believed to have traveled widely—through Thrace and Thessaly, to Athens and elsewhere. He is mentioned as a prominent physician twice in the dialogues of Plato, and once in the writings of Aristotle. He first separated superstition and vague speculation from medicine and recognized the importance of diet. He abandoned the idea that disorders of the human body were sent by the gods as punishment. Through his observations and recordings of symptoms and their comparison with those of other patients, Hippocrates was the first to place medicine on a scientific basis.

Hippocrates

His oath and aphorisms

The Hippocratic oath

I SWEAR BY Apollo Physician, by Aesculapius, by Hygiene, by Panacea and by all the gods and goddesses, making them my witnesses, that I will carry out according to my ability and judgment, this oath and this indenture.

To hold my teacher in this art equal to my own parents; to make him partner in my livelihood; when he is in need of money to share mine with him; to consider his family as my own brothers, and to teach them this art, if they want to learn it, without fee or indenture; to impart precept, oral instruction, and all other instruction to my own sons, the sons of my teacher, and to indentured pupils who have taken the physician's oath, but to nobody else.

I will use treatment to help the sick according to my ability and judgment, but never with a view to injury and wrongdoing.

9

Neither will I administer a poison to anybody when asked to do so, nor will I suggest a course. Similarly, I will not give to a woman an abortive remedy. But I will keep pure and holy both my life and my art.

I will not use the knife, not even verily, on sufferers from stone, but I will give place to such as are craftsmen therein.

Immortal Hippocrates —his oath is as respected today as it was by the men of his own time

Into whatever houses I enter, I will enter to help the sick, and I will abstain from all intentional wrong-doing and harm, especially from abusing the bodies of man or woman, bond or free.

And whatever I shall see or hear in the course of my profession in my intercourse with men, if it be what should not be published abroad, I will never divulge, holding such things to be holy secrets.

Now if I carry out this oath, and break it not, may I gain forever reputation among all men for my life and for my art; but if I transgress it and forswear myself, may the opposite befall me.

The aphorisms of Hippocrates

LIFE IS SHORT, and the Art long; the occasion fleeting; experience fallacious, and judgment difficult.

A slender and restricted diet is always dangerous in chronic diseases, and also in acute diseases, where it is not requisite. And again, a diet brought to the extreme point of attenuation is dangerous; and repletion, when in the extreme, is also dangerous.

Old persons endure fasting most easily; next, adults; young persons not nearly so well; and most especially infants, and of them such as are of a particularly lively spirit.

In whatever disease sleep is laborious, it is a deadly symptom; but if sleep does good, it is not deadly.

Both sleep and insomnolency, when immoderate, are bad.

It is better that a fever succeed to a convulsion, than a convulsion to a fever.

Persons who are naturally very fat are apt to die earlier than those who are slender.

In every movement of the body, whenever one begins to endure pain, it will be relieved by rest.

Observations that Hippocrates was the first to make and record, still have their place in modern textbooks

Phthisis (tuberculosis) most commonly occurs between the ages of eighteen and thirty-five years.

In persons who cough up frothy blood, the discharge of it comes from the lungs.

Sneezing coming on, in the case of a person afflicted with hiccup, removes the hiccup.

In acute diseases, complicated with fever, a moaning respiration is bad.

Persons are most subject to apoplexy between the ages of forty and sixty.

In acute diseases, coldness of the extremities is bad.

A chill supervening on a sweat is not good.

Those diseases which medicines do not cure, iron (surgery?) cures; those which iron cannot cure, fire cures; and those which fire cannot cure are to be reckoned wholly incurable.

Hippocrates today is a symbol rather than a doctor, a name more than a man, for his interest in medicine and his recognition of its potentials have gained him world-wide respect. His code of medical ethics is a legacy kept fresh by each year's army of medical school graduates.

ARCHIMEDES was born in Syracuse in 287 B.C., the son of Pheidias, an astronomer. Archimedes may have been related to Hiero II, king of Syracuse. At any rate, he and Hiero and Hiero's son Gelo were close friends. As a young man Archimedes spent two or three years studying in Alexandria, the great Greek city in Egypt. When he returned to Syracuse, he devoted himself to mathematics. Very little is known of what Archimedes looked like, or how he paid his bills. In the ancient world, mathematicians seemed to have earned their keep much as mathematicians do to this day— by conducting schools. But so far as is known, Archimedes did not conduct a school. Perhaps he was supported by grants from Hiero.

Archimedes

Father of experimental science

by Leonard Engel

ⅠN THE FAR-OFF year of 215 B.C., the Roman general Marcellus attacked Syracuse, a Greek city-state in Sicily. Rome and Greece were not at war, but Greeks in Sicily had aided Carthage in the mortal struggle between Rome and Carthage for mastery of the ancient world.

The redoubtable Marcellus appeared before Syracuse with a vast army and fleet. The army landed a short distance from the city and made ready to storm it from the landward side. The fleet deployed around Marcellus' "secret weapon" for firing over the walls of port cities—a catapult on a platform atop the masts of eight quinquiremes (five-banked galleys) lashed together.

Marcellus and his cohorts expected a speedy victory. They got the surprise of their lives. They were up against the first state in history to make systematic use of science for military purposes.

A super-colossal Syracusan catapult rained stones weighing over a quarter of a ton each on the Romans' floating "gun platform" and broke it up. Cranes caught ships that ventured in too close and up-ended them or hoisted them high in the air and then flung them back into the sea. Iron beaks seized other ships and smashed them into jutting cliffs, or held them fast while giant boulders were dropped on them. Meanwhile, other engines concealed behind the city walls showered the advancing army with rocks and arrows. Marcellus' legions fled in panic. Syracuse didn't fall until three years later, when Marcellus took it from the rear while the inhabitants were sleeping off the effects of a festival in honor of Artemis.

Artemis was one of the principal goddesses in Greek mythology. She is usually regarded as the goddess of chastity but, strangely enough, in some cases she has been referred to as the goddess of childbirth

The fantastic deviltries that accomplished the stunning defeat of Marcellus were engineered by a single citizen of Syracuse. His name was Archimedes. He was the greatest scientist and mathematician of antiquity. In fact, he was one of the few ancients who was a scientist in the modern sense of the word. In its Golden Age, the ancient world produced many philosophers, such as Aristotle and Lucretius, who speculated brilliantly on the nature of the world. Archimedes didn't speculate. He formulated exact laws and tested them, just as scientists do today. He founded the sciences of hydrostatics and mechanics; he built what we would now call a planetarium; and in mathematics, he made many of the important discoveries made, independently, by Sir Isaac Newton 1900 years later. Archimedes and Newton, remarks Eric Temple Bell, the historian of mathematics, would have understood each other perfectly, and with the aid of a post-graduate course in mathematics and physics, Archimedes would have had no trouble understanding Einstein.

Archimedes considered mathematics the only worthwhile science. He had no use for mere invention and what we know as physics. He seldom departed from his beloved mathematics and made no record of practically any of his nonmathematical discoveries. But one day Hiero presented him with a question he couldn't ignore.

Hiero had given a metalsmith enough gold to make a crown. The Syracusan king suspected that the smith had substituted silver for part of the gold. Could Archimedes find out for him?

Archimedes reasoned that an adulterated crown would have a larger volume of metal than a piece of pure gold of the same weight, since silver is lighter than gold. But how measure the volume of so intricately shaped an object as a royal crown? The answer came to the great mathematician when he noticed water overflowing as he stepped into his bath. A body immersed in water, he realized, displaces a volume of water equal to its own volume; he had but to compare the volume of water displaced by the crown and a piece of gold of the same weight.

The story of Hiero's crown and Archimedes' discovery of the basic law of displacement doesn't tell whether the crown was actually adulterated. It relates only that Archimedes was so elated at the discovery that he dashed out of the bath and ran naked through the streets of Syracuse shouting "Eureka! Eureka!" ("I have found it! I have found it!")

But that is only the beginning of the story. For Archimedes went on from there to the basic laws of hydrostatics. He formulated not only the famous Principle of Archimedes: *a body immersed in water is buoyed up by a force equal to the weight of the water displaced,* but its chief corollary: *a floating body sinks until it has displaced a volume of water with weight equal to the weight of the floating body.*

Below is a diagram of Archimedes' screw, invented by the Greek mathematician for removing water from the holds of ships; its lifting principle is sometimes used in wheat-handling machines

In addition, he worked out methods for calculating the stability of floating bodies, *i.e.*, for designing ships that won't turn turtle.

Some time later, Archimedes worked out the principle of levers and pulleys and their use to multiply effective force. Talking to Hiero and Gelo, he boasted that he could move any weight whatever, given a long enough lever and a proper fulcrum. "Give me a place to stand on," Archimedes cried, "and I will move the earth." Hiero asked for a demonstration. So Archimedes rigged a set of levers and pulleys with which he (or, according to one version of the story, Hiero) launched a fully loaded ship with one hand.

Though well versed in it, Archimedes had little interest in astronomy, the "queen of sciences" in the ancient world. His one contribution was to apply his marvelous mechanical ingenuity to constructing a model showing the motions of the sun, moon and five planets visible to the naked eye, according to ancient ideas of their movements. Archimedes' contrivance — the first "planetarium" — somehow survived nearly a century and a half after Archimedes' death. Cicero, who saw it in 75 B.C., describes it in one of his orations.

Another of the Syracusan's inventions was the "screw of Archimedes," essentially an oversized worm gear enclosed in a cylinder, a device used for centuries in many countries for pumping water. Still another was the "burning mirror"—a concave parabolic mirror for bringing the sun's rays to a sharp focus. With his burning mirror, Archimedes set fire to the sails of an approaching Roman fleet (though not in the battle in which he routed Marcellus).

There is some doubt as to whether Archimedes did construct and put into use a mirror large enough to burn the sails of an approaching enemy fleet

But Archimedes' greatest contributions were his discoveries in mathematics rather than the astonishing inventions that made him a popular hero from one end of the ancient world to the other. In Archimedes' time, mathematics consisted of an elementary form of arithmetic and the kind of plane geometry taught in high schools today. The Syracusan genius made advances in both these branches of mathematical calculation that would have saved more than 15 centuries of wasted effort if they had not been ignored.

In the ancient world, arithmetic was greatly handicapped by clumsy methods of writing numbers. (Try multiplying Roman numerals, say XLIII by XIV, for yourself some time without using our ordinary Arabic numerals.) Archimedes invented a compact, handy number system capable of expressing numbers up to 1 followed by

80,000 zeros—a feat completely beyond Greek and Roman numerals and awkward even with Arabic numerals before the invention of logarithms late in the 16th century. With his new number system, Archimedes devised numerous arithmetical procedures, including a convenient method for obtaining square roots.

In geometry, his ideas were even more revolutionary. Pythagoras and other mathematicians of the Golden Age of Greece had reduced geometry to a sort of parlor game, played according to a set of rigid rules. The only instruments permitted were compasses and straight-edge; rulers and other measuring instruments were taboo. Thus geometry became nothing but an exercise in formal logic and could not be used for solving practical problems.

With this "idea" of his, Archimedes laid the foundation for and started the fascinating field of experimental science

Archimedes had the modern idea that mathematics ought to be used for solving practical problems and that anything that helped solve problems was all right, regardless of what the rules of Pythagoras might say. He began by calculating the value of *pi*, the ratio of the circumference to the diameter of a circle, by a method which was to lead him to one of the great mathematical discoveries of all time.

The method was to draw polygons with an ever larger number of sides inside and outside a circle. As the number of sides increased, the polygons fitted the circle ever more closely, and their perimeters approached the circle's circumference. Since a polygon's perimeter is easily calculated, one can compute *pi* as accurately as one pleases by drawing polygons with enough sides.

Archimedes saw that this method of approximation could be applied much more widely. For example, the area of a circle can be calculated by dividing the circle into rectangular strips. And if one takes ever more strips, the area of the rectangles approaches ever more closely the area of the circle.

The Syracusan mathematician elaborated this into a general procedure for finding the area of any surface or the volume of any solid whatever. But this is exactly what is done in the great branch of mathematics known as integral calculus—invented by Newton and Leibnitz in the 17th century. And Archimedes used his procedure for just the sort of problems physicists and engineers employ integral calculus for today—finding centers of gravity, weight distributions, moments (tendency to turn) and so forth in all sorts of bodies and structures, from spheres and cylinders to ships and scales. Archimedes also made a start on what eventually became the differential calculus,

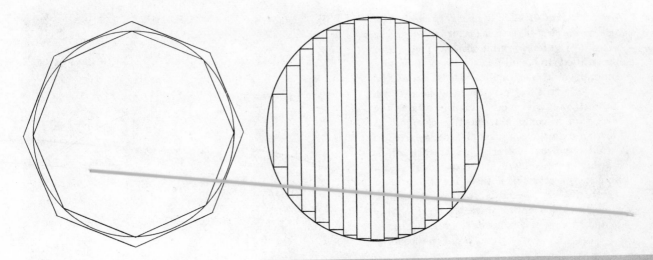

Science Digest

The figure at the left shows Archimedes' method for measuring the circumference of a circle and so calculating *pi*, by measuring perimeters of the inscribed and circumscribed polygons. At the right is his method for the computation of the area of a circle by breaking it up into a series of rectangular strips

the branch of mathematics dealing with the paths of the planets, bullet trajectories and so on.

By a curious irony, Archimedes' great mathematical discoveries were completely forgotten although he carefully wrote them out in eight very modern-sounding books and though he was revered everywhere as "the *great* geometer" and "the wise one." His mathematical manuscripts were not rediscovered until 400 years ago by which time others had rediscovered or were about to rediscover most of what they contain.

Archimedes was the archetype of the absent-minded mathematician. He drew geometrical diagrams incessantly. No sanded floor or square of dusted earth was safe from him. According to legend, he would also rake the ashes from his fire and draw in them. And, after bathing and anointing himself, he would sit for hours, tracing figures with his fingernail on his oiled skin. Archimedes met his end in 212 B.C. when Marcellus finally captured Syracuse. Marcellus gave orders that Archimedes was to be spared from the sack that invariably followed capture of a city. An irate soldier, however, ran Archimedes through with his sword when the aged mathematician refused to look up until he finished diagramming in the sand.

Thus died the one man of the ancient world who stands on the same plane with Newton and Albert Einstein

Although Eratosthenes is probably more well known as the first man to measure the earth, he was also quite a prolific writer. Two of his books entitled On Means dealt with mathematics. Another book, Geographica, helped to lay the foundation of mathematical geography. Eratosthenes is also given credit as being the first man to compile a scientific chronology. Starting with the conquest of Troy, he tried to place all important political and literary dates. But his writings were not restricted solely to subjects of a scientific nature. He also wrote a treatise on the old Greek comedy with a commentary on the principal comic works and several selections dealing with history and moral philosophy.

Eratosthenes

First measurer of the earth

by W. G. Lipsett

ERATOSTHENES—poet, athlete, astronomer and mathematician, the world's first geographer worthy of the title—was the first man to find a simple way of measuring the earth's size accurately and scientifically. We may find it strange then, to learn that his contemporary scientists regarded his achievements as no more than second-rate. They nicknamed him "Beta," Beta being the second letter of the Greek alphabet. They would surely have been surprised to learn that modern man acknowledges his genius, his intelligence and his foresight. More than one modern historian has compared his achievements with those of Pasteur and Newton. And it is not a wild comparison when we consider the crude equipment he had at his disposal.

Who was this man of over 2,000 years ago—a scientist who was born, perhaps, before his time?

We know little about the private life of Eratosthenes. We know that he was a friend of Archimedes and that he was often called "pentathlus," a champion of five sports. The "pentathlon" of the Greeks was similar to the modern version; it was a contest in which men competed against each other in jumping, javelin-throwing, running, quoit-throwing and wrestling.

Eratosthenes was born in 276 B.C., at Cyrene, and in 235, at the age of 41, he accepted the post of custodian of the Library at Alexandria. This library had been founded by Ptolemy Euergetes and was one of the wonders of the ancient world.

The library was part, only, of a great scientific institute, known as the Royal Museum. It was actually the world's first university and the greatest center of learning then in existence.

Here, situated opposite the royal palace in a large parkland, was a group of imposing marble buildings—lecture-rooms, halls, exhibition rooms, rest-rooms, living-rooms, reading-rooms and quarters for resident and visiting lecturers.

Added to and expanded by the Ptolemies of Egypt, the library finally contained over 700,000 volumes—not books as we know them today, but lengthy rolls of papyrus.

The first system of cataloging and indexing was developed here.

Eratosthenes, while lecturing at this university in old Alexandria, was one of the first men to discuss the nature of fossils, though it does not seem likely that he ever guessed what they really were.

Science Digest

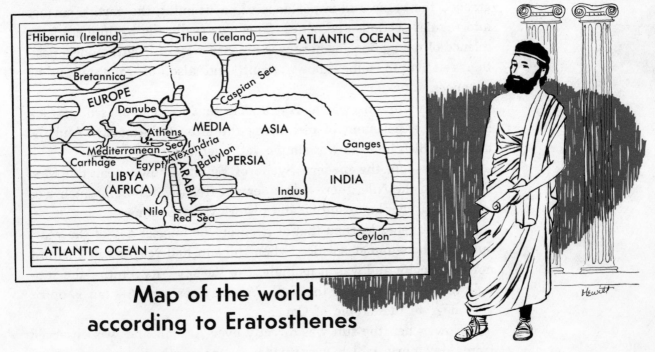

Map of the world
according to Eratosthenes

About 200 B.C., Eratosthenes drew a map of the then-known world. When we look at it today, we may, perhaps, be forgiven for smiling, for in the light of modern knowledge, it is a rather crude attempt. Nevertheless, it is an interesting map for it tells us that the ancient Greeks knew of the existence of the British Isles and of that mysterious country, India.

The map has a strange, "compressed" appearance, as if Eratosthenes felt that he was running out of paper and tried to condense his drawing.

The great continent of Africa is represented only by a small portion of Libya and India appears as a strange, square-shaped continuation of Persia. But the importance of this map lies in the fact that it is the first map on which appear lines of latitude and longitude.

Eratosthenes called his lines of latitude, "parallels"; for example, "the Parallel of Alexandria" and "the Parallel of Meroe" were drawn through these two towns. His lines of longitude he called "Meridians" and gave to them such romantic names as "the Meridian of the Pillars of Hercules" (a line of longitude passing through the present-day Straits of Gibraltar), "the Meridian of the Inuds," "the Meridian of Alexandria," and "the Meridian of the Ganges."

Here, for the first time in history was a man who seemed to have grasped the value and importance of partitioning the earth's surface into regular sections and zones. This was really the beginning of the science of navigation for here was an easy way of locating one's position relative to some known point, and also, of roughly finding distances.

It was while he was at Alexandria that Eratosthenes undertook his classic experiment of measuring the size of the earth. And the method which he used was simple yet ingenious.

At Assuan, the modern Syene of Egypt, a town near the First Cataract of the Nile, there was a certain fresh-water well which was to have a particular scientific and historical importance.

Eratosthenes learned that at noon on the longest day of the year, June 21, the summer solstice, when the sun had reached its farthest northerly point and was at its highest in the sky—its zenith—the sunlight shone directly into the well. We may see that Assuan is on or very near to the Tropic of Cancer.

Now, when the sun was directly over Assuan and was observed from Alexandria which was further to the north, it was seen to be

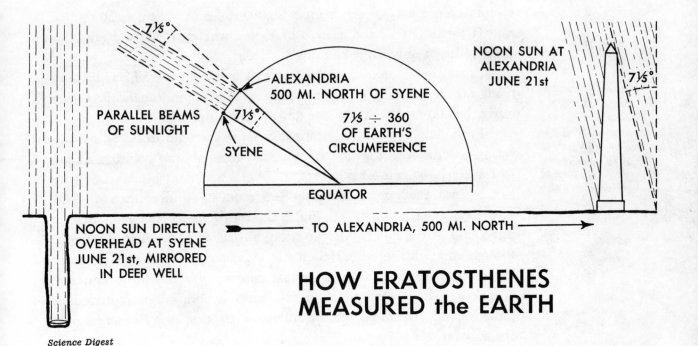

7⅕°

ALEXANDRIA
500 MI. NORTH OF SYENE

7⅕ ÷ 360
OF EARTH'S
CIRCUMFERENCE

PARALLEL BEAMS
OF SUNLIGHT

7⅕°

SYENE

7⅕°

NOON SUN AT
ALEXANDRIA
JUNE 21st

7⅕°

EQUATOR

NOON SUN DIRECTLY
OVERHEAD AT SYENE
JUNE 21st, MIRRORED
IN DEEP WELL

TO ALEXANDRIA, 500 MI. NORTH

HOW ERATOSTHENES
MEASURED the EARTH

Science Digest

lower on the horizon. In other words, when the sun was directly overhead at Assuan, it was not directly overhead at Alexandria.

From his observatory in Alexandria, Eratosthenes was able to determine with his crude instruments that when the sun was crossing its meridian (an imaginary north-south line) at Assuan, it was really 7-1/5 degrees south of its zenith at Alexandria.

By using simple Euclidian geometry, and assuming that the two towns lay on the meridian, which they almost do, Eratosthenes was able to prove that the distance between Alexandria and Syene was also equal to 7-1/5 degrees, or 1/50th of the earth's circumference, there being 360 degrees in a circle.

Eratosthenes knew that imaginary straight lines extended perpendicularly through the two towns must meet at the earth's center, since the earth was a sphere, and that the angle which they made with each other, whether as far away as the sun or at the surface of the earth, would remain the same. The fact that the sun was 93 million-odd miles away made no difference.

The distance between Alexandria and Syene was known to the Greeks; it was roughly 500 miles, though, of course, Eratosthenes used the ancient Greek unit-measure of distance, the "stadion."

It was an easy matter, then, for him to calculate that the earth's

Archimedes made some remarkable, if crude, attempts at calculating the size of the universe, but it remained for Eratosthenes to show how a knowledge of mathematics and clear reasoning, could solve the problem

circumference was approximately 25,000 miles or, 50 times 500 miles.

His estimate of the earth's diameter was even more accurate—7,850 miles or only some 50 miles too short.

Eratosthenes may have overlooked a few factors, he may have made one or two slight errors, errors which happily, cancelled each other, but these defects cannot detract from his achievement.

From this experiment of Eratosthenes, we can draw two interesting conclusions. Firstly, the ancients were able to measure angles as small as one fifth of a degree, no mean accomplishment when we realize that they possessed only the crudest of instruments. And, secondly, even as early as 200 B.C., the distance between certain important places had been accurately measured. We must not forget, though, that during the Hellenistic Age, the Greeks had invented ingenious machines, known as taximeters, with which to measure distances. They were wheeled machines which, when trundled or pulled along, measured off the miles on dials or by releasing stones or counters.

Eratosthenes is rightly famous because it was he who first put geography on a scientific basis. One or two of his other mathematical achievements, while not as remarkable as his effort to measure the size of the earth, are noteworthy.

He invented a simple mechanical device for duplicating the form of the cube, and he also found an easy way of finding prime numbers, a system which is known today as the "Sieve" method.

Eratosthenes died in 194 B.C., at the age of 82. He was a man, who, it is safe to say, would have been a successful scientist in any age.

The position and importance of the earth in the universe, and his own importance, have fascinated man throughout the ages. And man's imagination has given the universe and the earth some queer shapes. Some men, the ancient Babylonians for instance, claimed that the earth was a flat disc, others that it was a curved saucer; the Hindus of ancient India, that it was an inverted bowl resting on the heads of four giant elephants which stood, in turn, on the shell of an immense tortoise. The ancient Greeks were the first peoples to deduce that the earth was round—that it was a ball of matter suspended free in space—a fact which had to be discovered and accepted again, many centuries later.

VITRUVIUS (Marcus Vitruvius Pollio) was a Roman architect and military engineer in the time of Augustus, B.C. 63-A.D. 14. His great work De Architectura Libri Decem, written in Latin and dedicated to Augustus, had vast influence down to modern times. Based on earlier Greek theories, of which he was a student, and on his own practical experience as a builder, the treatise discussed the style, construction, materials and decoration of public buildings, private dwellings, and their many related subjects. For sixteen centuries it constituted a standard "handbook" for architects and city planners; its teachings flowered in the construction of the cathedrals and palaces of the Middle Ages and the Renaissance.

Marcus Vitruvius

. . . on acoustics

VOICE IS A FLOWING breath of air, perceptible to the hearing by contact. It moves in an endless number of circular rounds like the innumerably increasing circular waves which appear when a stone is thrown into smooth water, and which keep on spreading indefinitely from the center unless interrupted by narrow limits or by some obstruction which prevents such waves from reaching their end in due formation. When they are interrupted by obstructions, the first waves, flowing back, break up the formation of those which follow.

In the same manner the voice executes its movements in concentric circles; but while in the case of water the circles move horizontally on a plane surface, the voice not only proceeds horizontally but also ascends vertically by regular stages. Therefore, as in the case of the waves formed in the water, so it is in the case of the voice: the first wave, when there is no obstruction to interrupt it, does not break up the second or the following waves, but they all reach the ears of the lowest and highest spectators without an echo.

Hence the ancient architects (i.e., the Greeks), following in the

23

footsteps of nature, perfected the ascending rows of seats in theaters from their investigations of the ascending voice, and by means of the canonical theory of the mathematicians and that of the musicians, endeavored to make every voice uttered on the stage come with greater clearness and sweetness to the ears of the audience.

For just as musical instruments are brought to perfection of clearness in the sound of their strings by means of bronze plates or horn sounding boards, so the ancients devised methods of increasing the power of the voice in theaters through the application of the science of harmony. . . .

In accordance with the foregoing investigations on mathematical principles, let bronze vessels be made, proportionate to the size of the theater, and let them be so fashioned that, when touched, they may produce with one another the notes of the fourth, the fifth, and so on up to the double octave.

The value of Vitruvius' work on acoustics can well be appreciated in this age of stereophonic sound and other modern devices in motion picture presentation

Then, having constructed niches in between the seats of the theater, let the vessels be arranged in them, in accordance with musical laws, in such a way that they nowhere touch the wall, but have a clear space all round them and room over their tops . . . On this principle of arrangement the voice, uttered from the stage as from a center and spreading and striking against the cavities of the different vessels as it comes in contact with them, will be increased in clearness of sound and will wake a harmonious note in unison with itself. . . .

Somebody will perhaps say that many theaters are built every year in Rome and that in them no attention at all is paid to these principles; but he will be in error, from the fact that all our public theaters made of wood contain a great deal of boarding, which must be resonant. . . .

But when theaters are built of solid materials like masonry, stone, or marble, which cannot be resonant, then the principles of the resonator must be applied.

If, however, it is asked in what theater these vessels have been employed, we cannot point to any in Rome itself, but only to certain districts of Italy and in a good many Greek states.

We have also the evidence of Lucius Mummius who, after destroying the theater in Corinth, brought its bronze vessels to Rome and made a dedicatory offering . . . with the money obtained from their sale.

IN 1951 all the Americas joined the Old World in honoring the hardiest of all skippers on the occasion of the 500th anniversary of his birth. Thousands of tourists found their way to his native Genoa and to the International Columbian Exposition. Four halls in old Palazzo San Giorgio held Columbus material. Our Library of Congress lent papers and models of his ships. From other collections, private and public, came invaluable items: The anchor of his Santa Maria, a map of Hispaniola (Haiti) made by the navigator himself, and so on. Times have indeed changed since Mussolini's press deplored Columbus' discovery of a hemisphere that was to combat his fascist regime.

Christopher Columbus

Discoverer of a New World
by Walter Monfried

THOSE THOMASES who doubt that Columbus was born in 1451 may set their minds at ease. "There is no mystery about the birth, family or race of Christopher Columbus," declares Samuel Eliot Morison, the American historian, Columbus biographer and amateur seaman. Morison, alone among the Columbus biographers, has actually followed the routes of the great navigator in ships about the size of those Columbus used.

It is quite certain that Columbus was born in Genoa in 1451. He was undoubtedly of Italian blood and the Catholic faith. Various theorists have guessed that he was a Spaniard, a Jew, a Portuguese, an Armenian, a Greek and so forth.

There are a few misconceptions about Columbus, however, that can stand clearing up. His sailors on the first voyage did *not* believe that they would come to the edge of the world and fall over. Mariners and all intelligent people at that time knew the world was round. His sailors had the altogether reasonable fear that if they kept sailing too far westward without reaching land, they would not have supplies for the voyage back.

Columbus and his men had sound scientific data. Columbus worked the old "eclipse trick" on the American aborigines long before Mark Twain inspired his Connecticut Yankee to offer it in King Arthur's court.

In 1504, he was marooned on Jamaica for many weeks. The natives became ugly and Columbus sternly told them that if they did not behave and give him food he would turn off their heavenly light. Surely enough, on the night of Feb. 29 (just as his almanac had told him) the moon went into total eclipse. The Indians, after recovering from the shock, howled in fear, and loaded him with foods and begged him to restore their light.

Some admirers of Columbus argue that his discovery of America was not his greatest feat. To reach the New World was simply a matter of courage and stubbornness—it couldn't be missed. But to sail back

It has been said that every ship coming to America got its chart from Columbus

unerringly to Spain, and then to find again the American islands he had in mind—that was sheer genius of seamanship, when one considers his primitive instruments.

Although Columbus was a native of Italy, he did not speak, read or write Italian. The Genoese dialect of his boyhood could hardly be classed as Italian, and it was not written. Christopher, the son and grandson of wool weavers, didn't go to elementary school, much less to Pavia University, as his son inaccurately claimed many years later. When he did take up reading and writing seriously he found Castilian the most useful.

An unlettered boy, Christopher helped his father at the loom for several years. He went to sea at 14, but not permanently.

After he was 20, Columbus began to ship out more and more frequently. He was a crew member of a galley sponsored by a French duke to suppress the Barbary pirates. On one voyage Columbus was wounded, and his ship sank. Luckily he found a big oar in the water and clung to it till he reached the Portuguese shore.

In his 24th year Columbus was living in Lisbon, the busiest seaport of the continent. The Portuguese were forever seeking a better route to that fabled East of gold and silk and spices which had been so eloquently described by Marco Polo and other bold travelers.

The Portuguese navigators were feeling their way around Africa, to try to beat the costly overland route. But Columbus reasoned that, as the earth was round, a westward trip across the Atlantic would be a shorter route to the orient. Thousands of years before, a Greek named Eratosthenes had calculated that the earth was 25,000 miles around—an amazing deduction. Columbus concluded that the distance west from Lisbon to the orient was 3,000 miles. If he had realized the true distance, 14,000 miles, he probably would not have sailed across the Atlantic.

In his late twenties he married a Portuguese woman. He rose to a captain's rank and lived in Madeira. In 1482 he asked the king of Portugal to back him on a transatlantic expedition. The king's council scoffed at the idea. Columbus' brother, Bartholomew, was turned down by the kings of England and France. In 1485 Columbus trudged into Spain with his son, Diego, to try to interest the Spanish king and queen. Near Palos he chatted with Friar Juan Perez, a shrewd and experienced churchman who knew Queen Isabella well. The friar was strongly attracted to the visitor. Columbus was tall, powerfully built, with a long, intent face, a ruddy complexion and a big beaked nose. His hair, which had turned from blond to white when he was 30, gave him an even more dramatic appearance. It is regrettable that no authentic picture of Columbus has come down to us.

The friar secured Columbus' introduction to the keen-minded, ambitious queen. King Ferdinand put him on the pension rolls at a modest stipend to keep him at court. Spain at that time was driving out the Moors, and Columbus had to wait several more years. Early in 1492 the Moors were defeated, and the royal pair could consider Columbus' project. Their expert advisers derided it, but Santagnel, the royal treasurer, a converted Jew and a foresighted financier, thought it a good investment, and so convinced the queen. He supplied most of the funds, about $14,000 and Queen Isabella *didn't* have to pawn her jewels. Three stout ships, a percentage of profit, and the title "Admiral of the Ocean Sea" were provided. The amorphous title was meant to be distinct from that of the regular Spanish admirals, who would not admit this Genoese upstart to their level.

The *Santa Maria* with 39 men, the *Nina* with 22 and the *Pinta* with 26, left Palos on Aug. 3, 1492, stopped at the Canary Islands, and resumed the trip Sept. 7. The wind held from the east steadily, and the sea was smooth. After three weeks the men began to worry and grumble. "Adelante!" ("Sail on!") was the constant plea of the commander and Capt. Pinzon of the Pinta.

On Oct. 10 Columbus yielded to the pleas—if land were not sighted in three more days, they would turn around. On Oct. 12, by moonlight, they sighted the island which he named San Salvador. Two weeks later they cruised to Cuba.

Columbus, in all, led four expeditions to the New World, embracing a full 12 years. His shipwrecks, battles with Indians and white foes, his perilous coasting of the continents, his disgrace and imprisonment at the hands of treacherous rivals—all these experiences constitute the greatest adventure tale in seafaring history. And his final months spelled out a tale of deep, ironic tragedy.

Queen Isabella died before he could return to court. Ferdinand rejected his plea for the offices, fees and trade profit which had been promised him. He was crippled by rheumatism which the exposure on his later voyages caused. Vainly and painfully he padded after the king to repeat his prayer for justice. He was 54 years old when he died in a modest dwelling at Valladolid, in Castile.

In his will Columbus left a strange command —that the head of the household was to sign himself "The Admiral"

He was buried successively in Valladolid, in a Seville monastery, in San Domingo, in Cuba and finally in Seville. He himself had wished to be buried in the New World. He died in the belief that China lay just beyond the newly found territories, that Cuba was a tip of Asia. It was a delusion that endured. When Jean Nicolet in 1634 crossed Lake Michigan to Wisconsin, he thought he was entering China.

Columbus was virtually forgotten even before his death, and the oblivion lasted for more than two centuries. Meanwhile Amerigo Vespucci, a Florentine merchant, visited the New World a few times around 1500 and wrote about it. In 1507, just two years after Columbus' death, a German schoolmaster, Martin Waldseemueller, suggested that the New World be called America.

Well might Emerson exclaim: "Columbus discovered no isle or key so lonely as himself."

It is rather unfortunate that for all his voyages to the New World, Columbus was not given the honor of having the continent that he discovered named after him. Actually, the name America was first given to South America since this was the territory explored by Amerigo Vespucci. It was at a later date, however, that the name was applied to both continents.

LEONARDO DA VINCI, *whose intellectual range and capacity for action have been equalled by few, if any, of the grand geniuses in human history, was born in Tuscany in 1452. Da Vinci's energy, his originality of observation, his homely but penetrating experiments, and his insight which approached prophecy, are revealed in his thousands of pages of manuscript notes, written in the Florentine dialect in reversed mirror-image writing and illustrated with his own drawings. These, unpublished during his life, and little known until recent years, disclose Da Vinci's interest in mechanics, astronomy, physiology, optics and many other fields of which his grasp was centuries ahead of his time. He died in 1519.*

Leonardo da Vinci

. . . on flight

A BIRD IS AN instrument working according to mathematical law, which instrument it is within the capacity of man to reproduce with all its movements, but not with a corresponding degree of strength, though it is deficient only in the power of maintaining equilibrium.

We may therefore say that such an instrument constructed by man is lacking in nothing except the life of the bird, and this life must needs be supplied from that of man.

The life which resides in the bird's members will without doubt better conform to their needs than will that of man which is separated from them, and especially in the almost imperceptible movements which preserve equilibrium. But since we see that the bird is equipped for many obvious varieties of movements, we are able from this experience to declare that the most rudimentary of these movements will be capable of being comprehended by man's understanding; and that he will to a great extent be able to provide against the destruction of that instrument of which he has himself become the living principle and the propeller. . . .

Leonardo da Vinci
... on flight

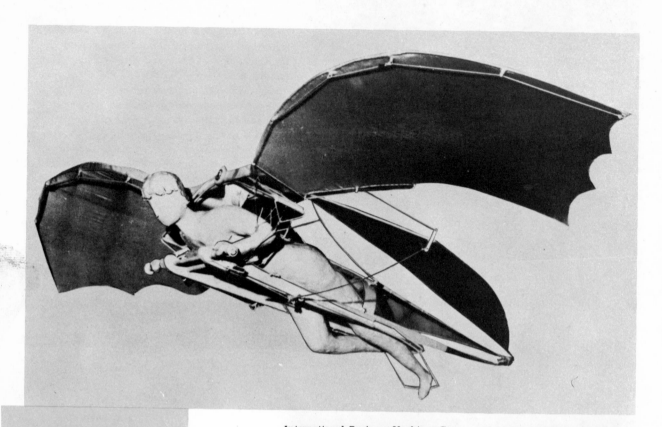

Above is a model of an airplane constructed by Leonardo da Vinci and actually flown by one of his servants or pupils. At the right is Da Vinci's famous "tent of linen"

International Business Machines Corp.

International Business Machines Corp.

Leonardo da Vinci's aerial screw, left, is the forerunner of the present-day helicopter. Motive power was to be supplied by a spring-driven mechanism operating in a manner similar to modern clockwork

There is as much pressure exerted by a substance against the air as by the air against the substance.

Observe how the beating of its wings against the air suffices to bear up the weight of the eagle in the highly rarefied air which borders on the fiery element! Observe also how the air moving over the sea, beaten back by bellying sails, causes the heavily laden ship to glide onwards!

So that by adducing and expounding the reasons of these things you may be able to realize that man when he has great wings attached to him, by exerting his strength against the resistance of the air and conquering it, is enabled to subdue it and to raise himself upon it.

If a man have a tent made of linen of which the apertures have all been stopped up, and it be twelve braccia (more than 25 feet) across and twelve in depth, he will be able to throw himself down from any great height without sustaining injury.

And if you wish to ascertain what weight will support this wing place yourself upon one side of a pair of balances and on the other place a corresponding weight so that the two scales are level in the air; then if you fasten yourself to the lever where the wing is and cut the rope which keeps it up you will see it suddenly fall; and if it required two units of time to fall of itself you will cause it to fall in one by taking hold of the lever with your hands; and you lend so much weight to the opposite arm of the balance that the two become equal in respect of that force; and whatever is the weight of the other balance so much will support the wing as it flies; and so much the more as it presses the air more vigorously.

From his observations of birds in flight, Leonardo conceived the idea of a machine to conquer air. Then the real genius that was Leonardo da Vinci took hold and he not only built this air-conquering machine but flew it to prove that it could be done

NICOLAS COPERNICUS was born in 1473 in Torun, a town in western Poland. His father was a merchant and town magistrate. The original spelling of Copernicus' name suggests that he was German in origin. But the family had been in Poland for generations and was, in the opinion of most Copernican scholars, to all intents and purposes, Polish. Copernicus' father died when the future astronomer was 10 years old, and the family was taken under the wing of an uncle, a priest who soon became Bishop of Ermland. The uncle saw to it that Copernicus was given the best education possible. Nicolas studied at the universities of Cracow, Bologna and Padua and became a doctor of medicine and church law.

Copernicus

Maker of the "new astronomy"

by Leonard Engel

AS EARLY as the fourth century B.C., a Greek astronomer named Heraclides had hit upon the idea that the earth and the planets revolve about the sun. Nevertheless, in 1543, nearly all educated men still believed that the sun and the planets revolved about the earth. Their view was not unreasonable. To earth-bound observers, it certainly looks that way. And the only tables of planet and star positions the world then had—the *Almagest* compiled by Ptolemy of Alexandria in the second century A.D.—were based on this view and agreed quite well with what observations could be made with the crude astronomical instruments of the time.

In 1543, however, ocurred an event which was finally to dethrone the earth as the center of the universe. The event, one of the great milestones in the history of science, was the publication of a folio titled *Six Books Concerning the Revolutions of the Heavenly Spheres*. The *Revolutions* (as it is usually called) was the work of Nicholas Koppernigk, better known under the Latin version of his name, Copernicus. It not only advanced anew the hypothesis that the planets known at that time turned about the sun, but furnished what was needed to put the theory over—a better set of planetary tables.

Even when well proved, new ideas take a long time to displace old ones; another century and a half passed before the new view of the solar system actually won general acceptance. The preparation of the *Revolutions* also took a long time—30 years, off and on, of the life of Copernicus. There were hundreds of observations and laborious calculations to be made for the tables in the *Revolutions*. Besides, Copernicus was an extremely busy man: a renowned physician, a prominent churchman and an able diplomat who played an important part in settling a devastating war between Poland and the Teutonic Order of Knights, an order of German knights whose sway once extended along the Baltic coast all the way to the Gulf of Finland. It was a wonder that Copernicus found time to carry through the great work for which he is remembered. It was a close thing, in fact. He finished the *Revolutions* only a few weeks before a stroke left him half paralyzed and scarcely able to speak. His memory failed so far that he did not recognize his own book when the first copy was brought to him from the printer on May 24, 1543—the day he died.

Copernicus awoke to the world of the heavens while in secondary school (they had secondary schools even then), where one of his teachers built sundials as a hobby. Two or three years later, shortly after arriving at the University of Cracow, he had already outlined his new scheme of the solar system. He liked a sun-centered universe better than the earth-centered universe of Ptolemy, he wrote in between the lecture notes in his university notebooks (which by a minor miracle, have survived), because it is simpler. But he attended no lectures on astronomy or mathematics, though some of the ablest mathematicians and astronomers of the day were at the universities where he studied. And he didn't get down to serious astronomical work until after the death of his uncle. The bishop kept him busy, during Copernicus' first years as a Frauenburg canon, as his personal physician and as a special envoy to the court of the Polish king.

Copernicus was now nearly 40 years old. If he had actually done little astronomy thus far, he had thought much. He understood clearly what had to be done. To make his new scheme stick, he would have to flesh it out with plots of the planets' paths. These would have to fit past observations and observations of the planets' present positions, and predict where the planets would be at future dates. And the fit

The effectiveness of the Revolutions *was marred by Andreas Osiander who, entrusted with the printing of the book, replaced Copernicus' original preface with one of his own contradicting the author's theory of a heliocentric system and labeling it as a mere working hypothesis*

33

of these observations would have to be better than in plots based on the earth-centered scheme of the *Almagest*.

All this was easier said than done. For telescopes, Copernicus had only his own eyes; telescopes were still three-quarters of a century in the future. For measuring instruments, he had only a crude quadrant for determining the altitude of the sun at noon, and a clumsy device, made up of three straight edges, called the *triquetrum* for measuring star altitudes. And Copernicus was a poor observer. "Other men can measure angles in the sky with an accuracy of a minute or two of arc," he told his friend, the German astronomer Rheticus; "I would be happy to measure celestial angles to within 10 minutes of arc."

Copernicus' observatory was a platform atop the fortified wall surrounding the Frauenburg Cathedral. The Frauenburg canons had apartments in the wall. Copernicus' quarters were in a turret opening onto the platform. His observation post commanded an unobstructed view in all directions except to the east.

Science Digest

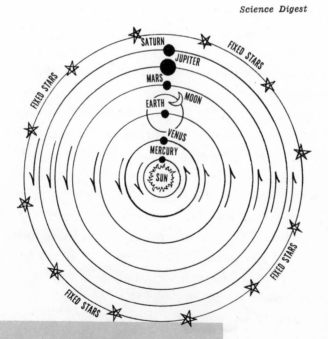

The sun-centered system of the universe, in broad outline, as visualized by Copernicus. The size of the planets and their distance from the sun are not drawn to scale. Note absence of Uranus, discovered in 1781; Neptune, 1846, and Pluto, 1930

Copernicus had few official duties during the next several years. He was able not only to make many observations, but to complete a first draft of his great work. In 1516, however, he was appointed manager of several large estates belonging to the cathedral and three days' journey away. And in 1519, war broke out between Poland and the Teutonic Knights over the allegiance of the bishopric of Ermland (which was a semi-independent church state rather than a mere diocese) and with Ermland as the principal battlefield.

All the canons except Copernicus and two others fled. The bishop who succeeded Copernicus' uncle died. So when the astronomer wasn't busy with the cathedral estates, he was on the go as one of the mediators who finally negotiated a truce in the war. And when he finished with the truce negotiations, he found himself "Administrator-General for Ermland," with the dual task of rebuilding a war-shattered countryside and managing church affairs until the selection of a new bishop. As the result, he was seldom in his observatory for nearly a decade. But he did complete a new draft of his book.

After the war, apart from his duties as a church official and astronomer, Copernicus found time to propose a unified monetary system for the Polish kingdom

With his rich experience in both church and state affairs, Copernicus might well have been chosen bishop himself. Fortunately for science, if not for the Church, he had never taken orders and was ineligible for the post. Another man received the bishopric and Copernicus returned to his turret apartment and observation post.

There he remained for the rest of his life, except for occasional trips as physician to the leading dignitaries of Poland and Prussia. Circumstances now finally conspired to leave the great astronomer alone so that he could get on with his work. The great issue of the day, in that far-off time, was the rise of Protestantism.

The new bishop was a militant foe of the "Protestant heresy"; Copernicus favored a more moderate policy for fear of irretrievably rending the "seamless fabric" of Christendom. Moreover, years before, Copernicus had written a short outline of his scheme of the solar system. Though he had not published it, he had given copies to a few friends and word of his revolutionary ideas had begun to spread. The supporters of the old were not to mobilize for their bitter but futile attempt to suppress the new until long after Copernicus' death. But the bishop found fewer and fewer church tasks for the star-gazing canon of Frauenburg.

Copernicus must have felt that he had little enough time, though he was still in his early fifties. He was a commanding figure, with harsh features; short, stiff, graying hair; a brooding glance; and an overwhelming urge toward perfection. Every clear night, however cold, found him out on his platform, his eyes glued to the *triquetrum*. Day after day, he sweated over his calculations. Many old observations of the planets proved especially difficult to fit into his scheme; he did not realize that they were grossly in error. The original manuscript of the *Revolutions*, which turned up in Czechoslovakia in the middle of the last century after being lost for 300 years, shows half a dozen revisions in many sections of the book. How many additional revisions Copernicus made and threw away we will never know.

In fact, Copernicus was never fully satisfied with his great work and almost decided not to publish it. It was saved for the world by his young German friend Rheticus, who visited Copernicus just before his final illness. In the nick of time, Rheticus, who had just published a brief account of Copernicus' work, persuaded the aging astronomer to allow the *Revolutions* to be printed. Rheticus not only arranged for publication, but gave the *Revolutions* its title.

The theories expressed in the Revolutions *were so radically different that for about 300 years the book was the object of constant attack by the Church and the universities*

The *Revolutions*, which was written in Latin like nearly all scientific works until two centuries ago, does not describe the solar system quite as we understand it today. Copernicus assumed that the earth and planets swept out circular paths around the sun—an assumption that caused him a good deal of difficulty. It took the more accurate observations of Tycho Brahe and the mathematical genius of Johannes Kepler, a generation later, to disclose the true state of affairs: that the paths of the planets are ellipses, with the sun at one focus. It was not until centuries later that the final proof of the sun-centered solar system, the demonstration of star parallax, came in. Since the earth, along with the other planets, moves around the sun, there must be motion relative to the stars. Copernicus looked for this shift, which is called the parallax, but could not find it. Because of the great distance of the stars, which Copernicus and his successors did not realize, the shift was not detected until a hundred years ago.

But the *Revolutions* fully accomplished what the great astronomer hoped it would. In the course of time, it led to better planetary tables and other practical applications, including the reform of the calendar by Pope Gregory XIII. And these led men to accept the revolutionary notion that the earth was not the center of things, but one among a family of planetary equals, all spinning their way through space around the mother of life, the sun.

THEOPHRASTUS Bombastus von Hohenheim took the name of Paracelsus from that of Celsus, a Roman physician, whose works on medicine were held in high regard by the men of Paracelsus' time. He probably picked the prefix of para to denote equality with the ancient Roman. Both his parents had medical backgrounds. His father was also a physician and, before her marriage, his mother was superintendent of a hospital in the town of Einsiedeln where the future scientist was born. Paracelsus concealed his scientific ideas in the seemingly obscure writings of a quack alchemist, and it wasn't until many years later that all of his discoveries and theories on the treatment of disease were brought to light.

Paracelsus

From alchemy to analysis

by Dr. Gordon R. Fonda

THE LATTER PART of the 15th century was a period of revolutionary changes. America had been discovered. Printing had been invented. Science was shaking off the shackles of tradition.

At the height of this period, in 1493, there was born in Switzerland a man who became a revolutionary leader in chemistry by changing its course from the vain pursuit of alchemy to a realistic search for new chemical compounds and to the investigation of their value in healing disease. He is known by the name which he gave himself, Paracelsus.

His family had christened him Theophrastus Bombastus. To many people, there was significance in that name, Bombastus. In the estimation of the professional class of his age and of some scholars even today, he was indeed nothing but the bombastic knave, a charlatan, an egoist who saw himself supreme and who arrogantly derided the leaders in his profession as incompetent and ignorant.

The truth is somewhat different. By nature his spirit was a fighting one and he attempted, single-handed, a rebellion in two sciences, chemistry and medicine.

After finishing college, he spent several years in mining laboratories and in them he became proficient in the chemistry of his day. "Why are not chemical compounds of the metals used in medicine?" he wondered. At the age of 24 he decided to study medicine and find out if they could be used.

On returning to the universities, he was appalled to find that the training of a physician included no laboratory work whatever. Medical training was little more than a parrot-like memorizing of ancient, mystical writings.

His experience in chemical laboratories had formed the habit of experimentation and of free inquiry as the means of acquiring knowledge. He left the universities in disgust and resolved on an unconventional method of training, to travel and to pick up his medical education as he went.

Paracelsus during these wanderings began to compile the material that was to be later included in his books

"In all corners of the world," he wrote later, "I questioned people and sought for the true and experienced arts of medicine. Not alone with the doctors; but with barbers, surgeons, learned physicians, women, magicians, alchemists; in the cloisters with the noble and the common, with the wise and the simple, I sought for a foundation of medicine which should be unspotted by fables and babble."

His travels carried him over the greater part of Europe. At the end of nine years, some of which had been spent as army surgeon and physician in the wars of the day, the fame of his cures had become widely known. In 1526 he was appointed city physician of Basel in Switzerland and made professor at the University in a new department of Chemical Medicine. Its emphasis on chemistry as the important factor in the treatment of disease, represented the philosophy of medicine which Paracelsus wished to establish.

He saw in it an opportunity for his fighting spirit. Tall, stocky, he had the strongly molded head of a Cicero but the face of an Old Testament prophet, a man of passionate convictions, with the sense of a mission. Appreciating the abyss that separated him from the physicians of the day, he decided upon an outright break with the accepted order. He denounced and derided the old school. His lectures were not in Latin, the accepted language of scholars, but in German, the language of the people. His appeal was to the younger generation.

He emphasized continuously the importance of chemistry. As he put it, "I praise the chemical physicians, for they do not consort with loafers or go about gorgeous in satin, silks and velvets, gold rings on

Shown above is an alchemist and his laboratory as pictured by the Dutch master David Teniers

their fingers, white gloves on their hands, but they tend their work at the fire patiently day and night.

"They do not go promenading but seek their recreation in the laboratory, wear plain dress and aprons on which to wipe their hands; they thrust their fingers amongst the coals, into dirt and rubbish and not into golden rings. They are sooty and dirty and hence make little show, they do not gossip with their patients, they well know that words and chatter do not help the sick nor cure them. Therefore they busy themselves with working over their fires and learning the art of chemistry."

When violent opposition arose, he redoubled his attacks upon the older school in remarks that became more and more virulent. He showed his derision for the ancient books by burning one of them in a public bonfire.

Not satisfied with having one good fight on his hands, he undertook another. He sought authority to inspect the offices of the local apothecaries, with the aim of improving the purity of their drugs and of reducing the price. The opposition which this excited, aroused another element of privileged society against him.

His lectures continued for a year and a half and then were suddenly closed by an incident that had no direct connection with his teaching. This incident led him to attack another important element of society, the judiciary.

A wealthy citizen had long been troubled with a baffling disease. Fearing that it would prove fatal, he offered 100 gulden to Paracelsus to cure him. After a few treatments, the man recovered so rapidly that he considered 100 gulden as altogether out of proportion to the medical treatment. With some derogatory remarks, he offered to settle for six gulden. Paracelsus was enraged and took the matter to the courts. The judges, however, were as unimpressed as the patient with the value of the medicine used, just a few small pills, resembling nothing so much as sweepings from a pantry infested with mice. At this, Paracelsus' sense of injustice burst out of bounds. He denounced the judges in court in such terms as to warrant charges of treason against him. Warned by his friends, he saw that the game was up. He left Basel that night and resumed the wanderings of his early years.

The remaining 13 years of his life found him continually unsettled, staying in no one place for long and encountering opposition from those in authority wherever he went. His one outstanding thought was to reduce to writing his revolutionary philosophy of the use of chemical compounds in the treatment of disease.

The cause of Paracelsus' death is a mystery. Friends of the physician claim he was killed by his enemies and his enemies claim he died as the result of a prolonged drinking bout

Of the many manuscripts that he wrote, however, few were allowed to be published because of the interference from universities. Occasionally his fortune was up but it was mostly down. Sometimes he would reside in a town for a year or so, sometimes he was feted at a public dinner as the guest of honor, but for the most part his life was one of wandering, and his only home the inn where travelers stayed. It was in Salzburg at such an inn that he died in 1541 at the age of 48, an old man, sick and worn out, his adherents few, his aims seemingly unaccomplished.

He was not to perish, however, with the death of his body. Unknown to the world at large, his rebellious spirit was still sputtering, enclosed in his manuscripts. It was they which were destined to accomplish his revolution. It was indeed 20 years before any search for them was made. An official inquiry from Vienna brought some to light and their publication aroused a demand for others. Soon a complete edition of his books appeared.

Then began the second period of Paracelsus' life, with his books renewing the revolution. The pen proved to be mightier than the tongue. The number and repute of his adherents increased.

Many of his writings are surprisingly modern in their point of view; a treatise, for instance, on the occupational disease of miners, smelters and metallurgists, emphasizing means of prevention as well as of cure; another on nervous diseases, insisting on physical cause rather than demon origin; another on surgery, opposing the practice of closing wounds with poultices and stressing the prevention of external infection.

It had been his insistence on the value of mineral remedies that aroused the strongest opposition. They included many salts of metals, largely mercury and antimony and also lead, arsenic, copper and iron. The human body is a combination of three properties, he maintained, and disease is due to the presence of a foreign parasite which disrupts the normal correlation between the three properties. The function of a medicine is to stimulate and strengthen the vital force within the body so that it may suffocate the parasite.

Ether, too, was discovered by Paracelsus but the formula was hidden in an obscure passage and was not revealed until many years later, after its use had already become widely recognized

Such conceptions were a complete break with the theories of the old school, which he discarded as well as their practices of blood-letting and purging. It was in chemistry, however, that his real revolution was effected.

Chemistry as a science had fallen to low estate. Its main attention had been given to alchemy, in the vain aim of transmuting base metals into gold. "The object of chemistry," as Paracelsus put it, "is not to make gold but to prepare medicines."

New leaders in chemistry arose who devoted their lives to this study, the pursuit of medicines. It is their work which makes up the history of chemistry for 150 years after the death of Paracelsus. These leaders were physicians. In time, they found that chemistry is too broad a science to be simply the hand-maiden of medicine. Their interest was growing in the composition of compounds, in identifying the constituents of matter and in isolating the fundamental elements. They were experimenting so as to understand and explain the processes of combustion and of oxidation.

People from many diverse fields were now calling themselves chemists. The outlook of Paracelsus, limited as it was, had invigorated men's minds and directed them into new paths which led to modern science.

BENVENUTO CELLINI, the famous Italian sculptor and artisan in silver and gold, was born in Florence in 1500, the son of a musician. His father tried to interest the boy in music but he failed, and at the age of fifteen Benvenuto was apprenticed to a goldsmith. In 1519 he went to Rome, where under the patronage of Pope Clement VII he became known as the most skillful and artistic metalworker of his time. For a while, upon the invitation of Francis I, he worked at the French court but after five years he left in disgust and returned to Italy. Cellini died in Florence in 1571, unmarried, leaving behind a wealth of memorials in the form of his many outstanding pieces of art.

Benvenuto Cellini

The casting of a statue

Cellini is about to cast the bronze statue of "Perseus with the Head of Medusa," which, surmounting a marble pedestal adorned with statuettes and carvings, stands in the Loggia dei Lanzi, in Florence.

ACCORDINGLY I strengthened my heart, and . . . employing what little money still remained to me, I set to work. First I provided myself with several loads of pine wood from the forests of Serristori. . . . While these were on their way, I clothed my Perseus with the clay which I had prepared many months beforehand, in order that it might be duly seasoned. After making its clay tunic (for that is the term used in this art) and properly arming it and fencing it with iron girders, I began to draw the wax out by means of a slow fire. This melted and issued through numerous air vents I had made; for the more there are of these the better will the mold fill. When I had finished drawing off the wax, I constructed a funnel-shaped furnace all around the model of my Perseus.

It was built of bricks, so interlaced, the one above the other, that numerous apertures were left for the fire to exhale at. Then I began to lay on wood by degrees, and kept it burning two whole days and nights. At length, when all the wax was gone, and the mold was well baked, I set to work at digging the pit in which to sink it. This I performed with scrupulous regard to all the rules of art. When I had finished that part of my work, I raised the mold by windlasses and stout ropes to a perpendicular position, and, suspending it with the greatest care one cubit above the level of the furnace, so that it hung exactly above the middle of the pit, I next lowered it gently down into the very bottom of the furnace and had it firmly placed with every possible precaution for its safety. When this delicate operation was accomplished, I began to bank it up with the earth I had excavated; and, ever as the earth grew higher, I introduced its proper air vents, which were little tubes of earthenware, such as folk use for drains and suchlike purposes.

At length I felt sure that it was admirably fixed and that the filling in of the pit and the placing of the air vents had been properly performed. I also could see that my work people understood my method, which differed very considerably from that of all the other masters in the trade. Feeling confident, then, that I could rely upon them, I next turned to my furnace, which I had filled with numerous pigs of copper and other bronze stuff. The pieces were piled according to the laws of art; that is to say, so resting one upon the other that the flames could play freely through them, in order that the metal might heat and liquefy the sooner.

At last I called out heartily to set the furnace going. The logs of pine were heaped in, and, what with the unctuous resin of the wood and the good draft I had given, my furnace worked so well that I was obliged to rush from side to side to keep it going. The labor was more than I could stand; yet I forced myself to strain every nerve and muscle. To increase my anxieties, the workshop took fire, and we were afraid lest the roof should fall upon our heads; while, from the garden, such a storm of wind and rain kept blowing in that it perceptibly cooled the furnace.

Battling thus with all these untoward circumstances for several hours, and exerting myself beyond even the measure of my powerful constitution, I could at last bear up no longer, and a sudden fever, of the utmost possible intensity, attacked me. I felt absolutely obliged to

This furnace, called manica, was like a grain hopper, so that the mold could stand upright in it as a cup

These air vents were introduced into the outer mold. They served the double purpose of drawing off the wax, whereby a space was left for the molten bronze to enter, and also of facilitating the penetration of this molten metal by allowing a free escape of air and gas from the outer mold

43

The statue of Perseus holding the head of the Gorgon Medusa, which was cast by Benvenuto Cellini. In spite of his wild frenzy, the statue, cast as a solid piece, was nearly perfect

go and fling myself upon my bed. Sorely against my will having to drag myself away from the spot. I turned to my assistants, about ten or more in all, what with master founders, hand workers, country fellows, and my own special journeymen, among whom was Bernardino Mannellini, of Mugello, my apprentice through several years. To him in particular I spoke: "Look, my dear Bernardino, that you observe the rules which I have taught you; do your best with all dispatch, for the metal will soon be fused. You cannot go wrong; these honest men will get the channels ready; you will easily be able to drive back the two plugs with this pair of iron crooks; and I am sure that my mold will fill miraculously. I feel more ill than I ever did in all my life, and verily believe that it will kill me before a few hours are over." Thus, with despair at heart, I left them and betook myself to bed.

No sooner had I got to bed than I ordered my serving-maids to carry food and wine for all the men into the workshop; at the same time I cried: "I shall not be alive tomorrow." They tried to encourage me, arguing that my illness would pass over, since it came from excessive fatigue. In this way I spent two hours battling with the fever, which steadily increased, and calling out continually: "I feel that I am dying." My housekeeper . . . kept chiding me for my discouragement; but, on the other hand, she paid me every kind of attention which was possible. . . . While I was thus terribly afflicted, I beheld the figure of a man enter my chamber, twisted in his body into the form of a capital S. He raised a lamentable, doleful voice, like one who announces their last hour to men condemned to die upon the scaffold, and spoke these words: "O Benvenuto! Your statue is spoiled, and there is no hope whatever of saving it."

No sooner had I heard the shriek of that wretch than I gave a howl which might have been heard from the sphere of flame. Jumping from my bed, I seized my clothes and began to dress. . . .

When I had got my clothes on, I strode with soul bent on mischief toward the workshop; there I beheld the men, whom I had left erewhile in such high spirits, standing stupefied and downcast. I began at once and spoke: "Up with you! Attend to me! Since you have not been able or willing to obey the directions I gave you, obey me now that I am with you to conduct my work in person. Let no one contradict me, for in cases like this we need the aid of hand and hearing, not of advice."

The canals or channels were sluices for carrying the molten metal from the furnace into the mold. The iron crooks were poles fitted at the end with curved irons, by which the openings of the furnace, plugs, could be partially or wholly driven back, so as to let the molten metal flow through the channels into the mold. When the metal reached the mold, it entered in a red-hot stream between the outside mold and the inner block, filling up exactly the space which had been occupied by the wax, previously extracted by a method of slow burning. The mold consisted of two pieces; one hollow, which gave shape to the bronze; one solid and rounded, which stood at a short interval within the former and regulated the influx of hot metal

When I had uttered these words, a certain Maestro Allesandro Lastricati broke silence and said: "Look you, Benvenuto, you are going to attempt an enterprise which the laws of art do not sanction and which cannot succeed."

I turned upon him with such fury and so full of mischief that he and all the rest of them exclaimed with one voice: "On then! Give orders! We will obey your least commands, so long as life is left in us." I believe they spoke thus feelingly because they thought I must fall shortly dead upon the ground. I went immediately to inspect the furnace and found that the metal was all curdled; an accident which we express by "being caked." I told two of the hands to cross the road and fetch from the house of the butcher Capretta a load of young oak wood, which had lain dry for above a year; this wood had been previously offered me by Mme. Ginevra, wife of the said Capretta. So soon as the first armfuls arrived, I began to fill the grate beneath the furnace. Now oak wood of that kind heats more powerfully than any other sort of tree; and for this reason, where a slow fire is wanted, as in the case of gun foundry, alder or pine is preferred. Accordingly, when the logs took fire, oh! how the cake began to stir beneath that awful heat, to glow and sparkle in a blaze! At the same time I kept stirring up the channels and sent men upon the roof to stop the conflagration, which had gathered force from the increased combustion in the furnace; also I caused boards, carpets, and other hangings to be set up against the garden, in order to protect us from the violence of the rain.

The Italian is bracciaiuola, *a pit below the grating, which receives the ashes from the furnace*

When I had thus provided against these several disasters, I roared out first to one man and then to another: "Bring this thing here! Take that thing there!" At this crisis, when the whole gang saw the cake was on the point of melting, they did my bidding, each fellow working with the strength of three. I then ordered half a pig of pewter to be brought, which weighed about 60 pounds, and flung it into the middle of the cake inside the furnace. By this means, and by piling on wood and stirring now with pokers and now with iron rods, the curdled mass rapidly began to liquefy. Then, knowing I had brought the dead to life again, against the firm opinion of those ignoramuses, I felt such vigor fill my veins that all those pains of fever, all those fears of death, were quite forgotten.

All of a sudden an explosion took place, attended by a tremendous flash of flame, as though a thunderbolt had formed and been discharged amongst us. Unwonted and appalling terror astonished everyone, and me more even than the rest. When the din was over and the dazzling light extinguished, we began to look each other in the face. Then I discovered the cap of the furnace had blown up, and the bronze was bubbling over from its source beneath. So I had the mouths of my mold immediately opened, and at the same time drove in the two plugs which kept back the molten metal. But I noticed that it did not flow as rapidly as usual, the reason being probably that the fierce heat of the fire we kindled had consumed its base alloy. Accordingly I sent for all my pewter platters, porringers, and dishes, to the number of some two hundred pieces, and had a portion of them cast, one by one, into the channels, the rest into the furnace. This expedient succeeded, and everyone could now perceive that my bronze was in most perfect liquefaction, and my mold was filling; whereupon they all with heartiness and happy cheer assisted and obeyed my bidding, while I, now here, now there, gave orders, helped with my own hands, and cried aloud: "O God! Thou that by Thy immeasurable power didst rise from the dead, and in Thy glory didst ascend to heaven!" . . .

When Cellini uncovered the statue he found, to his immense satisfaction, only one small imperfection—in the toe of Perseus

Even thus in a moment my mold was filled; and seeing my work finished, I fell upon my knees and with all my heart gave thanks to God.

Most of Cellini's pieces have not survived, and those that have are jealously guarded treasures in the museums that possess them. Although his statue of Perseus holding the head of Medusa is probably his most famous work, and one of the few that have survived, several others bear mentioning, notably the salt-cellar he made for Francis I—a gigantic statue of Mars, which adorns a magnificent fountain in France—and a life-size statue of another Roman god, Jupiter, done in silver. All three of these pieces have withstood the ravages of time. Cellini was adept with the chisel and the rapier—not the test tube and crucible. His classic autobiography is a diary of the loves, commissions and escapades of a profligate, flamboyant, artist-adventurer—not a record of scientific observation. But its presentation of Renaissance technology and the glimpse it provides of the metallurgical lore of the period, give it a place in the history of science.

ANDREAS VESALIUS (1514-1564), the founder of modern anatomy, did for medicine what Copernicus and Newton did for astronomy and physics. A Belgian, descended from distinguished physicians, Vesalius became professor of anatomy at the University of Padua before he was 23. At Padua he was able to lecture upon human cadavers as he dissected them before large groups of students—who were thereafter to spread the still forbidden knowledge. Discouraged and frightened by attacks upon his "unholy" demonstrations, Vesalius went to Spain as court physician to Charles V. Condemned to death for heresy by the Inquisition, his sentence was commuted on condition he make a pilgrimage to the Holy Land.

Andreas Vesalius

. . . on the human body

I SHALL PASS over all the other arts in silence and confine myself to a few remarks on that which presides over the health of mankind. This, of all the arts which the mind of man has discovered, is by far the most beneficial, necessary, abstruse, and laborious . . . Its primary instrument, the employment of the hand in healing, was so neglected that it was relegated to vulgar fellows with no instruction whatsoever in the branches of knowledge that subserve the art of medicine. . . .

In course of time the art of healing has been so wretchedly rent asunder that certain doctors, advertising themselves under the name of physicians, have arrogated to themselves alone the prescription of drugs and diet for obscure diseases, and have relegated the rest of medicine to those whom they call surgeons and scarcely regard as slaves, disgracefully banishing from themselves the chief, and most ancient branch of the medical art, and that which principally (if indeed there be any other) bases itself upon the investigation of nature . . .

The tyros in this art must by every means be exhorted to follow the Greeks in despising the whisperings of those physicians (save the mark!), and, as the fundamental nature and rational basis of the art prescribes, to apply their hands also to the treatment, lest they should rend the body of medicine and make of it a force destructive of the common life of man.

And they must be urged to this with all the greater earnestness because men today who have had an irreproachable training in the art are seen to abstain from the use of the hand as from the plague, and for this very reason, lest they should be slandered by the masters of the profession as barbers before the ignorant mob, and should henceforth lack equal gain and honor with those less than half doctors, losing their standing both with the uneducated commonalty and with princes.

For it is indeed above all other things the wide prevalence of this hateful error that prevents us even in our age from taking up the healing art as a whole, makes us confine ourselves merely to the treatment of internal complaints, and, if I may utter the blunt truth once for all, causes us, to the great detriment of mankind, to study to be healers only in a very limited degree. . .

Perverse distribution of the instruments of healing among a variety of craftsmen inflicted a much more odious shipwreck and a far more cruel blow upon the chief branch of natural philosophy (anatomy), to which, since it comprises the natural history of man and should rightly be regarded as the firm foundation of the whole art of medicine and its essential preliminary, Hippocrates and Plato attached so much importance that they did not hesitate to put it first among the parts of medicine. For though originally it was the prime object of the doctors' care, and though they strained every nerve to acquire it, it finally began to perish miserably when the doctors themselves, by resigning manual operations to others, ruined anatomy.

For when the doctors supposed that only the care of internal complaints concerned them, considering a mere knowledge of the viscera as more than enough for them, they neglected the structure of the bones and muscles, as well as of the nerves, veins, and arteries which run through bones and muscles, as of no importance for them.

And further, when the whole conduct of manual operations was entrusted to barbers, not only did doctors lose the true knowledge of the viscera, but the practice of dissection soon died out, doubtless for the reason that the doctors did not attempt to operate, while those to

Vesalius gave the first complete and accurate description of the construction of the human body—based on systematic dissections he performed himself, with instruments of his own design

49

*The body was Vesalius'
textbook, not the
writings of Galen, the
2nd century Greek
physician whose
authority was almost
absolute but whose
errors in anatomy
Vesalius laid bare as
he did the human
organs. Called a
"madman," he defied
the prohibitions of his
time even when a
student youth in
Paris, where on dark
nights he would steal
the bodies of hanged
criminals from the
public gibbets
and churchyards for
his dissection table*

whom the manual skill was resigned were too ignorant to read the writings of the teachers of anatomy . . .

I myself, having trained myself without guidance in the dissection of brute creatures, at the third dissection at which it was my fortune ever to be present (this, as was the custom there, was concerned exclusively or principally with the viscera), led on by the encouragement of my fellow students and teachers, performed in public a more thorough dissection than was wont to be done.

Later I attempted a second dissection, my purpose being to exhibit the muscles of the hand together with a more accurate dissection of the viscera. For except for eight muscles of the abdomen, disgracefully mangled and in the wrong order, no one (I speak the simple truth) ever demonstrated to me any single muscle, or any single bone, much less the network of nerves, veins, and arteries. . .

I have . . . made a completely fresh arrangement in seven books of my information about the parts of the human body in the order in which I am wont to lay the same before that learned assembly in this city, as well as at Bologna and at Pisa. Thus those present at the dissections will have a record of what was there demonstrated, and will be able to expound anatomy to others with less trouble.

And also the books will be by no means useless to those who have no opportunity for personal examination, for they relate with sufficient fullness the number, position, shape, substance, connection with other parts, use and function of each part of the human body, together with many similar facts. . .

Moreover, the books contain representations of all the parts inserted in the text of the discourse, in such a way that they place before the eyes of the student of nature's works, as it were, a dissected corpse.

I am aware . . . how little authority my efforts will carry by reason of my youth (I am still in my twenty-eighth year) and . . . how little, on account of the frequency with which I draw attention to the falsity of Galen's pronouncements, I shall be sheltered from the attacks of those who have not—as I have done in the schools of Italy—applied themselves earnestly to anatomy, and who, being now old men devoured by envy at the true discoveries of youth, will be ashamed, together with all the other sectaries of Galen, that they have been hitherto so purblind, failing to notice what I now set forth. . .

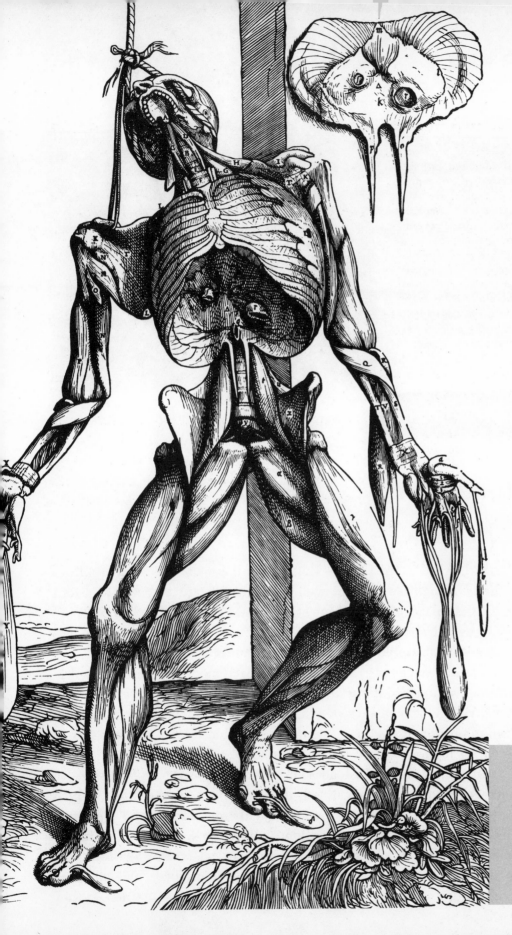

The woodcut, left, is from Vesalius' book, *De Humani Corporis Fabrica.* The work is composed of seven volumes and is distinguished by the vivid accuracy of its artwork

WILLIAM GILBERT (1540-1603), an early
investigator of magnetic and electrical
phenomena, was born in Colchester, England,
and educated at Cambridge and Oxford.
After traveling in Europe, he settled in London
and began to practice as a physician. He held
several important posts in the College of
Physicians to which he was admitted several
years after his return from the Continent. His
work in the field of physical research is
distinguished by the employment of genuine
scientific methods of investigation by experiment
—an approach unusual in his time. He became
court physician to Queen Elizabeth in 1601
and was reappointed to the post by her
successor, James I.

William Gilbert

. . . on magnetism

THE MANY QUALITIES exhibited by the loadstone itself, qualities
hitherto recognized yet not well investigated, are to be pointed out
in the first place, to the end the student may understand the powers of
the loadstone and of iron, and not be confused through want of knowledge at the threshold of the arguments and demonstrations.

In the heavens astronomers give to each moving sphere two poles;
thus do we find two natural poles of excelling importance even in our
terrestrial globe, constant points related to the movement of its daily
revolution, to wit, one pole pointing to Arctos (Ursa) and the north;
the other looking toward the opposite part of the heavens.

In like manner the loadstone has from nature its two poles, a
northern and a southern; fixed, definite points in the stone, which
are the primary termini of the movements and effects, and the limits
and regulators of the several actions and properties. It is to be understood, however, that not from a mathematical point does the force
of the stone emanate, but from the parts themselves; and all these
parts in the whole—while they belong to the whole—the nearer they

are to the poles of the stone the stronger virtues do they acquire and pour out on other bodies. These poles look toward the poles of the earth, and move toward them, and are subject to them.

The magnetic poles may be found in every loadstone, whether strong and powerful (male, as the term was in antiquity) or faint, weak, and female; whether its shape is due to design or to chance, and whether it be long, or flat, or foursquare, or three-cornered, or polished; whether it be rough, broken off, or unpolished: the loadstone ever has and ever shows its poles. . .

First we have to describe in popular language the potent and familiar properties of the stone; afterward, very many subtle properties, as yet recondite and unknown, being involved in obscurities, are to be unfolded; and the causes of all these (nature's secrets being unlocked) are in their place to be demonstrated in fitting words and with the aid of apparatus.

The fact is trite and familiar that the loadstone attracts iron; in the same way, too, one loadstone attracts another. Take the stone on which you have designated the poles, N. and S., and put it in its vessel so that it may float; let the poles lie just in the plane of the horizon, or at least in a plane not very oblique to it; take in your hand another stone the poles of which are also known, and hold it so that its south pole shall lie toward the north pole of the floating stone, and near it alongside; the floating loadstone will straightway follow the other (provided it be within the range and dominion of its powers), nor does it cease to move nor does it quit the other till it clings to it, unless by moving your hand away you manage skillfully to prevent the conjunction.

In like manner, if you oppose the north pole of the stone in your hand to the south pole of the floating one, they come together and follow each other. For opposite poles attract opposite poles. But now, if in the same way you present N. to N. or S. to S., one stone repels the other; and as though a helmsman were bearing on the rudder it is off like a vessel making all sail, nor stands nor stays as long as the other stone pursues. One stone also will range the other, turn the other around, bring it to right about and make it come to agreement with itself. But when the two come together and are conjoined in nature's order, they cohere firmly.

For example, if you present the north pole of the stone in your hand to the Tropic of Capricorn (for we so may distinguish with

Gilbert discovered by simple but original experiments that glass, sulphur, resin, and other substances would attract other bodies after excitation by friction, and that this "magical" power was not confined to amber, as had been supposed since the time of Thales

mathematical circles the round stone or terrella, just as we do the globe itself) or to any point between the Equator and the South Pole: immediately the floating stone turns round and so places itself that its south pole touches the north pole of the other and is most closely joined to it. In the same way you will get like effect at the other side of the Equator by presenting pole to pole; and thus by art and contrivance we exhibit attraction and repulsion, and motion in a circle toward the concordant position, and the same movements to avoid hostile meetings.

Gilbert introduced the terms axis, equator, *and others, and invented the magnetic "keeper," which he called an* armature

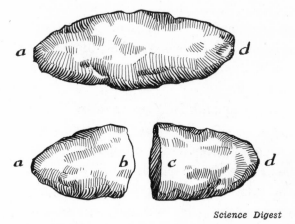

Science Digest

Furthermore, in one same stone we are thus able to demonstrate all this: but also we are able to show how the selfsame part of one stone may by division become either north or south. Take the oblong stone *ad* in which *a* is the north pole and *d* the south. Cut the stone in two equal parts, and put part *a* in a vessel and let it float in water.

You will find that *a*, the north point, will turn to the south as before; and in like manner the point *d* will move to the north, in the divided stone, as before division. But *b* and *c*, before connected, now separated from each other, are not what they were before. *B* is now south while *c* is north. *B* attracts *c*, longing for union and for restoration of the original continuity. They are two stones made out of one, and on that account, the *c* of one turning toward the *b* of the other, they are mutually attracted, and, being freed from all impediments and from their own weight, borne as they are on the surface of the water, they come together and into conjunction.

But if you bring the part or point *a* up to *c* of the other, they repel one another and turn away; for by such a position of the parts nature is crossed and the form of the stone is perverted: but nature observes strictly the laws it has imposed upon bodies: hence the flight of one part from the undue position of the other, and hence the discord unless everything is arranged exactly according to nature. And nature will not suffer an unjust and inequitable peace, or agreement, but makes war and employs force to make bodies acquiesce fairly and justly. Hence, when rightly arranged, the parts attract each other, i.e., both stones, the weaker and the stronger, come together and with all their might tend to union: a fact manifest in all loadstones, and not, as Pliny supposed, only in those from Ethiopia.

The Ethiopic stones, if strong, and those brought from China, which are all powerful stones, show the effect most quickly and most plainly, attract with most force in the parts nighest the pole, and keep turning till pole looks straight on pole. The pole of a stone has strongest attraction for that part of another stone which answers to it (the *adverse*, as it is called); e.g., the north pole of one has strongest attraction for, has the most vigorous pull on, the south part of another; so, too, it attracts iron more powerfully, and iron clings to it more firmly, whether previously magnetized or not. Thus it has been settled by nature, not without reason, that the parts nigher the pole shall have the greatest attractive force, and that in the pole itself shall be the seat, the throne, as it were, of a high and splendid power; and that magnetic bodies brought near thereto shall be attracted most powerfully. . . So, too, the poles are readiest to spurn and drive away what is presented to them amiss, and what is inconformable and foreign.

William Gilbert was one of the first to make a small-scale model for test and demonstration purposes. He showed that the earth itself is a huge magnet and that the behavior of the mariner's compass is due to that fact

Shown here are just a few examples of many different types of magnets in use

Indiana Steel Products Co.

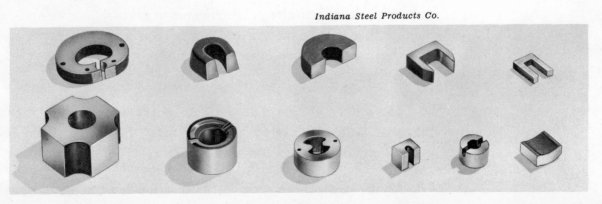

Francis Bacon

Interpretation of nature and of man

Man, AS THE MINISTER and interpreter of nature, does and understands as much as his observations on the order of nature, either with regard to things or the mind, permit him, and neither knows nor is capable of more.

It would be madness and inconsistency to suppose that things which have never yet been performed can be performed without employing some hitherto untried means.

Even the effects already discovered are due to chance and experiment, rather than to the sciences, for our present sciences are nothing more than peculiar arrangements of matters already discovered, and not methods for discovery or plans for new operations.

The sole cause and root of almost every defect in the sciences is this, that while we falsely admire and extol the powers of the human mind, we do not search for its real helps.

As the present sciences are useless for the discovery of effects, so the present system of logic is useless for the discovery of the sciences.

There are and can exist but two ways of investigating and discovering truth. The one hurries on rapidly from the senses and particulars to the most general axioms, and from them, as principles and their supposed indisputable truth, derives and discovers the intermediate axioms. This is the way now in use. The other constructs its axioms from the senses and particulars, by ascending continually and gradually, till it finally arrives at the most general axioms, which is the true but unattempted way.

If all the capacities of all ages should unite and combine and transmit their labors, no great progress will be made in learning by anticipations, because the radical errors, and those which occur in the first process of the mind, are not cured by the excellence of subsequent means and remedies.

Nor is it an easy matter to deliver and explain our sentiments; for those things which are in themselves new can yet be only understood from some analogy to what is old.

We have but one simple method of delivering our sentiments, namely, we must bring men to particulars and their regular series and order, and they must for a while renounce their notions, and begin to form an acquaintance with things.

Four species of idols beset the human mind, to which (for distinction's sake) we have assigned names, calling the first Idols of the Tribe, the second Idols of the Den, the third Idols of the Market, the fourth Idols of the Theatre.

The formation of notions and axioms on the foundation of true induction is the only fitting remedy by which we can ward off and expel these idols. It is, however, of great service to point them out; for the doctrine of idols bears the same relation to the interpretation of nature as that of the confutation of sophisms does to common logic.

The idols of the tribe are inherent in human nature and the very tribe or race of man; for man's sense is falsely asserted to be the standard of things; on the contrary, all the perceptions both of the

After his retirement from public office, Bacon was able to spend his full time in organizing—in both English and Latin—the ideas which he had developed during his career as an official. In his own words Bacon was "the trumpeter" of his time —that period in history when the printing press, gun powder, and the compass were about to create the "modern" world, with what Bacon considered to be its need for knowledge of nature, rather than understanding of ancient philosophy

senses and the mind bear references to man and not to the universe, and the human mind resembles those uneven mirrors which impart their own properties to different objects, from which rays are emitted and distort and disfigure them.

The idols of the den are those of each individual; for everybody (in addition to the errors common to the race of man) has his own individual den or cavern, which intercepts and corrupts the light of nature, either from his own peculiar and singular disposition, or from his education and intercourse with others, or from his reading, and the authority acquired by those whom he reverences and admires, or from the different impressions produced on the mind, as it happens to be preoccupied and predisposed, or equable and tranquil, and the like. . . .

There are also idols formed by the reciprocal intercourse and society of man with man, which we call idols of the market, from the commerce and association of men with each other; for men converse by means of language, but words are formed at the will of the generality, and there arises from a bad and unapt formation of words a wonderful obstruction to the mind. . . .

Lastly, there are idols which have crept into men's minds from the various dogmas of peculiar systems of philosophy, and also from the perverted rules of demonstration, and these we denominate idols of the theatre: for we regard all the systems of philosophy hitherto received or imagined, as so many plays brought out and performed, creating fictitious and theatrical worlds.

The human understanding resembles not a dry light, but admits a tincture of the will and passions, which generate their own system accordingly; for man always believes more readily that which he prefers. He, therefore, rejects difficulties for want of patience in investigation; sobriety, because it limits his hope; the depths of nature, from superstition; the light of experiment, from arrogance and pride, lest his mind should appear to be occupied with common and varying objects; paradoxes, from a fear of the opinion of the vulgar; in short, his feelings imbue and corrupt his understanding in innumerable and sometimes imperceptible ways.

But by far the greatest impediment and aberration of the human understanding proceeds from the dullness, incompetency, and errors

Bacon's importance as a philosopher is that he most clearly formulated and most eloquently proclaimed the inductive method of modern science. In the words of Benjamin Farrington, his most recent biographer, Bacon's idea was that "knowledge ought to bear fruit in works, that science ought to be applicable to industry, that men ought to organize themselves as a sacred duty to improve and transform the conditions of life."

of the senses; since whatever strikes the senses preponderates over everything, however superior, which does not immediately strike them. Hence contemplation mostly ceases with sight, and a very scanty, or perhaps no regard is paid to invisible objects. The entire operation, therefore, of spirits enclosed in tangible bodies is concealed, and escapes us. All that more delicate change of formation in the parts of coarser substances (vulgarly called alteration, but in fact a change of position in the smallest particles) is wholly unknown; and yet, unless the two matters we have mentioned be explored and brought to light, no great effect can be produced in nature. Again, the very nature of common air, and all bodies of less density (of which there are many) is almost unknown; for the senses are weak and erring, nor can instruments be of great use in extending their sphere or acuteness—all the better interpretations of nature are worked out by instances, and fit and apt experiments, where the senses only judge of the experiment, the experiment of nature and the thing itself.

. . . Nobody can successfully investigate the nature of any object by considering that object alone; the inquiry must be more generally extended.

Even when men build any science and theory upon experiment, yet they almost always turn with premature and hasty zeal to practise. . . .

Those who have treated of the sciences have been either empirics or dogmatical. The former, like ants, only heap up and use their store, the latter, like spiders, spin out their own webs. The bee, a mean between both, extracts matter from the flowers of the garden and the field, but works and fashions it by its own efforts.

. . . The empire of man over things is founded on the arts and sciences alone, for nature is only to be commanded by obeying her.

Lastly, let none be alarmed at the objection of the arts and sciences becoming depraved to malevolent or luxurious purposes and the like, for the same can be said of every worldly good; talent, courage, strength, beauty, riches, light itself, and the rest. Only let mankind regain their rights over nature, assigned to them by the gift of God, and obtain that power, whose exercise will be governed by right reason and true religion.

Bacon's greatest work was the Instauratio Magna, *or encyclopedia of all knowledge. He lived long enough to finish only its first two parts: the* Novum Organum, *or "The New Logic" (1620)— and the* De Dignitate et Augmentis Scientiarum, *or "The Advancement of Learning" (1623). The accompanying aphorisms are from the* Novum Organum

GALILEO GALILEI was born in 1564 and died in 1642. Between these dates four highlights stand out: The student Galileo timing with his pulse beat a swinging lamp in the Cathedral of Pisa in 1581 ... the young lecturer bent over a balustrade of the Leaning Tower about to drop two stones of different weights ... the mature professor of mathematics elated at his telescope's disclosure that the Milky Way is a great sea of stars—these three moments together with his other observations and experiments marked the foundation of modern mathematical physics. The fourth highlight in the great Italian's career is not so inspiring: that of the aged and infirm Galileo on his knees in Rome in 1633, forced to recant his life's beliefs.

Galileo

"The earth moves"

ABOUT TEN MONTHS ago a report reached my ears that a Dutchman* had constructed a telescope, by the aid of which visible objects, although at a great distance from the eye of the observer, were seen distinctly as if near; and some proofs of its most wonderful performances were reported, which some gave credence to, but others contradicted.

A few days after, I received confirmation of the report in a letter written from Paris by a noble Frenchman, Jacques Badovere, which finally determined me to give myself up first to inquire into the principle of the telescope, and then to consider the means by which I might compass the invention of a similar instrument, which after a little while I succeeded in doing, through deep study of the theory of Refraction; and I prepared a tube, at first of lead, in the ends of which I fitted two glass lenses, both plane on one side, but on the other side one spherically convex, and the other concave. Then bringing my eye to the concave lens I saw objects satisfactorily large and near, for they

* (Hans Lippershey)

appeared one-third of the distance off and nine times larger than when they are seen with the natural eye alone. I shortly afterwards constructed another telescope with more nicety, which magnified objects more than sixty times. At length, by sparing neither labour nor expense, I succeeded in constructing for myself an instrument so superior that objects seen through it appear magnified nearly a thousand times, and more than thirty miles nearer than if viewed by the natural powers of sight alone.

It would be altogether a waste of time to enumerate the number and importance of the benefits which this instrument may be expected to confer, when used by land or sea. But without paying attention to its use for terrestrial objects, I betook myself to observations of the heavenly bodies; and first of all, I viewed the Moon as near as if it

Yerkes Observatory

Two telescopes built and used by Galileo Galilei for his observations of the solar system

was scarcely two semi-diameters of the Earth distant. After the Moon, I frequently observed other heavenly bodies, both fixed stars and planets, with incredible delight. . .

There remains the matter, which seems to me to deserve to be considered the most important in this work, namely, that I should disclose and publish to the world the occasion of discovering and observing four planets, never seen from the very beginning of the world up to our own times, their positions, and the observations made during the last two months about their movements and their changes of magnitude. . .

Galileo was also the first man to see the phases of Venus, the spots on the sun, and the mountains of the moon

On the 7th day of January in the present year, 1610, in the first hour of the following night, when I was viewing the constellations of the heavens through a telescope, the planet Jupiter presented itself to my view, and as I had prepared for myself a very excellent instrument, I noticed a circumstance which I had never been able to notice before, owing to want of power in my other telescope, namely, that three little stars, small but very bright, were near the planet; and although I believed them to belong to the number of the fixed stars, yet they made me somewhat wonder, because they seemed to be arranged exactly in a straight line, parallel to the ecliptic, and to be brighter than the rest of the stars, equal to them in magnitude. The position of them with reference to one another and to Jupiter was as follows:

Ori.　☆　☆　●　☆　Occ.

On the east side there were two stars, and a single one towards the west. The star which was furthest towards the east, and the western star, appeared rather larger than the third.

I scarcely troubled at all about the distance between them and Jupiter, for as I have already said, at first I believed them to be fixed stars; but when on January 8th, led by some fatality, I turned again to look at the same part of the heavens, I found a very different state of things, for there were three little stars all west of Jupiter, and nearer together than on the previous night, and they were separated from one another by equal intervals, as the accompanying figure shows.

Ori.　●　☆　☆　☆　Occ.

At this point, although I had not turned my thoughts at all upon the approximation of the stars to one another, yet my surprise began

Yerkes Observatory

Galileo's original drawings of the satellites of Jupiter as he observed them day by day

to be excited, how Jupiter could one day be found to the east of all the aforesaid fixed stars when the day before it had been west of two of them; and forthwith I became afraid lest the planet might have moved differently from the calculation of astronomers, and so had passed those stars by its own proper motion. I, therefore, waited for the next night with the most intense longing, but I was disappointed of my hope, for the sky was covered with clouds in every direction.

But on January 10th the stars appeared in the following position with regard to Jupiter, the third, as I thought, being

Ori.　☆　☆　●　Occ.

hidden by the planet. They were situated just as before, exactly in the same straight line with Jupiter, and along the Zodiac.

When I had seen these phenomena, as I knew that corresponding changes of position could not by any means belong to Jupiter, and as, moreover, I perceived that the stars which I saw had always been the same, for there were no others either in front or behind, within a great distance, along the Zodiac—at length, changing from doubt to surprise, I discovered that the interchange of position which I saw belonged not to Jupiter, but to the stars to which my attention had been drawn, and I thought therefore that they ought to be observed henceforward with more attention and precision.

Accordingly, on January 11th I saw an arrangement of the following kind:

Ori.　☆　٭　●　Occ.

namely, only two stars to the east of Jupiter, the nearer of which was distant from Jupiter three times as far as from the star further to the east; and the star furthest to the east was nearly twice as large as the other one; whereas on the previous night they had appeared nearly of equal magnitude. I, therefore, concluded, and decided unhesitatingly, that there are three stars in the heavens moving about Jupiter, as Venus and Mercury around the Sun; which at length was established as clear as daylight by numerous other subsequent observations. These observations also established that there are not only three, but four, erratic sidereal bodies performing their revolutions round Jupiter. . .

These are my observations upon the four Medicean planets,

Only four of Jupiter's nine satellites were visible to Galileo, and it wasn't until 300 years later that scientists discovered the other five

recently discovered for the first time by me; and although it is not yet permitted me to deduce by calculation from these observations the orbits of these bodies, yet I may be allowed to make statements, based upon them, well worthy of attention.

And, in the first place, since they are sometimes behind, sometimes before Jupiter, at like distances, and withdraw from this planet towards the east and towards the west only within very narrow limits of divergence, and since they accompany this planet alike when its motion is retrograde and direct, it can be a matter of doubt to no one that they perform their revolutions about this planet while at the same time they all accomplish together orbits of twelve years' length about the centre of the world. Moreover, they revolve in unequal circles, which is evidently the conclusion to be drawn from the fact that I have never been permitted to see two satellites in conjunction when their distance from Jupiter was great, whereas near Jupiter two, three, and sometimes all four, have been found closely packed together.

Moreover, it may be detected that the revolutions of the satellites which describe the smallest circles round Jupiter are the most rapid, for the satellites nearest to Jupiter are often to be seen in the east, when the day before they have appeared in the west, and contrariwise. Also, the satellite moving in the greatest orbit seems to me, after carefully weighing the occasions of its returning to positions previously noticed, to have a periodic time of half a month. Besides, we have a notable and splendid argument to remove the scruples of those who can tolerate the revolution of the planets round the Sun in the Copernican system, yet are so disturbed by the motion of one Moon about the Earth, while both accomplish an orbit of a year's length about the Sun, that they consider that this theory of the universe must be upset as impossible; for now we have not one planet only revolving about another, while both traverse a vast orbit about the Sun, but our sense of sight presents to us four satellites circling about Jupiter, like the moon about the Earth, while the whole system travels over a mighty orbit about the sun in . . . 12 years.

The Copernican theory, ridiculed by all seemingly "learned men" of this era, had little definite proof of its validity until Galileo's discovery of Jupiter's satellites

WILLIAM HARVEY was born at Folkestone, on the south coast of England, on April 1, 1578. He received his B.A. degree at Cambridge at 19. His parents were wealthy and he was able to go to the famous Italian university at Padua and study medicine under Fabricus, then a co-teacher there with Galileo, and the man who discovered the little valves which permit blood to flow only one way in the veins. Harvey there began the dissection and experiments on many kinds of live animals— and upon himself—which led to his most important discovery, that of the circulation of the blood. In 1651 he published a prophetic treatise on generation. He died on June 3, 1657, after a long and prosperous life.

William Harvey

On the circulation of the blood

Wₕₐₜ REMAINS to be said upon the quantity and source of the blood . . . is of so novel and unheard-of character that I not only fear injury to myself from the envy of a few, but I tremble lest I have mankind at large for my enemies, so much does wont and custom . . . and doctrine once sown and that has struck deep root, and respect for antiquity influence all men.

Still the die is cast, and my trust is in my love of truth and the candor that inheres in cultivated minds.

And sooth to say, when I surveyed my mass of evidence, whether derived from vivisections, and my various reflections on them, or from the ventricles of the heart and the vessels that enter into and issue from them, the symmetry and size of these conduits—for nature, doing nothing in vain, would never have given them so large a relative size without a purpose—or from the arrangement and intimate structure of the valves in particular, and of the other parts of the heart in general, with many things besides, I frequently and seriously bethought me, and long revolved in my mind, what might be the quantity of blood which was transmitted, in how short a time its passage might be effected, and the like; and not finding it possible that this could be supplied by the juices of the ingested aliment (food taken into the body) without the veins on the one hand becoming drained, and the arteries on the other getting ruptured through the excessive charge of blood, unless the blood should somehow find its way from the arteries into the veins, and so return to the right side of the heart; I began to think whether there might not be a *motion, as it were, in a circle*.

Now this I afterwards found to be true; and I finally saw that the blood, forced by the action of the left ventricle into the arteries, was distributed to the body at large, and its several parts, in the same manner as it is sent through the lungs, impelled by the right ventricle into the pulmonary artery, and that is then passed through the veins and along the vena cava (the large veins which carry the blood to the right atrium, or chamber of the heart) and so round to the left ventricle. . . .

But lest anyone should say that we give them words only, and make mere specious assertions without any foundation, and desire to innovate without sufficient cause, three points present themselves for confirmation, which being stated, I conceive that the truth I contend for will follow necessarily, and appear as a thing obvious to all.

First, the blood is incessantly transmitted by the action of the heart from the vena cava to the arteries in such quantity that it cannot be supplied from the ingesta (foods), and in such wise that the whole mass must very quickly pass through the organ.

Second, the blood under the influence of the arterial pulse enters and is impelled in a continuous, equable, and incessant stream through every part and member of the body, in much larger quantity than were sufficient for nutrition, or than the whole mass of fluids could supply.

Third, the veins in like manner return this blood incessantly to the heart from all parts and members of the body.

These points proved, I conceive it will be manifest that the blood circulates, revolves, propelled and then returning, from the heart to the extremities, from the extremities to the heart, and thus that it performs a kind of circular motion.

Let us assume either arbitrarily or from experiment the quantity of blood which the left ventricle of the heart will contain when

Previously it was supposed that the blood moved forward and backward in the body, something like the ebb and flow of the tides; that the arteries transported air to various parts of the body; that blood was made from food in the liver, and that it then passed to the heart which sent it around the body through the veins; that the right side of the heart which is connected to the veins, and which is separated by a partition from the left side of the heart, was full of holes which acted as a filter

distended to be, say, two ounces, three ounces, one ounce and a half—in the dead body I have found it to hold upwards of two ounces.

Let us assume further how much less the heart will hold in the contracted than in the dilated state; and how much blood it will project into the aorta upon each contraction (and all the world allows that with the systole something is always projected, a necessary consequence . . . obvious from the structure of the valves); and let us suppose as approaching the truth that the fourth, or fifth, or sixth, or even but the eighth part of its charge is thrown into the artery at each contraction; this would give either half an ounce; or three drams (one eighth of an ounce), or one dram of blood as propelled by the heart at each pulse into the aorta; which quantity, by reason of the valves at the root of the vessel, can by no means return into the ventricle.

Harvey proved in this treatise that the pulse is the result of blood flowing into the arteries

Now, in the course of half an hour, the heart will have made more than one thousand beats, in some as many as two, three, and even four thousand. Multiplying the number of drams propelled by the number of pulses, we shall have either one thousand half ounces, or one thousand times three drams, or a like proportional quantity of blood, according to the amount which we assume as propelled with each stroke of the heart, sent from this organ into the artery; a larger quantity in every case than is contained in the whole body.

In the same way, in the sheep or dog, say that but a single scruple (one third of a dram) of blood passes with each stroke of the heart, in one half hour we should have one thousand scruples, or about three pounds and a half of blood injected into the aorta; but the body of neither animal contains above four pounds of blood, a fact which I have myself ascertained in the case of the sheep.

Upon this supposition, therefore, assumed merely as a ground for reasoning, we see the whole mass of blood passing through the heart, from the veins to the arteries, and in like manner through the lungs.

But let it be said that this does not take place in half an hour, but in an hour, or even in a day; anyway, it is still manifest that more blood passes through the heart in consequence of its action than either be supplied by the whole of the ingesta, or than can be contained in the veins at the same moment.

Nor can it be allowed that the heart in contracting sometimes propels and sometimes does not propel, or at the most propels but very little, a mere nothing, or an imaginary something: all this, indeed, has already been refuted; and is, besides, contrary both to sense and reason.

For if it be a necessary effect of the dilatation (enlargement) of the heart that its ventricles become filled with blood, it is equally so that, contracting, these cavities should expel their contents; and this

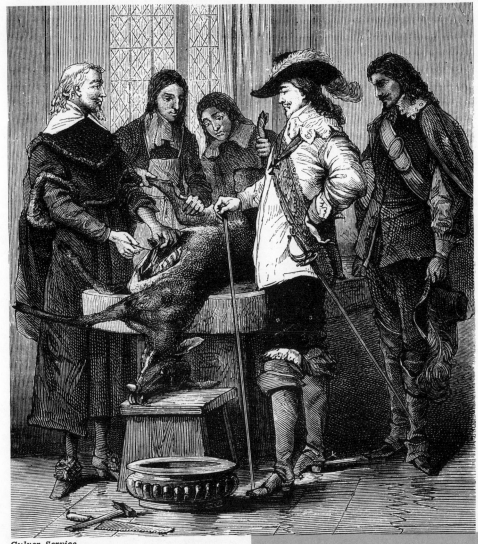

With the use of a live animal, William Harvey is demonstrating the remarkable phenomenon of the circulation of the blood to Charles I and several doctors of the Royal College of London

not in any trifling measure, seeing that neither are the conduits small nor the contractions few in number, but frequent, and always in some certain proportion, whether it be a third, or a sixth, or an eighth, to the total capacity of the ventricles, so that a like proportion received with each stroke of the heart, the capacity of the ventricle contracted always bearing a certain relation to the capacity of the ventricle when dilated.

Although Harvey inferred the existence of the capillaries, through which the blood passes from the arteries to the veins, they were discovered by Malpighi—and the microscope—four years after Harvey's death

And since, in dilating, the ventricles cannot be supposed to get filled with nothing, or with an imaginary something; so in contracting they never expel nothing or aught imaginary, but always a certain something, viz., blood, in proportion to the amount of the contraction.

Whence it is to be inferred that if at one stroke the heart in man, the ox, or the sheep ejects but a single dram of blood, and there are one thousand strokes in half an hour, in this interval there will have been ten pounds five ounces expelled: were there with each stroke two drams expelled, the quantity would of course amount to twenty pounds and ten ounces; were there half an ounce, the quantity would come to forty-one pounds and eight ounces; and were there one ounce, it would be as much as eighty-three pounds and four ounces; the whole of which, in the course of one half hour, would have been transfused (transferred) from the veins to the arteries.

The actual quantity of blood expelled at each stroke of the heart, and the circumstances under which it is either greater or less than ordinary, I leave for particular determination afterward, from numerous observations which I have made on the subject.

Meanwhile this much I know, and would here proclaim to all, that the blood is transfused at one time in larger, at another in smaller quantity; and that the circuit of the blood is accomplished now more rapidly, now more slowly, according to the temperament, age, et cetera, of the individual, to external and internal circumstances, to naturals and non-naturals—sleep, rest, food, exercise, affection of the mind, and the like.

But indeed, supposing even the smallest quantity of blood to be passed through the heart and the lungs with each pulsation, a vastly greater amount would still be thrown into the arteries and whole body than could by any possibility be supplied by the food . . . in short it could be furnished in no other way than by making a circuit and returning.

IN 1644, 17-year-old Robert Boyle returned to England from the then almost traditional educational grand tour of the Continent. From that year forward his life was devoted to scientific study—study which led in time to the discovery of a foundation stone of physics, Boyle's law. He discovered that gases, unlike liquids, can be compressed and that their volume, in fact, varies inversely with the pressure applied. Doubling the pressure squeezes a gas into half the space. A commonplace today, but a commonplace at the heart of steam and internal-combustion engines, sprayers, air- and gas-driven machinery of every kind. But a revolutionary notion in 1662, when Boyle announced his law.

Robert Boyle

The physical properties of gases
by Leonard Engel

ROBERT BOYLE, seventh son and fourteenth child of one of Elizabethan England's greatest sea rovers, the Earl of Cork, came into the world on January 25, 1627, at one of the earl's Irish castles.

It was the age of the poet Milton and the giant of science, Isaac Newton. Further, in science, it was the time when scientific research first began to emerge as a full-time pursuit, like medicine or law; when the first scientific societies were formed, and the first scientific journals published; when science began to whet its secret weapon of discovery, the experimental method. In all this, the Earl of Cork's youngest son was to play a starring role.

Boyle's father died in 1644, leaving him large estates in Ireland and southern England and a house in London. Just 17, Boyle decided to devote his life to "natural philosophy." He had acquired a taste for "natural philosophy"—as science was then called—while studying astronomy, optics, and mechanics in the Italian city of Florence in the year Galileo lay dying not many miles away.

Boyle conducted experiments at one time or another in nearly every branch of science then known except anatomy. The "tenderness of his nature," he explained, couldn't abide experimenting with animals, though he knew this to be "most instructing." Chemists honor him as the father of chemistry. He discovered many previously unknown substances, introduced the study of crystals as clues to chemical composition, distinguished between mixtures and chemical compounds, and gave the first real definition of an element. It was Boyle who sealed the stem of Galileo's water barometer and thus made the first real thermometer. With it, Boyle discovered the constancy of man's body temperature. He also carried out important experiments in electricity and magnetism and was the first to suggest that heat was due to the motion of molecules. But above all, Boyle is remembered for his experiments on gases and vacuums.

In the 1650's, the big questions among the *virtuosi* (as the early scientists referred to themselves) were whether air had weight and whether there was such a thing as a vacuum. Not long before, Galileo's disciple Torricelli had inverted the open end of a long tube filled with mercury in an open dish of mercury. The column of quicksilver fell to a height of about 30 inches, where it stayed. Torricelli guessed that the mercury column was held up by the weight of the air pressing down on the quicksilver in the dish, and that the clear space over the mercury in the tube was a vacuum.

In that day, many learned, intelligent men could not believe in "empty" space. Nature, it was widely believed, abhorred a vacuum. They were equally unconvinced that the column of mercury was held up by the weight of the air. Some argued that the mercury was kept in place by an invisible thread, called a "funiculus," between the quicksilver and the inner surface of the top of the glass tube.

What was needed was more direct proof of the weight of the air and the emptiness of the Torricellian space. Both were found by Boyle in Von Guericke's pump.

Boyle designed a vacuum pump with a large glass vacuum chamber and an arrangement for introducing various objects into it. Even more remarkable—this was centuries before the age of precision—he and Hooke got it built.

In one of his first experiments, Boyle placed a mercury barometer in the glass chamber. Then he started to work his "pneumatical engine." As more and more air was removed from the chamber, the mercury fell. (It didn't come all the way down to the level of the dish, though, because his pump couldn't create a high vacuum.) Plainly, it was the weight or pressure of the air *outside* the barometer that kept the mercury column up.

In another experiment, he hung a watch with a loud alarm by a thread inside the chamber. He was overjoyed to hear the ticking of the watch and the sound of the alarm fade away as air was pumped out of the chamber. By a fortunate circumstance, nearly all the learned men of Europe had already accepted the idea that sound was carried by the air. So perhaps they would accept the silence within the vacuum chamber as proof of its emptiness.

But wait a moment. In the course of his experiments, the alert Boyle noticed something else. The piston of his pneumatical engine was drawn up and down by a lever and ratchet. Boyle noticed that the piston kicked back against the lever toward the end of each stroke, very much like the piston of a tire pump when the tire is nearly inflated.

Nothing similar had ever been observed with water pumps. It was as though the air had a "spring" to it. Air was clearly an elastic medium, capable of both expansion and compression.

Boyle announced his findings in 1660 in a small book with a whopping title, *New Experiments Physico-Mechanicall, Touching the Spring of the Air, and Its Effects (Made, for the Most Part, in a New Pneumatical Engine)*. As happens so often, however, the book persuaded few who weren't already convinced. In fact, the opponents of the new science redoubled the attack. They were especially scornful of the "spring of the air," which Boyle had actually inferred rather than proved.

Boyle took up the challenge. To demonstrate the compressibility of the air beyond any possible doubt, he devised one of the first true controlled experiments in history.

He had a glass blower make a large glass tube in the shape of a J. The short leg, which was nearly 5 feet long, was closed by a stopcock; the other, about 12 feet in length, was open. Both legs were carefully graduated in sixteenths of an inch.

The mammoth double tube was set up in the stairwell of Boyle's London house. With the stopcock open, mercury was poured in until the space over the liquid metal in the short leg measured exactly 48 inches. The mercury was at the same level in the long leg, giving

As a scientific investigator Boyle is distinguished because he carried out the principles set down by Francis Bacon in his Novum Organum

73

Boyle, so to speak, 48 inches of air at atmospheric pressure when the stopcock was closed.

Boyle's assistant climbed the stairs and began adding mercury through the long leg of the tube. Boyle stayed below to watch what happened in the short leg.

As mercury was added in the long leg, it rose in the short branch, squeezing the entrapped air. When 29⅛ inches of quicksilver—an amount equivalent to the atmospheric pressure that day—had been poured in, thus doubling the pressure, the trapped air measured 24 inches—just half its volume at the start of the experiment. When 58¾ inches more of quicksilver was added, doubling the pressure once more, the length of the air column was halved again, to 12 inches. Thus Boyle not only proved directly the compressibility of air and other gases, but found the law governing the relation of pressure and volume.

Boyle nearly discovered the relation between the temperature and volume of a gas as well. A painstaking observer, he noticed a slight change in the length of the air column when he cooled the short leg of the tube with a wet cloth or warmed it with a candle. He was afraid, however, that increasing the heat would break the glass and prevent completion of the pressure experiments.

He never returned to the question of heat's effect on gas volume. He always had a dozen other experiments going. He was also a prolific writer—he wrote more than 40 books on a wide variety of topics, including religion—and he was one of the *virtuosi* who, in 1662, formed the oldest scientific society still in existence, Great Britain's august Royal Society. The relation between temperature and gas volume—the latter varies directly with the absolute temperature—wasn't worked out until a century and a quarter later. But Boyle did more than enough. He not only discovered one of the fundamental laws of physics, but by the clear, careful way in which he went about his experiments, helped show those who followed him how to wrest out nature's secrets and push back the boundaries of the unknown.

Like Galileo and many other early scientists, Boyle was ridiculed by the Church for "destroying religion." But unlike these earlier men, he lived in Great Britain and so was not persecuted for his ideas

CHRISTIAN HUYGENS was born in 1629, and died in 1695. Into the 66 years of his life he packed many lives; Huygens was many men. He was a searcher for things nobody else ever saw before in the sky—who ground lenses with his own hands. He was a philosopher who wondered about the nature of time—who junked the hourglass and made himself a clock. He was a physicist trying to pin down the composition and actions of light—who knotted together a net of numbers that snared a little of the secret heart of matter itself. And, although he never married, he was a gentleman of the world—as at ease at the French Court as when alone on his walks along the banks of the Zuyder Zee.

Christian Huygens

Astronomer, philosopher, physicist
by William P. Schenk

CHRISTIAN HUYGENS (frequently spelled Christiaan Huyghens) was born at The Hague in Holland on April 14, 1629. His father, Constantijn, a famous Dutch poet and statesman, tutored him, and then sent him to Leiden University where he studied law and mathematics. He finished his formal schooling at the *Collegium Arausiacum* at Breda in 1649. He then returned to The Hague and lived at home where he was able to devote himself as he wished to mathematics and to his own investigations in astronomy, mechanics and physics.

The mathematician Huygens having mastered geometrical optics, the mechanic Huygens soon developed and perfected a new technique in practical lens grinding.

Around 1650 he began work on a telescope having twice the power and clarity of its average contemporaries; with it he made two of the most astonishing discoveries of the age. In 1655 he discovered Titan, the largest and brightest of Saturn's moons. And in the following year he announced (in a Latin anagram he later translated) that Saturn was encircled "by a ring, thin, plane, nowhere attached, and inclined to the ecliptic!"

Christian Huygens
Astronomer, philosopher, physicist

He was an early explorer of Orion, and on November 28, 1659, he made the first drawing of Syrtis Major, the most prominent disk marking on Mars. His sketch many years later enabled the rotation period of Mars to be calculated to within 1/50th second.

In 1665 Huygens took time out to suggest that the temperature of boiling water be used as a fixed point on the thermometer scale.

This clock is now in the National Museum of the History of Science at Leiden

Meanwhile, keenly aware of the astronomer's need of a method of accurate measurement of small intervals of time, Huygens had been at work on the construction of a clock employing the principles of the pendulum—a task not solved by Galileo who had discovered the pendulum secret. It is now generally acknowledged that Huygens succeeded in inventing the world's first pendulum clock in 1656. (In 1675 he discovered the principle of the spiral-spring regulator and balance-wheel of the chronometer—basis of subsequent watches and clocks.)

Science Digest

Christian Huygens at the eye-piece of one of his famous "aerial" or "tubeless" telescopes

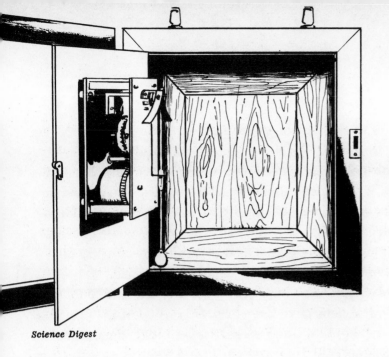

Science Digest

The oldest pendulum clock in existence, constructed under Huygens' personal supervision

Huygens lived in Paris from around 1668 until 1681, at the invitation of Louis XIV. These were fruitful years for the Hollander and for the advancement of science.

In 1669, by then having talked with Newton in England, and having been elected a Fellow, Huygens submitted his communication on the laws governing the collision of elastic bodies to the Royal Society.

In 1673 Huygens published his classic *Horologium Oscillatorium*, describing his improved pendulum clock and its theory, and presenting his work on the mechanical properties of the cycloid, and the theory of evolutes and involutes; this masterwork of mathematics laid the foundations of modern rigid dynamics.

One of Huygens' duties in Paris was to assist in founding the Académie des Sciences

Now a member of the newly founded *Académie des Sciences*, Huygens invented a "gunpowder machine" based on the principle of the internal combustion engine. And in the scholarly seclusion of the Bibliotheque du Roi, he turned his mind to the mysteries of the transmission of light. In 1677, one of the earliest students of polarization, he explained the laws of double refraction; in the following year he made his first formal announcement of his undulatory theory of light.

After his return to his native land, and the death of his father in 1687, Huygens lived out the rest of his life at the small country

Huygens is probably more well known for his outstanding work in the field of light than he is for his astronomical observations

seat of Hofwijck at the village of Voorburg, near The Hague. He now devoted himself to making lenses of enormous focal length, which, "mounted on high poles, and connected with the eyepiece by means of a cord, formed what were called 'aerial telescopes.' " Around this period he designed and ground the almost perfectly achromatic double-lens type of eyepiece named after him. His *Cosmotheoros*—a speculation on the inhabitants of the planets—was published after he died— "being a man of considerable property"—on June 8, 1695.

In his *Traité de la Lumiére,* written in French and published at Leiden in 1690, Huygens gave the world the results of his profound researches in physical optics. In this *Treatise on Light,* the concept of an "ether" is introduced for the first time, and light is explained as an undulatory, or *wave*—rather than as a corpuscular, or *particle*—phenomenon. But, as Peter van de Kamp, director of the Sproule Observatory wrote in his *Basic Astronomy,* "We do justice to both our knowledge and ignorance if we abandon any specific description, but simply say that light has both particle and undulatory properties."

From Huygen's treatise on light

IT IS INCONCEIVABLE to doubt that light consists in the motion of some sort of matter. For whether one considers its production, one sees that here upon the earth it is chiefly engendered by fire and flame which contain without doubt bodies that are in rapid motion, since they dissolve and melt many other bodies, even the most solid; or whether one considers its effects, one sees that when light is collected, as by concave mirrors, it has the property of burning as fire does, that is to say, it disunites the particles of bodies. . . .

Further, when one considers the extreme speed with which light spreads on every side, and how, when it comes from different regions, even from those directly opposite, the rays traverse one another without hindrance, one may well understand that when we see a luminous object it cannot be any transport of matter coming to us from this object, in the way in which a shot or an arrow traverses the air; for assuredly that would too greatly impugn these two properties of light, especially the second of them. It is then in some other way that light spreads; and that which can lead us to comprehend it is the knowledge which we have of the spreading of sound in the air.

We know that by means of the air, which is an invisible and impalpable body, sound spreads around the spot where it has been produced, by a movement which is passed on successively from one part of the air to another; and that the spreading of this movement, taking place equally rapidly on all sides, ought to form spherical surfaces ever enlarging and which strike our ears.

Now there is no doubt at all that light also comes from the luminous body to our eyes by some movement impressed on the matter which is between the two; since, as we have already seen, it cannot be by the transport of a body which passes from one to the other. If, in addition, light takes time for its passage . . . it will follow that this movement, impressed on the intervening matter, is successive; and consequently it spreads, as sound does, by spherical surfaces and waves; for I call them waves from their resemblance to those which are seen to be formed in water when a stone is thrown into it. . . .

Now if one examines what this matter may be in which the movement coming from the luminous body is propagated, which I call ethereal matter, one will see that it is not the same that serves for the propagation of sound. For one finds that the latter is really that which we feel and which we breathe, and which, being removed from any place, still leaves there the other kind of matter that serves to convey light. This may be proved by shutting up a sounding body in a glass vessel from which the air is withdrawn by the machine which Mr. Boyle has given us, and with which he has performed so many beautiful experiments.

The "machine" mentioned here is the vacuum pump built by Boyle

But in doing this of which I speak care must be taken to place the sounding body on cotton or on feathers, in such a way that it cannot communicate its tremors either to the glass vessel which encloses it or to the machine; a precaution which has hitherto been neglected. For then, after having exhausted all the air, one hears no sound from the metal, though it is struck.

One sees here not only that our air, which does not penetrate through glass, is the matter by which sound spreads; but also that it is not the same air but another kind of matter in which light spreads; since if the air is removed from the vessel the light does not cease to traverse it as before. . . .

But the extreme velocity of light, and other properties which it has, cannot admit of such a propagation of motion, and I am about to show here the way in which I conceive it must occur. For this, it is needful to explain the property which hard bodies must possess to transmit movement from one to another.

When one takes a number of spheres of equal size, made of some very hard substance, and arranges them in a straight line, so that they touch one another, one finds, on striking with a similar sphere against the first of these spheres, that the motion passes as in an instant to the last of them, which separates itself from the row, without one's being able to perceive that the others have been stirred. And even that one which was used to strike remains motionless with them. Whence one sees that the movement passes with an extreme velocity which is the greater, the greater the hardness of the substance of the spheres.

Huygens' theory of light waves was put aside for many years in favor of the more popular "corpuscular" theory of light, advanced by Isaac Newton

But it is still certain that this progression of motion is not instantaneous, but successive, and therefore must take time. For if the movement, or the disposition to movement, if you will have it so, did not pass successively through all these spheres, they would all acquire the movement at the same time, and hence would all advance together; which does not happen. For the last one leaves the whole row and acquires the speed of the one which was pushed. Moreover there are experiments which demonstrate that all the bodies which we reckon of the hardest kind, such as quenched steel, glass, and agate, act as springs and bend somehow, not only when extended as rods but also when they are in the form of spheres or of other shapes. That is to say, they yield a little in themselves at the place where they are struck, and immediately regain their former figure. . . .

Now in applying this kind of movement to that which produces light there is nothing to hinder us from estimating the particles of the ether to be of a substance as nearly approaching to perfect hardness and possessing a springiness as prompt as we choose. . . .

I will say . . . in passing, that we may conceive that the particles of the ether, notwithstanding their smallness, are in turn composed of other parts and that their springiness consists in the very rapid movement of a subtle matter which penetrates them from every side and constrains their structure to assume such a disposition as to give to this fluid matter the most overt and easy passage possible. . . .

I have then shown in what manner one may conceive light to spread successively, by spherical waves, and how it is possible that this spreading is accomplished with as great a velocity as that which experiments and celestial observations demand.

Van Leeuwenhoek

"The little animals"

IN THE YEAR 1675 I discovered very small living creatures in rain water, which had stood but few days in a new earthen pot glazed blue within. This invited me to view this water with great attention, especially those little animals appearing to me ten thousand times less than those represented by Monsieur Swammerdam, and by him called water fleas, or water lice, which may be perceived in the water with the naked eye.

The first sort I several times observed to consist of five, six, seven, or eight clear globules without being able to discern any film that held them together, or contained them. When these animalcula or living atoms moved, they put forth two little horns, continually moving.

The space between these two horns was flat, though the rest of the body was roundish, sharpening a little toward the end, where they had a tail, near four times the length of the whole body, of the thickness, by my microscope, of a spider's web; at the end of which appeared a globule of the size of one of those which made up the body.

These little creatures, if they chanced to light on the least filament

81

Enthusiastically, Leeuwenhoek turned his microscopes on bees' stings, seeds, ants, urine, tadpoles' tails, the tartar from his teeth—almost everything excited his curiosity. In his observations of tadpoles' tails, he saw the tiny capillary blood vessels which were the missing link in solving the mystery of the circulation of the blood

or string, or other particle, were entangled therein, extending their body in a long round and endeavoring to disentangle their tail.

Their motion of extension and contraction continued awhile; and I have seen several thousands of these poor little creatures, within the space of a grain of gross sand, lie fast clustered together in a few filaments. I also discovered a second sort, of an oval figure; and I imagined their head to stand on a sharp end. These were a little longer than the former. The inferior part of their body is flat, furnished with several extremely thin feet, which moved very nimbly. The upper part of the body was round, and had within eight, ten, or twelve globules, where they were very clear.

These little animals sometimes changed their figure into a perfect round, especially when they came to lie on a dry place. Their body was also very flexible; for as soon as they struck against the smallest fibre or string their body was bent in, which bending presently jerked out again.

When I put any of them on a dry place I observed that, changing themselves into a round, their body was raised pyramidal-wise, with an extant point in the middle; and having lain thus a little while, with a motion of their feet, they burst asunder, and the globules were presently diffused and dissipated, so that I could not discern the least thing of any film, in which the globules had doubtless been enclosed; and at this time of their bursting asunder I was able to discover more globules than when they were alive.

I observed a third sort of little animals that were twice as long as broad, and to my eye eight times smaller than the first. Yes, I thought I discerned little feet, whereby they moved very briskly, in a round as well as a straight line.

There was a fourth sort, which were so small that I was not able to give them any figure at all. These were a thousand times smaller than the eye of a large louse. These exceeded all the former in celerity.

I have often observed them to stand still as it were on a point, and then turn themselves about with that swiftness, as we see a top turn round, the circumference they made being no larger than that of a grain of small sand, and then extending themselves straight forward, and by and by lying in a bending posture.

I discovered also several other sorts of animals; these were generally made up of such soft parts, as the former, that they burst asunder as soon as they came to want water.

May 26, it rained hard; the rain growing less, I caused some of that rain water running down from the housetop to be gathered in a clean glass, after it had been washed two or three times with water. And in this I observed some few very small living creatures, and seeing them, I thought they might have been produced in the leaded gutters in some water that had remained there before.

I perceived in pure water, after some days, more of those animals, as also some that were somewhat larger. And I imagine that many thousands of these little creatures do not equal an ordinary grain of sand in bulk; and comparing them with a cheese mite, which may be seen to move with the naked eye, I make the proportion of one of these small water creatures to a cheese mite to be like that of a bee to a horse; for the circumference of one of these little animals in water is not so large as the thickness of a hair in a cheese mite.

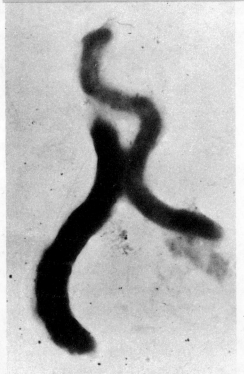

Two of the "little animals" that Anton van Leeuwenhoek might have seen with his simple yet ingenious microscopes. These microorganisms are found in selected specimens of rain water

Drs. Katherine Polevitzky and Robert Picard

In another quantity of rain water, exposed for some days to the air, I observed some thousands of them in a drop of water, which were of the smallest sort that I had seen hitherto. And in some time after I observed, besides the animals already noted, a sort of creatures that were eight times as large, of almost a round figure; and as those very small animalcula swam gently among each other, moving as gnats do in the air, so did these larger ones move far more swiftly, tumbling round as it were, and then making a sudden downfall.

In the waters of the river Maese I saw very small creatures of different kinds and colors, and so small that I could very hardly discern their figures; but the number of them was far less than those found in rain water.

In the water of a very cold well in the autumn I discovered a very great number of living animals, very small, that were exceedingly clear, and a little larger than the smallest I ever saw.

One of the 247 microscopes Leeuwenhoek built for his observations of bacteria. In addition he designed more than 419 lenses. Most of these were double-convex lenses

In sea water I observed at first a little blackish animal, looking as if it had been made up of two globules. This creature had a peculiar motion, resembling the skipping of a flea on white paper, so that it might very well be called a water flea; but it was far less than the eye of that little animal, which Dr. Swammerdam calls the water flea.

I also discovered little creatures therein that were clear, of the same size with the former animal, but of an oval figure, having a serpentine motion. I further noticed a third sort, which were very slow in their motion; their body was of a mouse color, clear toward the oval point; and before the head and behind the body there stood out a sharp little point anglewise. This sort was a little larger. But there was yet a fourth somewhat longer than oval.

Yet of all these sorts there were but a few of each. Some days after viewing this water I saw a hundred where before I had seen but one; but these were of another figure, and not only less, but they were also very clear, and of an oblong oval figure, only with this difference, that their heads ended sharper; and although they were a thousand times smaller than a small grain of sand, yet when they lay out of the water in a dry place they burst in pieces and spread into three or four very little globules, and into some aqueous matter, without any other parts appearing in them.

Having put about one third of an ounce of whole pepper in water, and it having lain about three weeks in the water, to which I had twice added some snow water, the other water being in great part exhaled, I discerned in it with great surprise an incredible number of little animals, of divers kinds, and among the rest, some that were three or four times as long as broad; but their whole thickness did not much exceed the hair of a louse.

They had a very pretty motion, often tumbling about and sideways; then when the water was let to run off from them they turned round like a top; at first their body changed into an oval, and afterwards, when the circular motion ceased, they returned to their former length.

The second sort of creatures discovered in this water were of a perfect oval figure, and they had no less pleasing or nimble a motion than the former; and these were in far greater numbers. There was a third sort, which exceeded the two former in number, and these had tails like those I had formerly observed in rain water.

The fourth sort, which moved through the three former sorts,

Leeuwenhoek was the first man actually to see living bacteria and infusoria, the red blood corpuscles, striated muscle fibers, human and animal spermatozoa, and hundreds of other marvels previously invisible to man

were incredibly small, so that I judged that if one hundred of them lay one by another they would not equal the length of a grain of coarse sand; and according to this estimate, one million of them could not equal the dimensions of a grain of such coarse sand. There was discovered a fifth sort, which had near the thickness of the former, but almost twice the length.

In snow water, which had been about three years in a glass bottle well stopped, I could discover no living creatures; and having poured some of it into porcelain teacup and put therein half an ounce of whole pepper, after some days I observed some animalcula, and those exceedingly small ones, whose body seemed to me twice as long as broad, but they moved very slowly, and often circularly. I observed also a vast multitude of oval-figured animalcula, to the number of eight thousand in a single drop.

Bausch & Lomb Optical Company

This modern research microscope is
quite a contrast to the ones used by Leeuwenhoek

ISAAC NEWTON, English mathematician and natural philosopher, called one of the greatest intellects who ever lived, was born in 1642. A farmer's son, Newton entered Cambridge in 1661. From that year on the world was to have cause to remember him. As an undergraduate he discovered the Binomial Theorem; had he done nothing else his name would still appear in the histories of science. But he went on to invent mathematical tools without which modern science would be impossible, to evolve the first formula for the velocity of sound, to formulate the laws of universal gravity and motion, and to work out many other laws of the physical world. White-haired and venerable, Newton died in 1727.

Isaac Newton

On light and color

The dispersion of light

IN THE YEAR 1666 (at which time I applied myself to the grinding of optick glasses of other figures than spherical) I procured me a triangular glass prism, to try therewith the celebrated phaenomena of colors. And in order thereto, having darkened my chamber, and made a small hole in my window-shuts, to let in a convenient quantity of the sun's light, I placed my prism at its entrance, that it might be thereby refracted to the opposite wall.

It was at first a very pleasing divertissement, to view the vivid and intense colors produced thereby; but after a while applying myself to consider them more circumspectly, I became surprised, to see them in an oblong form; which, according to the received laws of refraction, I expected should have been circular. They were terminated at the sides with straight lines, but at the ends, the decay of light was so gradual that it was difficult to determine justly, what was their figure; yet they seemed semicircular.

Comparing the length of this colored Spectrum with its breadth, I found it about five times greater, a disproportion so extravagant, that it excited me to a more than ordinary curiosity to examining from whence it might proceed.

I could scarce think that the various thicknesses of the glass, or the termination with shadow or darkness, could have any influence on light to produce such an effect; yet I thought it not amiss, first to examine those circumstances, and so tried what would happen by transmitting light through parts of the glass of divers thicknesses, or through holes in the window of divers bignesses, or by setting the prism without, so that light might pass through it, and be refracted, before it was terminated by the hole: But I found none of these circumstances material. The fashion of the colors was in all these cases the same. . . .

Newton divided sunlight into its component parts and put them together again

Bausch & Lomb Optical Company

Through his extensive experiments with light, Sir Isaac Newton became one of the founders of modern optical science. He also worked out the laws governing color production

The gradual removal of these suspicions led me to the Experimentum Crucis, which was this: I took two boards, and placed one of them close behind the prism at the window, so that the light might pass through a small hole, made in it for the purpose, and fall on the other board, which I placed at about 12 feet distance, having first made a small hole in it also, for some of the incident light to pass through.

Then I placed another prism behind this second board, so that the light trajected through both the boards might pass through that also, and be again refracted before it arrived at the wall.

This done, I took the first prism in my hand, and turned it to and fro slowly about its axis, so much as to make the several parts of the image cast, on the second board, successively pass through the hole in it, that I might observe to what places on the wall the second prism would refract them.

And I saw by the variation of those places, that the light, tending to that end of the image, towards which the refraction of the first prism was made, did in the second prism suffer a refraction considerably greater than the light tending to the other end.

And so the true cause of the length of that image was detected to be no other, than that light is not similar or homogenial, but consists of *Difform Rays, some of which are more Refrangible than others;* so that without any difference in their incidence on the same medium, some shall be more Refracted than others; and therefore that, according to their *particular Degrees of Refrangibility,* they were transmitted through the prism to divers parts of the opposite wall. . . .

The phenomenon of Refrangibility *is now called* Dispersion

The origin of colors

THE COLORS of all natural bodies have no other origin than this, that they are variously qualified, to reflect one sort of light in greater plenty than another. And this I have experimented in a dark room, by illuminating those bodies with uncompounded light of divers colors. For by that means any body may be made to appear any color. They have therefore no appropriate color, but ever appear of the color of the light cast upon them, but yet with this difference, that they are most brisk and vivid in the light of their own daylight color.

Minimum appeareth there of any color indifferently, with which

Bise, also bice,
*is the color
of malachite or
azurite; bice blue
is azurite blue,
bice green is
malachite green*

it is illustrated, but yet most luminous in red, and so bise appeareth indifferently of any color, but yet most luminous in blue. And therefore minimum reflecteth rays of any color, but most copiously those endowed with red, that is, with all sorts of rays promiscuously blended, those qualified with red shall abound most in that reflected light, and by their prevalence cause it to appear of that color.

And for the same reason bise, reflecting blue most copiously, shall appear blue by the excess of those rays in its reflected light; and the like of other bodies. And that this is the entire and adequate cause of their colors, is manifest, because they have no power to change or alter the colors of any sort of rays incident apart, but put on all colors indifferently, with which they are enlightened.

These things being so, it can be no longer disputed, whether there be colors in the dark, or whether they be the qualities of the objects we see, no nor perhaps, whether light be a body. For, since colors are the quality of light, having its rays for their entire and immediate subject, how can we think those rays qualities also, unless one quality may be the subject of, and sustain another; which in effect is to call it substance.

We should not know bodies for substances; were it not for their sensible qualities, and the principle of those being now found due to something else, we have as good reason to believe that to be a substance also.

*Written on Newton's
tomb is this
epitaph: "Mortals,
congratulate
yourselves that so
great a man has
lived for the honor
of the human race"*

Besides, whoever thought any quality to be a heterogeneous aggregate, such as light is discovered to be? But to determine more absolutely what light is, after what manner refracted, and by what modes or actions it produceth in our minds the phantasms of colors, is not so easie; and I shall not mingle conjectures with certainties.

Newton's two most important works were the famous *Principia Mathematica Philosophiae Naturalis* published in 1687 and his *Opticks*, published in 1704. His own estimate of his achievements is in his statement: "I seem to have been only like a boy playing on the seashore, and diverting myself in now and then finding a smoother pebble or a prettier shell than ordinary, whilst the great ocean of truth lay all undiscovered before me."

EDMUND HALLEY, *English astronomer, mathematician and classical scholar, was the first man to predict the return of a comet— subsequently named after him—and to fix the date of its arrival. He was born in London on Oct. 29, 1656, and was educated at St. Paul's and at Oxford. In 1676 he made a series of observations from St. Helena which resulted in his catalog of 341 stars of the Southern Hemisphere. His work also included the discovery of the proper motions of the stars, the acceleration of the moon's mean motion, and the use of transits of Venus for the determination of the parallax of the sun. He died on Jan. 14, 1742.*

Edmund Halley

"I venture to foretell"

HITHERTO I have considered the orbits of comets as exactly parabolic; upon which supposition it would follow that comets, being impelled toward the sun by a centripetal force, would descend as from spaces infinitely distant, and by their falling acquire such a velocity as that they may again fly off into the remotest parts of the universe, moving upwards with a perpetual tendency, so as never to return again to the sun.

But since they appear frequently enough, and since some of them can be found to move with a hyperbolic motion, or a motion swifter than what a comet might acquire by its gravity to the sun, 'tis highly probable they rather move in very eccentric elliptic orbits, and make their returns after long periods of time. For so their number will be determinate, and, perhaps, not so very great.

Besides, the space between the sun and the fixed stars is so immense that there is room enough for a comet to revolve, though the period of its revolution be vastly long.

Now the *latus rectum* of a ellipsis is to the *latus rectum* of a parabola, which has the same distance in its perihelium, as the distance in the aphelium in the ellipsis is to the whole axis of the ellipsis. And the velocities are in a subduplicate ratio of the same. Wherefore in very eccentric orbits the ratio comes very near to a ratio of equality; and the very small difference which happens on account of the greater velocity in the parabola is easily compensated in determining the situation of the orbit.

The principal use, therefore, of this table of the elements of their motions, and that which indeed induced me to construct it, is that whenever a new comet shall appear we may be able to know, by comparing together the elements, whether it be any of those which has appeared before, and consequently to determine its period, and the axis of its orbit, and to foretell its return.

Aside from astronomy, Halley calculated An Estimate of the Degrees of the Mortality of Mankind, which is considered to be the scientific foundation of the life insurance business

And indeed there are many things which make me believe that the comet which Apian observed in the year 1531 was the same with that which Kepler and Longomontanus more accurately described in the year 1607; and which I myself have seen return, and observed in the year 1682.

All the elements agree, and nothing seems to contradict this my opinion besides the inequality of the periodic revolutions; which inequality is not so great neither, as that it may not be owing to physical causes. For the motion of Saturn is so disturbed by the rest of the planets, especially Jupiter, that the periodic time of that planet is uncertain for some whole days together.

How much more, therefore, will a comet be subject to suchlike errors, which rises almost four times higher than Saturn, and whose velocity, though increased but a very little, would be sufficient to change its orbit from an elliptical to a parabolical one.

And I am the more confirmed in my opinion of its being the same; for that in the year 1456, in the summertime, a comet was seen passing retrograde between the earth and the sun, much after the same manner; which, though nobody made observations upon it, yet from its period and the manner of its transit I cannot think different from those I have just now mentioned. And since looking over the histories of comets I find, at an equal interval of time, a comet to have been seen about Easter in the year 1305, which is another double period of 151 years before the former.

Hence I think I may venture to foretell that it will return again in the year 1758.

And if it should then so return we shall have no reason to doubt

Halley's comet as it appeared when last seen in 1909. The comet is due again in 1984

but the rest may return also. Therefore astronomers have a large field wherein to exercise themselves for many ages, before they will be able to know the number of these many and great bodies revolving about the common center of the sun, and to reduce their motions to certain rules.

DANIEL BERNOULLI (1700-1782) was one of a Swiss family of which at least eight members became distinguished in the history of science and mathematics. The family originated in Antwerp, and later settled in Switzerland. Daniel, a philosopher, mathematician and physician, advanced the kinetic theory of gases and fluids in his most important work, the Hydrodynamica, *devoted to a theoretical and practical exploration of the equilibrium, pressure, reaction and velocities of fluids. He won or shared some ten prizes offered by the Academy of Sciences of Paris and devoted the rest of his life to study of probabilities.*

Daniel Bernoulli

"Air, like water, is a fluid"

by Ruth Wolfe

A CROW CAN FLY from tree to tree quite well without understanding the principles of flight. A pilot doesn't *have* to know what holds a plane up in order to fly it. But right there is where the pilot has the advantage over the crow. Man has not learned to fly, but he knows *why* he can fly.

Daniel Bernoulli (ber-NEW-ye) was the scientist who helped us to understand one of the main secrets of flight. Bernoulli lived in the eighteenth century. He never saw an airplane. In fact, Bernoulli didn't even work with air in figuring out his valuable principle. Bernoulli worked with water. His theorem deals with fluids. Air, like water, is a fluid. Bernoulli's theorem helps to explain one of the four major forces in flight. That force is lift. The other three are gravity, thrust, and drag.

Bernoulli was concerned with the flow of water through pipes. He discovered that if the speed of a moving fluid is increased at any point, the pressure is decreased. It is not hard to find examples of Bernoulli's theorem around you. You can see Bernoulli's theorem at work in many ways.

(1) Try blowing between two thin sheets of paper. The moving air between the sheets will have less pressure than the atmospheric pressure. They will be forced together.

(2) Place a card over the end of a spool. Hold it there with a pin to keep it from slipping sidewise. The harder you blow, the tighter the card will stick.

(3) A ball or balloon will balance in a stream of compressed air. The velocity of the moving air is greater than the surrounding air, but its pressure is less.

(4) The moving air passing through the throat of an atomizer has less pressure than the atmospheric pressure acting on the surface of the liquid.

Now how does Bernoulli's principle apply to the airplane? First, let's take a look at the shape of an airplane wing. The shape is called an airfoil. The airfoil is slightly curved on the top and nearly flat on the bottom. As it moves through the air, the stream of air is divided. The air which flows over the top has farther to go. Consequently, it travels faster than the air moving along the underside. Remember our principle. When the speed increases, the pressure decreases. If the air is moving faster over the top of the wing than it is below the wing, then the pressure above the wing must be less. The air below the wing will try to rise into the lower pressure area. It pushes the wing up with it, providing lift.

Greater lift is produced with greater speed. The design of the wing will also determine the amount of lift

There does not have to be a great amount of difference in pressure between the two areas to provide enough lift for a plane to fly. You will remember that at sea level, air has a pressure of 14.7 pounds per square inch. Let us suppose that the air beneath the wing has 14.7 lbs. of pressure and the air moving above the wing has 14.5 lbs. of pressure per square inch.

The difference of .2 lb. does not seem very great. We know that there are 144 square inches in a square foot. By multiplying 144 by .2, we find that there would be a difference of 28.8 lbs. per square foot between the pressure below the wing and the pressure above the wing.

If an airplane has a wing area of 200 square feet, then there would be (200 x 28.8) a force of 5,760 lbs. lifting the plane. That's nearly three tons of lift!

Bernoulli's theorem accounts for the way a wing gets about three fourths of its total lift. There are other factors to be considered. The wing must meet the airstream at the proper angle. This angle is called the angle of attack.

This article can give only the briefest explanation of lift.

Every plane in flight is acted upon by four forces—lift, gravity, thrust, and drag. We have seen how lift is provided. For our purposes, we can say that *gravity* is the weight of the plane. Before a plane can take off, the lift must be greater than the weight.

In jet aircraft, thrust is provided by the backward expulsion of air

Thrust is provided by the propeller, which is in itself an airfoil. As it turns, the propeller bites into the air, pulling the plane forward. It also sends a current of air back over the wing.

Drag is the resistance of the plane to the air. You have met drag on a windy day when you tried to run against the wind. Before a plane can increase in speed, thrust must be greater than drag. In level flight, lift is equal to gravity; the thrust is equal to the drag.

Lift is the force that makes an airplane differ from other vehicles. Cars, trains, and bicycles all have thrust, gravity, and drag. Only aircraft have the fourth force of lift.

Bernoulli's principle in action!
This theory, worked out with fluids not air,
explains to man the principle of lift in aircraft flight

ALTHOUGH Benjamin Franklin's ministrations to the newborn Republic made him an American hero, they do not, in the opinion of historians of science, outweigh his contributions to the whole field of natural philosophy—from medicine and stoves and fertilizers and lightning rods —to lead poisoning, electric shocks, the course and origin of rivers, and the luminosity of the sea. Franklin's early experiments and the letters in which he described them, won him membership in the Royal Society of London, the Royal Academy in Paris, and in many other learned societies of Europe. He was born in 1706 and died in 1790.

Benjamin Franklin

First American scientist

The experiment which Franklin proposed, to prove whether electricity and lightning were identical, and his own separate demonstration with the kite, must be ranked with the most fundamental as well as the most striking experiments in scientific history.—Carl Van Doren

Electric fire from the clouds

AS FREQUENT MENTION is made in public papers from *Europe* of the success of the *Philadelphia* experiment for drawing the electric fire from clouds by means of pointed rods of iron erected on high buildings, etc., it may be agreeable to the curious to be informed, that the same experiment has succeeded in *Philadelphia,* though made in a different and more easy manner, which is as follows:

Make a small cross of two light strips of cedar, the arms so long as to reach to the four corners of a large thin silk handkerchief when extended; tie the corners of the handkerchief to the extremities of the cross, so you have the body of a kite; which being properly ac-

97

commodated with a tail, loop, and string, will rise in the air, like those made of paper; but this being of silk, is fitter to bear the wet and wind of a thunder-gust without tearing. To the top of the upright stick of the cross is to be fixed a very sharp pointed wire, rising a foot or more above the wood. To the end of the twine, next the hand, is to be tied a silk ribbon, and where the silk and twine join, a key may be fastened.

This kite is to be raised when a thunder-gust appears to be coming on, and the person who holds the string must stand within a door or window or under some cover, so that the silk ribbon may not be wet; care must be taken that the twine does not touch the frame of the door or window. As soon as any of the thunder-clouds come over the kite, the pointed wire will draw the electric fire from them, and the kite, with all the twine, will be electrified, and the loose filaments of the twine will stand out every way, and be attracted by an approaching finger.

And when the rain has wet the kite and twine, so that it can conduct the electric fire freely, you will find it stream out plentifully from the key on the approach of your knuckle. At this key the phial may be charged; and from electric fire thus obtained, spirits may be kindled, and all the other electrical experiments be performed, which are usually done by the help of a rubbed glass globe or tube, and thereby the sameness of the electric matter with that of lightning completely demonstrated.—*From a letter from Benjamin Franklin to Peter Collinson, dated October 19, 1752.*

The conduction of heat

D AMP WINDS, though not colder by the thermometer, give a more uneasy sensation of cold than dry ones. Because, to speak like an electrician, they conduct better: that is, are better fitted to convey the heat away from our bodies. The body cannot feel *without* itself; our sensation of cold is not in the air *without* the body, but in those parts of the body that have been deprived of their heat by the air.

My desk and its lock are, I suppose, of the same temperature when they have been long exposed to the same air; but now, if I lay my hand on the wood, it does not seem so cold to me as the lock; because, as I imagine, wood is not so good a conductor, to receive and convey away the heat from my skin and the adjacent flesh, as metal is. Take a piece of wood of the size and shape of a dollar between the thumb and fingers of one hand, and a dollar in like manner with the other hand; place the edges of both at the same time in the flame of a candle; and though the edge of the wooden piece takes flame, and the metal piece does not, yet you will be obliged to drop the latter before the former, it conducting the heat more suddenly to your fingers.

Thus we can without pain handle glass and china cups filled with hot liquors, as tea, etc., but not silver ones. A silver teapot must have [a] wooden handle. Perhaps it is for the same reason that woolen garments keep the body warmer than linen ones equally thick: woolen keeping the natural heat in, or, in other words, not conducting it out to the air.—*From a letter from Benjamin Franklin to Cadwallader Colden, dated December 6, 1753.*

Bifocal spectacles

...B̲Y MR. DOLLOND'S saying, that my double spectacles can only serve particular eyes, I doubt he has not been rightly informed of their construction. I imagine it will be found pretty generally true, that the same convexity of glass, through which a man sees clearest and best at the proper distance for reading, is not the best for greater distances. I therefore had formerly two pair of spectacles, which I shifted occasionally, as in travelling I sometimes read, and often wanted to regard the prospects. Finding this change troublesome, and not always sufficiently ready, I had the glasses cut, and half of each kind associated in the same circle. . . .

By this means, as I wear my spectacles constantly, I have only to move my eyes up or down, as I want to see distinctly far or near, the proper glasses being always ready. This I find more particularly convenient since my being in France, the glasses that serve me best at table to see what I eat, not being the best to see the faces of those on the other side of the table who speak to me; and when one's ears are not well accustomed to the sounds of a language, a sight of the movements in the features of him that speaks helps to explain, so that I understand French better by the help of my spectacles.—*From a letter from Benjamin Franklin to George Whatley, dated May 23, 1785.*

With the invention of these glasses Franklin gave the gift of youthful vision back to many middle-aged spectacle wearers

JOSEPH PRIESTLEY, an English clergyman, was born in 1733. His first researches were in the newborn field of electricity. Soon his experiments resulted in his discovery of a number of gases and compounds—including ammonia, nitrous oxide, hydrogen chloride and sulphur dioxide. Priestley's unorthodox views on England's colonial policy and later his sympathy to the French Revolution, finally led to the destruction of his laboratory by a mob, and in 1794 to his emigration to the United States. He settled in Northumberland, Pa., where after uninterrupted writing and Franklin-like experiments, he died in 1804.

Joseph Priestley

On a "new kind of air"

AFTER MY RETURN from abroad, I went to work upon the *mercurius calcinatus* (red mercuric oxide), which I had procured from Mr. Cadet; and with a very moderate degree of heat I got from about one fourth of an ounce of it an ounce measure of air, which I observed to be not readily imbibed, either by the substance itself from which it had been expelled (for I suffered them to continue a long time together before I transferred the air to any other place) or by water, in which I suffered this air to stand a considerable time before I made any experiment upon it.

In this air, as I had expected, a candle burned with a vivid flame; but what I observed new at this time (November 19), and which surprised me no less than the fact I had discovered before, was that, whereas a few moments' agitation in water will deprive the modified nitrous air of its property of admitting a candle to burn in it, yet, after more than ten times as much agitation as would be sufficient to produce this alteration in the nitrous air, no sensible change was produced in this.

A candle still burned in it with a strong flame; and it did not in the least diminish common air, which I have observed nitrous air . . . does.

But I was much more surprised when, after two days in which this air had continued in contact with water (by which it was diminished about one twentieth of its bulk), I agitated it violently in water about five minutes and found that a candle still burned in it as well as in common air. The same degree of agitation would have made phlogisticated nitrous air fit for respiration indeed, but it would certainly have extinguished a candle.

These facts fully convinced me that there must be a very material difference between the constitution of air from *mercurius calcinatus,* and that of phlogisticated nitrous air, notwithstanding their resemblance in some particulars. But though I did not doubt that the air from *mercurius calcinatus* was fit for respiration, after being agitated in water, as every kind of air without exception, on which I have tried the experiment, had been, I still did not suspect that it was respirable in the first instance; so far was I from having any idea of this air being, what it really was, much superior, in this respect, to the air of the atmosphere.

The "air" Priestley gleaned from mercurius calcinatus *was later named oxygen by Antoine Lavoisier*

In this ignorance of the real nature of this kind of air I continued from this time (November) to the first of March following; having, in the meantime, been intent upon my experiments on the vitriolic acid air above recited, and the various modifications of air produced by spirit of niter, an account of which will follow. But in the course of this month, I not only ascertained the nature of this kind of air, though very gradually, but was led to it by the complete discovery of the constitution of the air we breathe.

Till the first of March 1775 I had so little suspicion of the air from *mercurius calcinatus,* et cetera, being wholesome, that I had not even thought of applying it to the test of nitrous air; but thinking (as my reader must imagine I frequently must have done) on the candle burning in it after long agitation in water, it occurred to me at last to make the experiment; and putting one measure of nitrous air to two measures of this air, I found, not only that it was diminished, but that it was diminished quite as much as common air, and that the redness of the mixture was likewise equal to that of a similar mixture of nitrous and common air.

After this I had no doubt but that the air from *mercurius calcinatus* was fit for respiration, and that it had all the other properties of genuine common air. But I did not take notice of what I might have observed, if I had not been so fully possessed by the notion of there being no air better than common air, that the redness was really deeper, and the diminution something greater than common air would have admitted.

Moreover, this advance in the way of truth, in reality, threw me back into error, making me give up the hypothesis I had first formed, viz., that the *mercurius calcinatus* had extracted spirit of niter from the air; for I now concluded that all the constituent parts of the air were equally, and in their proper proportion, imbibed in the preparation of this substance, and also in the process of making red lead. For at the same time that I made the above-mentioned experiment on the air from *mercurius calcinatus* I likewise observed that the air which I had extracted from red lead, after the fixed air was washed out of it, was of the same nature, being diminished by nitrous air like common air; but at the same time I was puzzled to find that air from the red precipitate was diminished in the same manner, though the process for making this substance is quite different from that of making the two others. But to this circumstance I happened not to give much attention.

I wish my reader be not quite tired with the frequent repetition of the word "surprise" and others of similar import; but I must go on in that style a little longer. For the next day I was more surprised than ever I had been before, with finding that, after the above-mentioned mixture of nitrous air and the air from *mercurius calcinatus* had stood all night (in which time the whole diminution must have taken place; and, consequently, had it been common air, it must have been made perfectly noxious and entirely unfit for respiration or inflammation), a candle burned in it, and even better than in common air.

I cannot, at this distance of time, recollect what it was that I had in view making this experiment; but I know that I had no expectation of the real issue of it. Having acquired a considerable degree of readiness in making experiments of this kind, a very slight and evanescent motive would be sufficient to induce me to do it. If, however, I had not happened, for some other purpose, to have had a lighted candle before me I should probably never have made the trial; and the whole train of my future experiments relating to this kind of air might have been prevented.

Priestley made important advances in the study of gases. He devised the modern pneumatic method of collecting gases, although he did not appreciate its significance

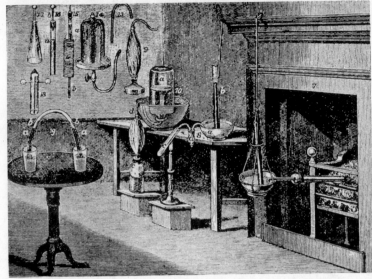

The chemical laboratory of Joseph Priestley showing some of the equipment and methods which the famous scientist used to perform his historic experiments with *mercurius calcinatus*

Still, however, having no conception of the real cause of this phenomenon, I considered it as something very extraordinary; but as a property that was peculiar to air that was extracted from these substances, and adventitious; and I always spoke of the air to my acquaintance as being substantially the same thing with common air.

I particularly remember my telling Dr. Price that I was myself perfectly satisfied to its being common air, as it appeared to be so by the test of nitrous air; though, for the satisfaction of others, I wanted a mouse to make the proof quite complete.

On the eighth of this month I procured a mouse and put it into a glass vessel, containing two ounce measures of the air from *mercurius calcinatus*. Had it been common air, a full-grown mouse, as this was, would have lived in it about a quarter of an hour. In this air, however, my mouse lived a full half hour; and though it was taken out seemingly dead, it appeared to have been only exceedingly chilled; for, upon being held to fire, it presently revived and appeared not to have received any harm from the experiment.

Priestley, by further experiments, showed that oxygen was restored to the air by growing plants

By this time I was confirmed in my conclusion that the air extracted from *mercurius calcinatus*, et cetera, was at least as good as common air; but I did not certainly conclude that it was any better; because, though one mouse would live only a quarter of an hour in a given quantity of air, I knew it was not impossible but that another mouse might have lived in it half an hour; so little accuracy is there in this method of ascertaining the goodness of air; and indeed I have never had recourse to it for my own satisfaction, since the discovery of that most ready, accurate, and elegant test that nitrous air furnishes. But in this case I had a view to publishing the most generally satisfactory account . . . that the nature of the thing would admit of.

103

James Watt

The perfection of an engine
by Henry Thomas and Dana Lee Thomas

THE LIFE of James Watt demonstrates the proposition that genius is an infinite capacity for taking pains. Owing to his parents' poverty, he was unable to get an adequate academic education. Yet, through his sheer persistence, he kept fighting for his knowledge—against want, discouragement, and disease—until he became not only a supreme inventor but a superior exponent of the liberal arts. . . .

Before long his school days were over. His mother died (1753); his older brother, John, had gone to sea and had been shipwrecked; his father's business affairs had reached a low ebb; and Jamie Watt was compelled to go to work.

A sober young mechanic who was anxious to find work, Watt went to live with his mother's family, the Muirheads, in Glasgow.

And his clever fingers came to his aid. He entered the service of an optician who, in addition to grinding glasses, repaired fiddles, tuned spinets, made fishing rods, upholstered furniture and offered to "fix or fashion anything useful to man."

And thus, at seventeen, James Watt became apprenticed to a

jack-of-all-trades—and managed to master them all. "Never saw such amazing versatility in my life!" exclaimed his employer as he watched him at his work. . . .

A year's apprenticeship as an instrument maker in London, amazing progress, and considerable heartache. For he was compelled, during this period, to rely upon his father's support. It wasn't much —only $2 a week—but it irked him to strain his father's resources even to this trifling extent. "I long for the day when I can take care of myself and repay you for all you have done."

But taking care of himself wasn't such an easy matter. Before his year of apprenticeship was over, he wrote to his father that he had made "a brass sector . . . which is reckoned as nice a piece of . . . work as is in the trade." He applied for membership in the Glasgow Guild of Hammermen—and his application was rejected. A seven years' apprenticeship was necessary as a qualification for membership in the Guild. Watt had learned his trade in one year. He was "too good to be true." He asked the Guild for permission to rent a small shop—"not for business but for scientific experiments." This request was also turned down. Here was one of the leading toolmakers in Scotland, forbidden to make tools!

At this juncture, his friends at the university (of Glasgow) came to the rescue. In accordance with the university charter, the faculty had supreme authority for assigning and accepting work within its campus. And so they gave him a workroom in one of the college buildings. Here he was at liberty, without the Guild's sanction, to make and sell his instruments and to conduct his "strange but fascinating" experiments. . . .

It was through Professor Robison (of the Glasgow faculty) that Watt became interested in steam engines. The university at that time owned a Newcomen engine—a mechanism that had been purchased for experimental use in the natural philosophy department. It was a crude contraption of pipes and boilers and pistons that generated a maximum of sound and fury and a minimum of practical power.

The engine was a challenge to Watt's ingenuity. He began to read up on the subject and to experiment with various models built upon the principles of this machine. He made the models himself, using apothecaries' vials for boilers and hollowed canes for pipes. But the idea refused to work. Theoretically it seemed all right; but practically

Apprenticeship was hard work and after a year young Watt came home for a much-needed rest before setting off on his own

105

it resulted in failure after failure. Every time you started the piston, both in the original and in the models, there would be a few gasping strokes and then the power would sputter out.

But Watt never gave up. "Every obstacle," observed Professor Robison, "was to him the beginning of a new and serious study, and I knew he wouldn't quit until he had either discovered its worthlessness or had made something of it."

One of the improvements Watt made on the Newcomen engine was the addition of a steam jacket to preserve the heat formerly lost through radiation

Infinite patience, assiduous application, inspired thought. *"The thing has worth, and I propose to make it work."*

And then came the clue to the final unleashing of the secret power. In the course of his experiments, he had discovered the principle of latent heat. This principle, briefly stated, means that a tremendous amount of heat lies hidden in nature until it can be set mechanically free. Thus, for example, *one pound of steam* inserted into freezing water will bring *five pounds of the water* to a boiling point. In other words, a quantity of water converted into steam will release enough latent energy to bring five times its own weight of water into steam heat.

And now that the generating power of heat had been discovered, it was merely a matter of time—Watt insisted—before he would find a way to harness it to the service of man. Build an engine to capture all this latent energy so that as little of it as possible can escape, and then direct this energy to the pushing of a piston, the pumping of a mine or the turning of a wheel.

Easier said than done. It wasn't enough merely to harness the steam in the engine. It was necessary to regulate its power when released. And this release of the steam, both in the Newcomen engine and in Watt's early models, resulted in the loss of about four-fifths of its energy. This loss was due to the cooling of the cylinder during the action of the engine; and the cooling of the cylinder in turn was due to the fact that the piston, after its upward stroke, could not be sent to the bottom for another upward stroke without the injection of a stream of cold water. It was a long time before Watt discovered the second secret of the steam engine—how to preserve the latent heat in the cylinder after he had succeeded in harnessing it.

The idea of this discovery came to him as he was walking on a Sabbath afternoon, in 1765. "I knew that in order to make a perfect steam engine it was necessary that the cylinder should always be as hot as the steam which entered it. . . . Suddenly the idea came to my

James Watt working with an experimental model of his famous steam pumping engine. After a great many failures, Watt was finally able to give the world its first practical steam engine

mind that as steam was an elastic body it would rush into a vacuum, and if a communication were made between the cylinder and an exhausted vessel it would rush into it, and might be there condensed without cooling the cylinder. . . ."

A simple idea—this separate condenser—once you happened to think of it. But it took infinite pains and patience for the preparation of the mind to *receive* this revolutionary idea. Years later, when publicly hailed as the conqueror of steam, Watt remarked that the contrivance of the condenser had just happened to occur to him. "There it was; somebody had to stumble upon it." But—as he failed to add in his modest way—it had to be somebody with the inventiveness and the tenacity of a James Watt.

The principle of the modern steam engine was now—to all practical purposes—complete. The condenser carried the steam into a separate vessel, leaving the cylinder uniformly hot. A circular piston kept pumping the steam through this cylinder, maintaining the cylinder at the same high temperature as the steam that entered it. In this way there was very little loss of the latent heat of the steam as it be-

Watt did not take out a patent on his steam engine until four years after all his improvements had been made, so as to give him time to test its efficiency

came transformed into the energy that "revolutionized the labor of the world."

Marriage, incessant toil, an unresponsive public, disappointments, headaches, heartaches, poverty, despondency, and the untimely death of his wife. He formed a partnership with Dr. Roebuck, founder and proprietor of the Carron Iron Works. But the venture brought only ruin to his partner. For invention and business remained at odds in the character of James Watt. "I would rather face a loaded cannon," he wrote, "than settle a disputed account or make a bargain."

Engine after engine, though built upon a plan which was theoretically sound, refused to come up to specifications when put to practical use. Often it was the fault of the workmen. At times, as he was honest enough to admit, it was his own fault. A failure to tighten this or that joint—"my engine sniffs at many opening"; a misfit between piston and cylinder that resulted in the breakdown of the entire machine—"my old White Iron man is dead"; a thousand and one other little oversights that resulted in leakage and loss of power. And always, when a customer complained, Watt agreed with the complaint, "My work, I know, is poor enough; but I am trying to make it better."

He was anxious, in short, not for profit but for perfection. He acknowledged his "intermediate failures and uncouth constructions"

Right, James Watt's first single-acting, steam engine built in 1768-9. Below, countless improvements in his earlier models resulted in Watt's new, double-acting, rotative engine, 1783

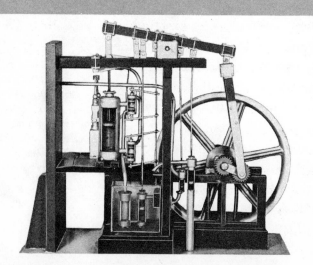
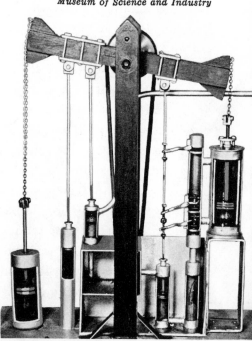

as the stepping stones toward the "faultless machine." But he was greatly disturbed at the inconveniences that his failures occasioned to other people. "You cannot conceive," he wrote to a friend concerning one of his imperfect machines, "how mortified I am with this disappointment. . . . I cannot bear the thought of other people becoming losers by my schemes."

And the dissatisfaction of his customers with his earlier machines was not always due to a defect in the mechanism. When one of his better engines was completed, a number of scientists and mining experts were invited to inspect it. "All the West Country captains (of industry) were there to see the prodigy," he wrote. "The . . . horrible noise of the engine gave universal satisfaction . . . I once or twice trimmed the engine to end the stroke gracefully and to make less noise." Whereupon many of the observers expressed their displeasure at the "reduced efficiency" of the machine. "The noise," he whimsically observed, "seems to convey great ideas of its power to the ignorant, who seem to be no more taken with modest merit in an engine than in a man."

But finally both the man and the engine were recognized at their true value. Another partnership—this time with a friend who had an amplitude of business ability as well as a sufficiency of funds—and Watt for the first time knew the happiness of a secure livelihood.

Another partner, and another wife. He was as happy in his second marriage as in his second business venture. His wife gave him the necessary courage—and his partner, the necessary capital—for the perfection of his engine.

The business partnership developed into an ardent friendship. James Watt and Matthew Boulton took to each other from the start. Mr. Boulton, a manufacturer of Birmingham, was one of the founders of the modern idea of low prices through mass production. But he was a philanthropist as well as a business man. He employed only one class of apprentices—"fatherless children, parish wards and hospital boys"—and he maintained a home in which his apprentices were properly sheltered, fed and educated. But it was his head as well as his heart that induced him to accept the inventor as a partner. Watt needed a sponsor—and the sponsorship, he was convinced, would ultimately result in profit to the beneficiary and the benefactor alike.

And so it turned out. The firm of Boulton and Watt—the one "running his business like a romance" and the other "perfecting his

Aside from his inventive abilities, Watt was quite well known and respected as a civil engineer

Watt, in later years, patented the idea of a steam locomotive for highway, not railway, use, but he never followed through with the plan

engine like a poem" compelled the world to waken to a new era. The Age of Steam Power, of the Industrial Revolution.

At the start, there were still many hardships to overcome. Incompetent mechanics, inadequate tools, plans and drawings stolen and sold to rival companies, spies from Germany, France and Russia masquerading as workers and trying to appropriate the secrets of the new agency "that threatened to revolutionize the world."

One of their best engines was deliberately ruined by the engineer whom the representatives of a competitive concern had bribed with money and stupefied with drink.

At another time a tempting offer was held out to Watt himself to leave his partner and to enter the imperial service of Russia. When Boulton heard of this offer, he wrote to Watt: "Your going to Russia staggers me. . . . I wish to advise you for the best without regard to self; but I find I love myself so well that I should be very sorry to have you go."

Watt didn't go to Russia. He remained loyal to his partner, and together they surmounted their difficulties and rode to final success.

Orders for the Watt engine began to pour in, and Watt attended personally not only to planning but to the installation of every machine. He had to be continually on the go. "I fancy," he wrote to his family from one of his trips to Cornwall "that I must be cut in pieces and a portion sent to every tribe in Israel."

Incessant work on his steam engine—and, in his leisure hours, more work on all sorts of other inventions. A copying-press for manuscripts, a machine for drying clothes, a surveying-quadrant, a micrometer for the measuring of fine angles, a drawing machine, a sculpture reproducer, an instrument for the computation of distances between planets and stars, a method for determining the specific gravity of liquids, a reading lamp—and so on and on.

This idea of the composition of water was contained in a letter to Joseph Priestley, the discoverer of oxygen

It was Watt, too, who discovered the composition of water. "Are we not authorized," he wrote (April 26, 1783), "to conclude that water is a compound of two gases—oxygen and hydrogen . . .?"

And with all this, he found time to play. He joined the famous Lunar Society—an organization of writers and scientists devoted to an exchange of original ideas and mutual goodwill. The intimacy of this group, in the words of one of its members, "was never broken except by death." And the last surviving member of this "coterie of gifted minds" was James Watt.

LUIGI GALVANI (1737-1798) was born in Bologna, Italy. He studied theology at the University of Bologna and at 23 married a professor's daughter. He soon forsook theology for medicine and received his doctorate in 1762. In that year he was appointed public lecturer in anatomy at the institute—and his skill was soon rewarded with the professorship of anatomy at the university. After Napoleon conquered Italy, Galvani refused to take a loyalty oath as required by the French and consequently lost his job. He was later reinstated but by then his wife had died and he was a broken man. He lived only a few months longer.

Luigi Galvani

He discovered that electricity flows
by Hugh Hildreth Skilling, Ph.D.

DOCTOR LUIGI GALVANI—whose name is immortalized in the words *galvanic, galvanize, galvanometer,* and many more—was a pioneer in the newly discovered world of electricity. He lived in Bologna, taught anatomy in the medical college of the University of Bologna, and carried on a private practice of medicine among the citizens of the Italian town.

Sometimes called Aloisio Galvani, he worked in what we term the biological sciences—the life sciences—and had done a good deal of work on the anatomy of birds.

He had worked particularly on their organs of hearing, and some of their internal organs, carefully measuring the tiny bones in what are called the semicircular canals of the ear. He would note the measurements, and make sketches, and compare the organs of one kind of bird with those of another kind, and with animals. He did all this work in a private laboratory; sometimes his advanced students helped him, and sometimes his wife worked with him.

Doctor Galvani had an electrical machine in his laboratory. He used it to study the effect of electric shocks on animals and people, for to him, electricity was a tool to be used for its biological effect. Perhaps it would cure people who suffered from some types of disease; there were a good many doctors who thought so then, even as there have been ever since.

Galvani was inclined to believe in electricity as a cure for certain nervous disorders, but as a good scientist he worked patiently to find by experiment whether or not he was right.

His electrical machine was not very different from the one that Benjamin Franklin used, except that it developed the electricity in a disc of glass instead of a glass tube. Thirty years had passed since the time of Franklin's experiments with lightning, but there had been no revolutionary discoveries in electrical science. There had been progress, of course, for a great many men had been very much interested in electricity during that time, but there had been no advance to compare with the one that Galvani was about to make.

Franklin, at this time, was too busy with state affairs to take notice of the work being done in Italy by Galvani. He died just two short years before Galvani's book on electricity was published

One day Galvani was working with frogs in his laboratory. It was November, 1780. Mrs. Galvani and one or two assistants were working with him. Dr. Galvani, with an assistant, was dissecting and preparing frogs, "in the usual way," he wrote in his notebook. For some entirely different purpose the electrical machine was running, and every now and then a spark cracked. Galvani and his helper were working on the leg of a frog; it had been cut entirely off the body, and yet, as they worked on it, it jumped. A little later it jumped again.

Mrs. Galvani called her husband's attention to it. Again it jumped, and again and again. At first it seemed to twitch each time the assistant's knife touched a certain nerve. But sometimes he touched the nerve and nothing happened. Then someone noticed that the frog's leg jerked each time the electric machine sparked, if the knife touched the nerve at the same time. This was tried, and tried again. It always worked. It was electricity that made the dead frog jump.

Galvani was thrilled. All other work was forgotten, and electricity alone held his thoughts. Electricity and life, life and electricity, what was the relation? Was electricity a manifestation of life? Galvani worked on the problem for a month or more, and then, on Christmas Day, he decided, yes.

"The electric fluid," he wrote in his notebook, "ought to be considered simply as a means designed to excite the nervo-muscular force." That was the first step.

The electric machine gave something that was very closely related to life. But would electricity from other sources have the same effect? Would Franklin's electricity from the clouds cause twitching of the frogs' legs?

Doctor Galvani decided to find out. That was necessarily a matter of some time; rods and wires were needed to bring electricity down from the sky, and not every day would do for the experiment. He must wait for storms, perhaps.

Little by little he had success in getting electricity from the clouds. He found that it had the same effect on frogs' legs as the frictional electricity from his machine. He tried the experiment several ways. Sometimes he collected atmospheric electricity in a Leyden jar, and when the jar was allowed to discharge through the nerve of the frog's leg, the muscle of the leg contracted and the leg jerked and twitched. Sometimes he connected a wire, that ran from the roof of

Galvani's lab. Note the famous frogs' legs, electrical machine (left) and Leyden jar (right)

Science Digest

his house to collect electricity, directly to the nerve of the frog, and again the effect was the same.

The experiments continued year after year. The work was of such importance that Dr. Galvani did not wish to publish any announcement of his discovery until he had tested his conclusions in every way. If he could prove that electricity was a part of life, it would be a very great discovery.

Now, what Dr. Galvani had actually discovered was a sensitive indicator of electricity. He used the leg of a frog as a means of knowing when there was a flow of electricity. The frog's leg was, in a sense, an electric meter. There had never before been any device to show electric current. Galvani found that a frog's leg would serve that purpose.

The early experimenters, up to about the time of Benjamin Franklin, had been able to detect the presence of electricity only by the force of attraction that it exerts on oppositely charged or uncharged bodies, or by the repulsive force that it exerts on a similarly charged body. Various electroscopes had been devised that operated in this way.

The "gnomon" was such an electroscope; when electricity flowed onto it an electric charge was imparted to a vertical rod and a charge of the same sign flowed onto a thread that hung beside the rod. The thread was repelled from the rod, and so hung out in space at an angle, and the angle between thread and rod was an indication of the amount of electricity. But all such instruments showed the *presence* of electricity as electric charge, but not the *motion* of it as electric current.

Franklin, and others of his time, had a means of detecting electric current, and even of comparing current intensities in different cases. But the method was an inconvenient one and likely to be uncomfortable. They would permit themselves to be shocked by the current, and they deduced that the more unpleasant the shock the stronger the current. Galvani's discovery substituted the nerve and muscle of a frog for the nerve and muscle of the scientist. It was a much more satisfactory arrangement—for the scientist.

There was another advantage, too, in the use of the frog's leg to indicate current. The leg would react to much smaller currents than could be felt by a human as an electric shock. The frog was the more delicate instrument.

In memory of his outstanding work in the field of electricity, a statue of Galvani was erected in front of the old Anatomical Building of the Medical College at Bologna. A pair of frog legs is sculptured upon a tablet-like dissection plate he is holding

For six years Galvani worked on the subject of muscular motion produced by electricity, and then there was a second fortunate accident that led to a second great discovery. One day some frogs were prepared "in the accustomed manner," with hooks of copper through their spinal cords.

Six years seems like a long time but it must be remembered that Galvani was a doctor and therefore his experiments could only be carried out in leisure time

Galvani tells of this in his notebook of October, 1786. He took the frogs' legs out onto the flat roof of the building and hung them, by the copper hooks, on a iron railing. The day was stormy, and Galvani hoped to get electricity from the clouds. While he was working with the necessary wires the wind blew the frogs' legs against the iron bars of the railing. Every time one touched a rail it twitched as if electricity had passed through it. But how could there be electricity? No electricity had been brought from the clouds or from an electric machine. Could there possibly be some entirely new source of electricity?

Doctor Galvani took the frogs into the laboratory and laid them on an iron plate. When the leg and the copper hook touched the plate at the same time, the leg jerked. He touched the muscle with a piece of iron, the nerve with a piece of copper, and when the copper and iron touched each other the leg jerked again. He used two pieces of copper, and nothing happened. He used two pieces of iron, and nothing happened. But every time the nerve and muscle were touched with *different* metals, and the metals were touched together, the leg twitched.

He then began a new series of experiments. It now appeared even more strongly than before that electricity was part of life. To a doctor, a biologist, this was what made electricity interesting.

Galvani had written in his notebook, several years before, that "the electric spark produces a current in the nerves of the frog," and he knew that "a frog is therefore an electrometer—an electrometer more delicate than any previously discovered."

Now, however, the frog was indicating a current of electricity when there was no electric machine and no spark. The current plainly flowed in a circuit of three parts: it flowed through the leg of the frog, from nerve to muscle, then into the iron, through the iron to the point at which the iron touched the copper, then through the copper to the nerve of the frog again.

Somewhere in that circuit there was a source of electricity, for when the circuit was closed the frog's leg twitched.

115

Where was the driving force of the electricity? Was it in the common copper and iron? In the dead, dull metal? Or did the electricity take its life from the leg of the frog that had so recently been living tissue? Electricity was surely no dead force: it was alive, active, vivid. It sparked and crackled. It brought life to dead flesh. It tingled in one's body.

How could Dr. Galvani, a student of life, say that it came from mere metal? How could there be any doubt that electricity came from the nerve of the frog? It was *animal electricity,* and the "metallic arc" of iron and copper was needed only to complete the circuit by providing a return path for electric current.

In fact, a "metallic arc" was not needed. It could be replaced by a nonmetallic conductor which would do just as well to provide a return path for the electricity. The electricity would flow through a jar of water, or even through the arms of people who were holding hands. But one thing, oddly enough, was absolutely essential: the two points that touched the leg of the frog must be of different materials. Iron and copper, silver and tin, carbon and zinc—no matter; some would produce more lively contractions of the frog's leg than others. Only if the two points of contact were the same material would there be no action at all. Galvani never quite grasped the importance of this clue—which might have led him to discover the electric battery.

Galvani's book had just been published when he heard of Alessandro Volta, who was also experimenting with animal electricity

For five more years Dr. Galvani studied "animal electricity." Then, after 11 years of work, he condensed all his results into a short *Commentary on the Forces of Electricity in Muscular Motion.* This monograph was published in 1791 as a contribution to the Institute of Sciences at Bologna.

"If all the frogs' legs in the world were made of gold," wrote Alfred P. Morgan, historian of electricity, "they would not be worth the results of Galvani's and Volta's patient curiosity concerning them." Alessandro Volta actually discovered dynamical electricity. He knew the frogs' legs were not needed to produce electricity, and that their twitching when stimulated was an *effect,* not a *cause.* But on the other hand, were it not for the original experiment and observation of Luigi Galvani, the Electrical Age might have been long postponed.

ANTOINE LAVOISIER *was born in Paris in 1743, the son of a wealthy tradesman. His early studies were guided by the most eminent chemists of his time. He was admitted to the Academy of Sciences in 1768, and soon wandered down paths others had never tried. In 1771 he married Marie Anne Pierette. A skilled artist and engraver, she became her husband's most faithful laboratory assistant and illustrated his publications. His* Traité élémentaire Chimie *(1789) was his major work. Because of his prominence in public affairs, Lavoisier was condemned to death (1794) during the Reign of Terror by a Revolutionary Tribunal.*

Antoine Lavoisier

The respiration of animals

OF ALL THE PHENOMENA of the animal economy, none is more striking, none more worthy the attention of philosophers and physiologists than those which accompany respiration. Little as our acquaintance is with the object of this singular function, we are satisfied that it is essential to life and that it cannot be suspended for any time without exposing the animal to the danger of immediate death. . . .

The experiment of some philosophers, and especially those of Messrs. Hales and Cigna, had begun to afford some light on this important object; and Dr. Priestly has lately published a treatise in which he has greatly extended the bounds of our knowledge; and has endeavored to prove, by a number of very ingenious, delicate, and novel experiments, that the respiration of animals has the property of phlogisticating air, in a similar manner to what is effected by the calcination of metals and many other chemical processes; and that the air ceases not to be respirable till the instant when it becomes surcharged, or at least saturated, with phlogiston.

However probable the theory of this celebrated philosopher may at first appear; however numerous and well conducted may be the experiments by which he endeavors to support it, I must confess I have found it so contradictory to a great number of phenomena that I could not but entertain some doubts of it. I have accordingly proceeded on a different plan and have found myself led irresistibly, by the consequences of my experiments, to very different conclusions.

Now air which has served for the calcination of metals is, as we have already seen, nothing but the mephitic residuum of atmospheric air, the highly respirable part of which has combined with the mercury, during the calcination: and the air which has served the purpose of respiration, when deprived of the fixed air, is exactly the same; and, in fact, having combined with the latter residuum about one half of its bulk of dephlogisticated air, extracted from the calx of mercury, I reestablished it in its former state and rendered it equally fit for respiration, combustion, et cetera, as common air by the same method as that I pursued with air vitiated by the calcination of mercury.

It was Lavoisier who first presented the true explanation of combustion, and forever destroyed the false "phlogiston theory" which had previously accounted for the phenomenon of burning. He was the first to explain the role of oxygen in the respiration of animals and plants

The result of these experiments is that, to restore air that has been vitiated by respiration to the state of common respirable air, two effects must be produced: first, to deprive it of the fixed air (carbon dioxide) it contains, by means of quicklime or caustic alkali; secondly, to restore to it a quantity of highly respirable or dephlogisticated air, equal to that which it has lost. Respiration, therefore, acts inversely to these two effects, and I find myself in this respect led to two consequences equally probable, and between which my present experience does not enable me to pronounce. . . .

The first of these opinions is supported by an experiment which I have already communicated to the Academy. For I have shown in a memoir, read at our public Easter meeting, 1775, that dephlogisticated air (oxygen) may be wholly converted into fixed air by an addition of powdered charcoal; and in other memoirs I have proved that this conversion may be effected by several other methods: it is possible, therefore that respiration may possess the same property, and that dephlogisticated air, when taken into the lungs, is thrown out again as fixed air. . . .

Does it not then follow, from all these facts, that this pure species of air has the property of combining with the blood and that this combination constitutes its red color? But whichever of these two opinions we embrace, whether that the respirable portion of the air combines with the blood, or that it is changed into fixed air in passing through the lungs; or lastly, as I am inclined to believe, that both these effects take place in the act of respiration, we may, from facts alone, consider as proved:

1. That respiration acts only on the portion of pure or dephlogisticated air contained in the atmosphere; that the residuum or mephitic part is a merely passive medium which enters into the lungs and departs from them nearly in the same state, without change or alteration.

2. That the calcination of metals, in a given quantity of atmospheric air, is effected, as I have already often declared, only in proportion as the dephlogisticated air, which it contains, has been drained and combined with the metal.

3. That, in like manner, if an animal be confined in a given quantity of air, it will perish as soon as it has absorbed, or converted into fixed air, the major part of the respirable portion of air, and the remainder is reduced to a mephitic state.

4. That the species of mephitic air, which remains after the calcination of metals, is in no wise different, according to all the experiments I have made, from that remaining after the respiration of animals; provided always that the latter residuum has been freed from its fixed air; that these two residuums may be substituted for each other in every experiment, and that they may each be restored to the state of atmospheric air by a quantity of dephlogisticated air equal to that of which they had been deprived.

A new proof of this last fact is that, if the proportion of this highly respirable air, contained in a given quantity of the atmospheric, be increased or diminished, in such proportion will be the quantity of metal which we shall be capable of calcining in it, and, to a certain point, the time which animals will be capable of living in it.

The chemist's balance—and his was the most accurate in France—was Lavoisier's magic key. With it he was able to make the first truly quantitative determinations in the investigation of chemical reactions. With it he established the composition of water and other compounds and formulated the law of the conservation of matter

Lavoisier laid down the foundation of the modern
system of chemical nomenclature; he listed 33 chemical elements,
and among others, coined the words *hydrogen, oxygen* and *caloric.*
Not content in the seclusion of his laboratory, Lavoisier
served France as trustee of the Bank of Discount, on the Commission of
Weights and Measures, and as Commissary of the Treasury. He
introduced reforms in lighting and housing, and suggested
new monetary, banking and taxation systems.

EDWARD JENNER, the son of a clergyman, was born in 1749. He began his study of medicine under Daniel Ludlow, a surgeon, but left him in 1770 to study under John Hunter in London. Jenner first became interested in the relationship between cowpox and smallpox about 1775. After receiving his M.D. in 1792 he began his history-making study of cowpox virus. In 1803 a society was established bearing his name to assist in the spread of vaccinations throughout London, and the yearly average of smallpox deaths dropped from 2,018 to 622. Jenner, one of the few scientists to receive recognition during his lifetime, died in 1823.

Edward Jenner

The conquest of smallpox

THIS IS THE STORY of the work of a country doctor who was born more than 200 years ago and the disease he conquered. He saved millions of lives with one of the greatest medical discoveries of his or any other day when he proved the effectiveness of cowpox vaccine against smallpox.

This great benefactor of humanity was Dr. Edward Jenner.

Jenner's discovery was more than a discovery of vaccination against smallpox, however. It was a basic medical discovery that founded the science of preventive medicine, and even in this day of accelerated advances in medicine it is still a major weapon in man's war on disease.

To make it seem even more remarkable, Jenner's work was the only event of the period, including the first half of the 19th century, that had any pronounced influence on the betterment of preventive and clinical medicine.

Just what were the factors that influenced this country doctor and led him to his discovery?

More important than any other factor, probably, that influenced Jenner in his work was his environment. Jenner lived almost all his life in a rural atmosphere. There, cowpox and its seemingly mysterious power to prevent infection by the dreaded smallpox which killed 60,000,000 Europeans during the 18th century was widely known and accepted.

Closely related to the primary circumstance of environment, but a somewhat different factor to a scientific man, was the period in which Jenner lived. The revival of the scientific spirit was in full swing during the 18th century.

The third factor that influenced Jenner's work was the instruction he received as a pupil of John Hunter, one of the most distinguished physicians of the century. Hunter wholeheartedly believed and taught the principle of Hippocrates which was revived only a few years before Jenner's time: the principle of intelligent, patient observation followed by experimentation.

It was Hunter who inspired Jenner to do more than just think about the use of vaccination to stop the spread of smallpox.

Jenner has been widely acclaimed as the founder of preventive medicine for his work on vaccinations

Dr. D. Gordon Sharp
Duke University

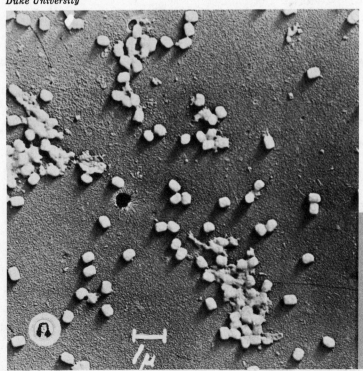

Cowpox virus magnified to about 3,000 times. Vaccination with cowpox virus will achieve more or less lasting immunity to small-pox — at one time one of man's most feared diseases

Jenner followed the advice of Hunter and began a concerted fight against smallpox in 1780. Finally, in 1796, he performed the first controlled experiment which scientifically proved the effectiveness of vaccination.

Before the first vaccination, Jenner proved to his own satisfaction that the diseases of "the grease" (a disease of horses' heels characterized by secretion), cowpox in cows, and smallpox, were the same and differed only in virulence, and that a patient could be infected with the virus only at a certain stage of the disease.

Greatly enthused by the result of this first controlled vaccination, Jenner wrote an account of the experiment and sent it to the *Transactions of the Royal Society.* He was disappointed when the society rejected the paper. They believed the evidence inconclusive.

To provide added proof of the success of his original experiment Jenner collected histories of 23 cases during the succeeding two years, and in 1798 published in pamphlet form his history-making article, *An Inquiry Into the Causes and Effects of Variolae Vaccinae.*

After the publication of Jenner's pamphlet, the superiority of vaccination over inoculation was quickly recognized

The effect of Jenner's article at first was similar to that of many other great announcements of science. Some authorities accepted Jenner's work, others denounced it, and the majority were completely unconcerned.

Soon the results of vaccination, however, began to be felt through a decrease in the death rate from smallpox.

Napoleon Bonaparte had vaccinated all of his soldiers who never had contracted smallpox. He was so grateful with the results that even though the two men never met, and England and France were at war with each other, the mention of Jenner's name was command enough for the dictator to grant Jenner a favor.

The success of Jenner's vaccination penetrated even to the wilds of North America from which came wampum and the prayers of the American Indians. From India came money, and accolades came from Spain, Italy and other countries.

On the other hand opposition to vaccination grew in England. Ministers denounced it from their pulpits as man's interference with the ways of God. Anti-vaccinationist societies were formed (some remain even today) and even poets denounced vaccination in verses which warned the people that they would "grow furry ears and have a bovine tail."

Luckily, however, thousands continued to be vaccinated, with

Fisher Scientific Company

Jenner vaccinating hundreds himself, until evidence of the effectiveness of vaccination became difficult to denounce.

Finally, recognition came in his own country. The British Parliament officially recognized the work of Jenner and granted him 10,000 pounds, and a few years later granted an additional 20,000 pounds. This led one historian to write that "England gave Jenner 30,000 pounds for saving the lives of 30,000 Britishers a year."

While Jenner's work was widely accepted over Europe and led to his election in many scientific societies, England was slower to recognize his merits

The world finally possessed a weapon to use against the terrible disease which could be traced back at least to Egyptian mummies more than 3,000 years ago.

At the end of the 18th century, 33 out of every 100 children who died before they were 10 years old died from smallpox, and 10 percent of all deaths were from the disease.

Those statistics were invalidated soon after 1800, however. During the long European wars connected with and following the French Revolution an estimated five to six million lives were lost, but vaccination saved more lives than were lost during the wars.

As one biographer said: *"The lancet of Jenner saved far more human lives than the sword of Napoleon destroyed."*

Experience proved the effectiveness of Jenner's vaccine, but nothing prevented ignorance and complacency of officials and the people. They no longer feared the once dreaded smallpox.

Consequently, there were sporadic outbreaks in all parts of a world which possessed a weapon against smallpox which it did not use as effectively as it should.

There were a few encouraging spots in the world where smallpox was fought systematically, such as New York City where the Department of Health vaccinated all vagrants found in the city.

Yet, isolation of those contracting smallpox, and systematic vaccination were not used until there was the threat of an epidemic. Then, the public did not always willingly submit to restrictions and compulsions.

The direct cause of smallpox is unknown, but it is spread, indirectly, by people already affected

Even today in a so-called enlightened world there are outbreaks of smallpox because so many people are not vaccinated.

For example, the fear of smallpox gripped New York City in April, 1947, when one death and three cases were first announced. Public officials quickly cleared the way for the use of public buildings, and medical men vaccinated over 5,000,000 residents in the metropolitan area.

Even more recent outbreaks are recorded. In February, 1948, 406 deaths from smallpox were reported from Calcutta, and in May of the same year, 57 died in Shanghai. Another scare was in March, 1949, in Havana, where U.S. Navy pilots flew in vaccine.

The modern production of smallpox vaccine is more or less standardized in all parts of the civilized world.

First step in the production of modern smallpox vaccine is the careful selection of a five to seven-month-old calf that is free from infection or disease. Then, the calf is clipped and placed in isolation for a week. After its isolation period the calf is removed to a laboratory where its abdomen and both thighs are shaved. Technicians then scarify the shaved area with a dull-pointed instrument in parallel lines about one-half inch apart, and smallpox virus is applied to the area.

The calf spends the next seven days in a humidified, controlled-temperature room where the virus grows rapidly.

After the incubation period technicians collect the virus from the calf, and send it to laboratories in crude form where it is refined and packaged.

The tremendous benefits derived from the work of one man should be remembered by those who condemn science because of its contributions to wars.

ELI WHITNEY was born on
December 8, 1765. His father was a farmer.
As a boy Eli preferred the farm workshop
to the fields. After the Revolutionary
War he entered Yale and was graduated in 1792.
A few years later he turned to manufacturing
arms and the perfection of mass-production
techniques. Eli was 52 years old when
he married Henrietta Edwards, the daughter of
an old friend. They had a son, Eli Whitney,
Jr., and three daughters. Despite a
lingering illness and extreme pain that
threatened to overwhelm him from time to time,
Whitney continued to work out new processes
almost to the day he died, in 1825.

Eli Whitney

Father of mass production
by Jeannette Mirsky and Allan Nevins

IN 1792 while visiting a plantation in Georgia, Eli Whitney learned
of a problem bedeviling the growers of upland cotton, a variety that
could be grown in most of the South. Unlike the sea island cotton—
restricted to the coastal areas—whose black seeds could be readily
separated from the fibers by a simple device called the roller gin, it
was practically impossible to separate the fibers of upland cotton from
its green seeds.

Fascinated with the problem, Whitney stayed on at the plantation and applied his mechanical talents to perfecting a machine—the
now-famed cotton gin (technically a saw gin)—that would clean the
green-seed cotton successfully. He patented it and set up a factory in
New Haven, Conn., to manufacture the device.

Although Whitney's gin—"gin" is an old form of "engine"—
revolutionized the Southern economy and made the South the "Cotton
Kingdom" for decades, it brought Whitney little but trouble and
hard work. Southern planters copied it, and little could be done
about these patent infringements except to file fruitless lawsuits.

In 1795 Whitney's New Haven factory burned to the ground, destroying all his tools and several nearly completed gins. After years of disappointment and unremunerative hard work, in 1798 Whitney, almost hopelessly in debt, was eager to turn to something else—something profitable. The following material tells the story of his greatest technological contribution—the use of interchangeable parts which made possible for the first time the mass manufacture of the products we now take for granted.

Whitney's cotton gin was worked by hand and would clean 50 pounds of lint a day—a pitifully small amount compared with modern production standards but a tremendous step, indeed, in that day and age

AS HIS INVENTION of the cotton gin had altered forever the history of the American South, so Whitney's sustained work in the manufacture of muskets changed the social and economic growth of the North and gave it its industrial might.

Whitney fathered the American system of interchangeable manufacture which shortly was producing quantities of cheap, serviceable clocks and watches, hardware, and sewing machines—the first fruits of the new industrial era to enter into the everyday life of peoples all over the world. Men who were trained by him continued the method he had pioneered and translated its concept into other fields. Whitney invented many tools and machines, but the one that assumed a major role in the genealogy of machine tools was the milling machine. He established a business that remained, in the hands of his son and grandson, one of the country's leading private armories for 90 years, until it was sold to the Winchester Arms Co.—a clear indication that from the onset Whitney understood the economics of the new business structure and that he was able to analyze problems very different from the mechanical ones which gained him his fame.

On May 1, 1798, Whitney wrote to Secretary of the Treasury Wolcott; "By the Debates of Congress I observe that they are about making Some appropriations for procuring Arms etc for the U.S. Should an actual War take place or the communication between the U.S. and the West India Islands continue to be as hazardous and precarious as it is now, my present Business of making The Patent Machines for Cleansing Cotton (his famous cotton gin) must, in the meantime be postponed. I have a number of workmen & apprentices whom I have instructed in working Wood & Metals and whom I wish to keep employed. These circumstances induced me to address you and ask the privilege of having an opportunity of contracting for the supply of some of the Articles which the U.S. may want. I should like

to undertake to Manufacture ten or fifteen thousand Stand of Arms."
(A stand of arms in this instance refers to the complete arms needed
to equip a soldier—the musket, bayonet, ramrod, wiper, and screw-
driver.)

Ten or fifteen thousand stand of arms! A notion as fantastic and
improbable as aviation was before Kitty Hawk. Only three years before, Whitney had bemoaned the loss of 20 cotton gins by fire and now
he was calmly offering to manufacture muskets in astronomical numbers, though he had never made a firearm before. To his way of
thinking, familiarity with a particular article—be it a gin, screw
press, a cartridge box, or a gun—was a secondary consideration, since
the operations of forging, boring, grinding, or polishing could be
directed to form any object.

Whitney sought to compensate for the dearth of artisans in
America, and the system he had been evolving since he had been
faced with the need to make gins in number and in haste for the cotton growers bypassed the time required to train workmen such as
Europe had. Whitney was but taking the next step to expedite production—that it was the decisive step that carried an economy from
the watershed of handicraft organization over into the unexplored
watershed of industrial manufacture has been revealed by time.

Whitney's proposal might have been postponed or mutilated by
heartbreaking hurdles had it been put forward at any other time.
Normally, new ideas have to fight for their lives—the slightest jolt to
an accepted way of looking at things automatically, as it were, mobi-
lizes the words that defend habitual techniques: "impractical," "visionary," "dubious," "rash." Familiar words to safeguard familiar
ways. A grim need can override this hostility to an original way of
looking at an old pattern; extreme danger permits people to grasp at
straws. Certainly President Adams, Wolcott, and Timothy Pickering,
Secretary of War, were eager to make the United States as self-suf-
ficient as possible; but stated policy could not have pierced through
their normal prudent attitudes.

A month after he had made his first inquiry, Whitney submitted
a draft contract to supply the government "with Ten Thousand Stand
of Arms, on the following terms & conditions." On June 14, 1798, just
12 days later, the contract was executed.

Looking at the goal Whitney had set himself, one can see that
at various times since boyhood he had been concerned with the same

*Later Whitney
signed a third
government contract,
again for 15,000
muskets. By this
time other musket
manufacturers—
both private
contractors and the
public arsenals—
were beginning
to use Whitney's
mass-production
methods. The third
contract was for
a new, standard
musket, and among
the manufacturing
problems it presented
was a series of new
and much more rigid
inspection procedures*

Eli Whitney
Father of mass production

problem. When he had made a model pen for his pupils to copy, he had intuitively expressed his awareness of the benefits derived from setting a model for form and size and demanding that each replica reproduce the pattern as exactly as possible. Later when he made gins, the advantages of standardizing the machines became obvious. What most delighted Whitney was that the contract to produce 10,-000 muskets provided the only opportunity he could have found to allow him to develop his ideas.

The "Charleville Musket," which Whitney took as his model, was the 1763 model of the standard musket made at the French Charleville armory. In 1777 several thousand of these guns had been obtained, through devious means, by representatives of the new American government. One of the three ships carrying the muskets from France to America was intercepted by the British blockade, but the other two brought their cargo of 23,000 muskets safely to American ports in time to share in the honor of defeating Burgoyne in the decisive battle of Saratoga.

Breech view of Whitney's famous musket made on the Charleville model. By producing the lock, most complex part of the weapon, on a mass production scale, Whitney ushered in a new era

Milwaukee Public Museum

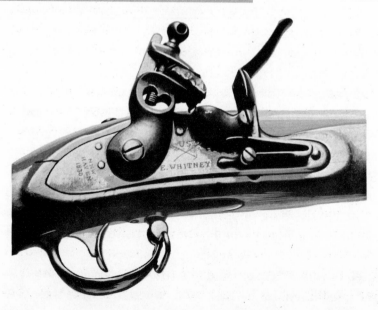

Whitney's familiarity with production problems had convinced him that for the United States their solution lay in reducing a complex form which required labor skill to simpler procedures which workers could learn in a short time. This had been demonstrated in England by Hargreaves, Arkwright, and Crompton when they replaced the spinner's skill with cunning machines.

But Whitney, exploring still further the laws that govern production, concluded that to increase the production of an article as intricate as a musket, methods and tools and machines would have to be created which would themselves be endowed with some of the armorer's skill and which would give uniformity and accuracy to make the parts interchangeable.

The system would also solve the related problem of maintenance by making available parts for repair. A logic derived from his experience and mechanical instinct assured him it was quite reasonable to assume a contract for 10,000 guns when the other 26 bidders, manufacturing by existing methods, together dared undertake a total of slightly over 30,000.

The rise of modern mass-production methods—basis of American industry today

"My general plan," Whitney wrote, "does not consist in one great complicated machine, wherever one small part being out of order or not answering to the purpose expected, the whole must stop & be considered useless. If the mode in which I propose to make one part of the musket should prove by experiment not to answer, it will in no way affect my mode of making any other part. One of my primary objects is to form the tools so the tools themselves shall fashion the work and give to every part its just proportion—which when once accomplished, will give expedition, uniformity, and exactness to the whole.

"If each individual workman must form and fashion every part according to his own fancy & regulate the size & proportion by his own Eye or even by a measure, I should have as many varieties as I have members of each part—many of them would require an inscription upon them to point out the use for which they were designed, & it would require treble the number of hands to do the same work. By long practice and many trials mere Mechanics who have no correct taste, acquire the art of giving a particular uniformity, I hope, to particular substances. But very few really good experienced workmen in this branch of business are to be had in this country. In order to supply ourselves in the course of the next few years with any considerable number of really good muskets, such means must be devised as will preclude the necessity of every workman's being bred to the business. An accurate eye, close attention and much time are necessary (where experience is wanting) to form things rightly; but few among the great mass can proportion things accurately.

"In short, the tools which I contemplate are similar to an engraving on copper plate from which may be taken a great number of impressions perceptibly alike."

At first, progress was necessarily slow, since special tools had to be made, processes worked out, and workmen trained—the first batch of 500 muskets was not, in fact, delivered until September, 1801, more than three years after the contract was signed. Whitney, meanwhile, required advances from the government if he was to keep going. Luckily, he was able to obtain them from Secretary Wolcott.

An early example of experimentation financed by the U.S. treasury

But on November 8, 1800, Wolcott resigned as Secretary of the Treasury. With Wolcott gone, written explanations and proposals, letters conveying reassurance fortified by impartial recommendations, bonds and sureties—all the paraphernalia by which Whitney had wrested additional time and moneys from the government—were useless; their efficacy had depended upon one man in authority who was friendly to Whitney's talent.

It became imperative that Whitney present himself at the seat of government as soon as possible. He was reassured by the progress he had made; he would not have to plead—this time he could show those in authority what he had been doing and the end to which he had worked. The muskets themselves would convince the most skeptical.

Whitney's demonstration of his musket to various government authorities, including Thomas Jefferson, was triumphant. By allowing the officials to assemble the parts of the locks—selecting the constituent parts at random—he dramatized the concept of interchangeability and made its advantages obvious.

Ten and a half years had passed from the time Whitney accepted the first contract when, on January 23, 1809, he informed the Secretary of War that "you will receive vouchers for a further delivery of 500 Muskets which compleats my Contract for fabricating 10,000 stands of arms for the Use of the U States. Upon the receipt of which be pleased to Direct the sum of Six Thousand Dollars to be remitted to me at this Place. I suppose the whole Balance due me from the U States is about Eight thousand Dollars . . . I propose to come to

Washington in a few weeks for the purpose of Closing up my accounts."

When Whitney deducted the cost of the stocks which had been furnished him from the Public Stores, when he next added the price of the 400 boxes he had made in which to pack his muskets properly and the cost of a "Proof House & Battery" which he had been asked to build at the government's cost, the balance owed him on the 10,000 arms he had manufactured and delivered was the small sum of $2,450.

But he had succeeded. He had carried through a new system of manufacturing, a revolutionary system that replaced a skill with the uniformity of a machine; he had been able to give tangible expression to an idea that could be adapted to other manufactures. And he had, to his own great satisfaction, established his own business.

After graduation from college, Eli Whitney visited the Mulberry Grove, Ga., plantation of the late Revolutionary War hero, Gen. Nathaniel Greene. It was while he was at Mulberry Grove that Whitney invented the cotton gin and that, with Phineas Miller, a fellow Yankee and manager of the plantation, he entered into a partnership to manufacture the new product. The rest, of course, is now history.

Science Digest

The cotton gin is Eli Whitney's most famous but not necessarily his most outstanding achievement

ROBERT FULTON, builder of the first steamboat, was born in 1765. He went to England at the age of 25 to study painting under Benjamin West. Partly influenced by James Watt and others, Fulton took up engineering. After publishing a Treatise on the Improvement of Canal Navigation in 1796, he went to France, where he built and experimented with submarines and steamboats. Fulton returned to the United States in 1806 and married Harriet Livingston. The next three years were busy ones: He built and rebuilt the Clermont, blew up a brig in New York Harbor with a torpedo and took his steamboat on its first voyage. Seven years later, in 1815, he died.

Robert Fulton

A boat propelled by steam

by Henry Thomas and Dana Lee Thomas

ONE NIGHT in 1806, Robert Fulton was lecturing to a large audience in New York. He had just returned from Europe, where he had astounded the scientific world with his experiments on steamships, torpedoes, and submarines. The public was especially interested in that "most diabolical" of his inventions—an "underwater contraption of cylinders and explosives" which, regulated by clockwork, could be placed under an enemy ship and blow it up.

Fulton was explaining to his audience the mechanism of this invention. "The torpedo which you see before you is charged with a hundred and seventy pounds of powder. Attached to it, as you will note, is a bit of clockwork which regulates the timing of the explosion. Now let me remove the peg which plugs up the powder charge." An apprehensive stir in the auditorium.

"Next," he continued, paying no attention to the uneasiness of his audience, "let me set the clock . . . There . . . And now, ladies and gentlemen, if I let this clock run ten minutes longer, we shall all be blown into kingdom come. . . ." He tried to go on with his lecture, but there was no one left to listen to him—the entire audience, in a panic, had made for the nearest exits.

His father was Scotch and his mother was Irish—a background which gave Robert the combined advantage of a tenacious will and a vivid imagination. He had need of both these characteristics from the start, for at the age of three he was left fatherless—a tough proposition for a youngster whose widowed mother had five children to feed and no income to fall back upon. He didn't care for the three Rs, which his mother taught him, nor for his lessons in school—which he entered at the age of eight.

Robert wouldn't learn his grammar. But he learned how to make all sorts of little gadgets in the blacksmith shops and the tinsmith shops of Lancaster, Pa. And he drew original designs for ornamenting the rifles that were manufactured in the village arsenal. "A pretty good draughtsman and a very good mechanic."

Robert couldn't make up his mind as to his future career. Should he devote himself to mechanics or to painting? Or, perhaps, to fighting? George Washington needed plenty of fighting men. However Robert was neither strong enough nor old enough for the rigors of a military life. "You are meant for the peaceful pursuits, my boy," said his mother. She sent him to Philadelphia, where for three years he knocked about as a jeweler's apprentice, an architect's assistant, and an occasional painter of miniature portraits.

His career, as it turned out, needed both his mechanical and artistic abilities

One of the men whose portraits he painted was Benjamin Franklin. The elderly statesman encouraged him in his work and secured him commissions from several personages of "manners and means."

Fulton had planned to try his fortune in England. He asked Franklin's advice about this plan. "You are right, young man. England is the place for an artist. America is too young, too eager to achieve. We have no time here for the leisurely appreciation of art."

He gave Fulton a letter of introduction to Benjamin West, the American painter who had made his mark in England. Fulton invested the greater part of his savings in a farm for his mother, and set sail for England with a capital of 40 guineas (about 200 dollars). "How foolish of him," said a friend, "to have decided upon the two most unprofitable careers in the world."

London, and a devoted intimacy with Benjamin West. Under the elder artist's inspiration, Fulton made rapid progress as a portrait painter. On two occasions his pictures were exhibited at the Royal

Academy. His artistic career was bringing him not only profit but prestige. "His portraits," wrote an eminent critic, "are well drawn, good in design, delicately colored, and well executed technically."

Yet Fulton was not content. If he stuck to his art, he would remain a competent painter all his life. But that was not enough. What he wanted was not competency, but mastery. And so he gave up the promise of his artistic career for the uncertainty of his engineering adventures.

Fulton possessed that rare combination of genius—Leonardo da Vinci was another man who possessed it—he was at once scientific in his art and artistic in his science. He reduced every object to a specific design and developed every design into a provocative picture. It was therefore an easy transition for him to transform his canvases into blueprints—to advance from the copying of existing shapes to the shaping of new existences.

Like so many others before him, Fulton was too far ahead of his time—held back by the lack of foresight of others

In rapid succession he invented a machine for spinning flax, an appliance for twisting ropes, and a mill for polishing marble. First the thought, then the plan, and finally the finished product. "He never made a model of an invention until he had completed a drawing which showed every part projected on the proper scale."

All these inventions, however, were but a preparation for his life's work—the lessening of the distance, both mental and material, between man and man. It was his ambition from now on to facilitate travel, to stimulate commerce, and to discourage dissension and war. For his interests were not only artistic and scientific; they were also political. "The establishment of Republicks throughout Europe . . . and the study of the art of Peace should be the aim of everybody." Certainly it was the aim of his own inventive labors.

He tried to develop a system of canals in England and on the European continent, so that the Old World might be more closely united into a confederation of free and friendly states. He spent a number of years on the invention of the submarine and the torpedo —two weapons whose destructiveness, he hoped, would bring about "the end of naval oppression and the establishment of peace through an agreement of nations." And he worked incessantly on his new "eagle of the sea"—a steam-propelled ship whose speed would in the future "narrow the sea into a strait and turn America and Europe into next-door neighbors."

It was through a friend, Madame de Gontaut, that Fulton was

able to interest the French ministers in his submarine and steamboat experiments. In December, 1797, he made his first attempt—on the Seine—to blow up a ship with a submarine. The attempt was a failure, both Fulton and his assistant escaping narrowly with their lives. Undeterred by the setback, he went ahead and built another submarine. This "undersea battleship" aroused the interest of Napoleon, who was at the time (1801) planning an invasion of England. "The sea which separates you from your enemy," Fulton wrote to Napoleon, "gives him an immense advantage over you. Aided . . . by the winds and the tempests, he defies you from his inaccessible island. I have it in my power to cause this obstacle which protects him to disappear. In spite of all his fleets, and in any weather, I can transport your armies to his territory (and destroy his ships) in a few hours . . . I am prepared to submit my plans."

Napoleon invited him to submit the plans and to demonstrate their effectiveness. In the summer of 1801, Fulton succeeded in "blowing a boat into atoms." The submarine was a proved success. Fulton was elated. "At long last we have an instrument that will do away with the erroneous system of exclusive commerce and distant possessions . . . the obstacles which hinder nations from arriving at a lasting peace."

But Napoleon and his ministers were not so sanguine about the usefulness of the submarine. "It would be impossible," said the Minister of Marine, "to give commissions to men using such an instrument in war, as these men would surely be hanged if captured." Fulton's invention was turned down.

Disappointed with his failure to interest the world in the submarine, Fulton now turned his entire effort to his next idea—the steamship. In this idea—the possibility of steam navigation—he was not alone. Both in America and in Europe there were a number of scientists preoccupied with experiments in this field. One of these scientists, Robert R. Livingston, was appointed American minister to France. The two Roberts—Fulton and Livingston—were drawn together through their similarity in temperament and taste. Fulton had the ideas, and Livingston had the funds. They formed a partnership which turned out to their mutual advantage and that of the world.

At the outset, however, they had anything but smooth sailing. In the early spring of 1803 they were ready with their model steamboat. It was anchored on the Seine, waiting for its initial experiment. One

135

morning Fulton was roused from his bed. His boat, he was told, had sunk in the night. He rushed to the spot. Sure enough, the boat was split in two. The iron machinery in the center had proved too heavy for the wooden structure.

What did it matter that the framework was wrecked—after all wasn't the machinery most important? And now, knowing the weakness of his craft, Fulton could build a better vessel

Plunging into the icy water and working incessantly for 24 hours, Fulton succeeded in raising the boat. The machinery was intact, but the framework was a wreck. So too, for a time, was his health. But Fulton went right on rebuilding the boat, and in the summer of that same year was ready for the test.

On August 10, 1803, the following account of the historic event appeared in the *Journal des Debats*:

". . . During the past two or three months there has been seen at the end of the quay Chaillot (on the Seine) a boat of curious appearance, equipped with two large wheels, mounted on an axle like a chariot, while behind these wheels was a kind of large stove with a pipe, as if there was some kind of a small fire engine intended to operate the wheels of the boat. . . .

"The day before yesterday, at six in the evening, the inventor . . . put his boat in motion . . . and for an hour and a half he produced the curious spectacle of a boat moved by wheels, like a chariot, these wheels being provided with paddles or flat plates, and being moved by a fire engine.

"The boat ascended and descended the stream four times from Les Bons-Hommes as far as the pump of Chaillot; it was maneuvered with facility, turning to the right and left, came to anchor, started again, and passed by the swimming school. . . .

"This mechanism, applied to our rivers—the Seine, the Loire, and the Rhone—will have most advantageous consequences upon our internal navigation. The tows and barges which now require four months to come from Nantes to Paris would arrive promptly in 10 to 15 days. . . ."

Again Fulton had offered a valuable gift to the French government, and again the offer was turned down. Napoleon and his ministers gave due consideration to the "experiment on the Seine," and decided that the steamship, like the submarine, was a "useless toy."

Fulton was now thoroughly disgusted with France—not only for personal but also for political reasons. It was a great shock to him to see the accession of Napoleon to the office of First Consul. "The French Revolution is dead. The French people have merely exchanged one despot for another." Fulton longed to breathe once more the air of a free country. He took passage to America.

And to final glory. Together with Livingston, who had returned from his diplomatic post in the Old World, he built a steamship—the *Clermont*—in the East River, and one day quietly sailed around the tip of New York and over to the New Jersey shore. It was a most successful trip. Fulton and Livingston were now ready for their first public test.

The public, however, had nothing but jeers for "Fulton's Folly" —the nickname given to the boat by one of the New York wits. "The thing," wrote a journalist who had gone down to examine the boat, "is an ungainly craft looking precisely like a backwoods' sawmill mounted on a scow and set on fire."

Yet on the day of the trial—August 17, 1807—a large number of spectators gathered on the banks of the Hudson River. "While we were putting off from the wharf," wrote Fulton in a letter to a friend, "I heard a number of sarcastic remarks." Excitement, incredulity, ridicule, scorn—and then silence, followed by a shout of spontaneous applause. "Holy Jupiter, the thing does work!" yelled one of the spectators hysterically as the *Clermont* wheeled across the river, made a clean-cut turn upstream, overtook sloop after sloop and "parted with them as if they had been at anchor."

Three weeks after the trial—from the 7th to the 11th of September—the *Clermont* sailed up the Hudson to Albany and back. The trip was a continuous triumph. Throngs of people on the banks and in boats looked on "with awe almost amounting to terror," as the water chariot rolled over the Hudson, her funnel spouting forth a pillar of cloud by day, a pillar of fire by night. A scene reminiscent of the Old Testament—the finger of God pointing the way to a new Canaan, the Promised Land of speedier communication and better understanding between man and man. "The power of propelling boats by steam," as Fulton wrote to one of his sponsors, "is now fully proved."

The government, impressed with the success of Fulton's steamboat, commissioned him to construct a 38-ton warship for the United States Navy

BORN IN SOUTHERN England in 1769, William Smith had little chance for formal education. But he was an avid reader, especially fascinated by mathematics—notably algebra and surveying. At 18 Smith qualified as a surveyor's assistant. And while on surveying jobs, he first began to notice the consistent arrangement of fossils in the earth's strata. Smith, through constant research, rearranged this strata into its proper geological order. Before his death in 1839, at the age of 70, William Smith had been honored by the Geological Society of London, and the British Association for the Advancement of Science.

William Smith

Rearranging the geologic calendar
by Edgar O. Bowles

THE EARLY HISTORY OF the science of geology is replete with the names of distinguished, wealthy, brilliant devotees who pursued their studies without being forced to seek a livelihood from their scientific work. James Hutton, the Scottish physician; Sir Charles Lyell, friend of royalty and social reformer; Sir Roderick Impey Murchison, traveler and writer on a host of geological subjects—all these made notable contributions to our fund of geological knowledge although they all were, according to modern classification, strictly amateurs. Against this sparkling background, the drab figure of William Smith, whose name was as inconspicuous as were his latent talents, stands in somber contrast.

The closing years of the 18th century marked an important period of transition in the whole economy of England. They were the days of industrial expansion, and some cheap method of mass transportation for raw materials, fuels, and finished goods was essential. The steam locomotive had not yet been developed, and the answer to the transportation bottleneck seemed to be more and larger canal systems.

Many potential routes were surveyed across England, and Smith was fortunate enough, although only 25, to become the engineer and surveyor of the Somerset Coal Canal. He personally supervised the surveying of the route, and through six work-filled years he managed the excavation and construction of the canal itself. Although the details of the job took much of his time, he still could devote himself to observations on the strata, or successive horizontal or tilted layers of rock, through which the canal passed, and collect the fossils that abounded in the sediments of that part of England. Fossils—the remains of plants and animals of past geological ages, found in the rock sediments which preserved them—were popular curiosities among the country-folk of the Somerset region, although there was little understanding of their derivation and no significance was attached to them.

William Smith was blessed not only with an observing eye, but also with that rarest and most satisfying of human attributes—intellectual curiosity. To Smith's technically trained observation, the fossils were more than mere curiosities for cabinet display. He noted that certain distinctive types of curiously formed petrified materials occupied definite layers in the rocks, and that layers above and below had their own peculiar assemblages of fossils remains. No matter where you encountered a certain layer, its fossils were like its own and no other's.

Idly at first, and then with an increasing interest in the results, William Smith began a determinative study that revealed that the fossils were true to their own strata, and that they always occurred at the specific levels he had first observed them. The order in which the levels were stacked never changed. Thus, he could not only identify a particular stratum but could anticipate the succession of strata below it and above it, even though the outcrops he was studying were completely unconnected.

Although a man of more than average intelligence, William Smith was no scholar. He was, basically, a very inarticulate man. To a few of his associates he revealed the interesting results of his casual researches, only to be met by the 18th-century British equivalent of "so what?" The industrial expansion had brought with it an eagerness for the advancement of practical and economically profitable innovations, but pure knowledge was of interest only to the

Smith's prosaic name has been relieved somewhat by the addition of a descriptive nickname, and to this day geology students refer to him casually as William "Strata" Smith, the recognized father of stratigraphic geology

scholar and philosopher, and the canal surveyor had little contact with either.

The uninterested listeners could conceive of no possible commercial value in a system of rock classification based on fossils—and to be truthful Smith had to agree reluctantly with them. This lack of appreciation might have had a serious effect on Smith's later researches, for he was a shy, sensitive, retiring man, had he not encountered a stimulating and encouraging adherent.

It is to the credit of the contemporary scientists of England that William Smith, simple surveyor that he was and continued to be, received full credit for his pioneering work

The Rev. Benjamin Richardson, a rural pastor, had made a collection of the local fossils that occurred in great abundance around the town of Bath, and a hodgepodge of the most characteristic specimens was on display in his study, just as similar cabinet displays adorned the houses of many of his parishioners. During a chance call on the pastor, Smith startled his host by identifying specimens from the unlabeled and casually arranged collection, not only by their common names, but also by a description of the beds in which they occurred.

Richardson was fascinated. He could hardly believe that Smith really had this apparently uncanny insight into the occurrence of fossils. It was particularly difficult for Richardson to credit this simple and comparatively untutored surveyor with the ability to arrive at a conclusion that was hitherto unknown to the geologic giants who were then holding sway. Could it be possible that the layers of rock were actually always found in the same order, and containing the same distinctive assemblages of fossils? Richardson doubted it, but he was willing to put his doubt to the test of demonstration. Smith assured him that he could tell *in advance* what fossils would be in the sediments on any particular hillside, and not only that, but also what fossils would be in the beds above and below. He demonstrated his accuracy again and again on the hills around Bath, and eventually convinced Richardson that his assumption was valid.

It was one thing to prove a point to a rural pastor, and another, Smith found to his discouragement, to bring it to the attention of the scientific world. Publication, urged by Richardson, was out of the question. The author of a scientific text, in those days at least, was required to finance the complete publication, and Smith's resources were limited. He did, under the continued prodding of his now eager advocate, publish a card showing the succession of British strata, and, rather to his surprise, the brief card caused considerable favorable comment.

To understand the full impact of Smith's apparently prosaic discovery about fossils and the strata that contain them, it is only necessary to look at the unsatisfactory classification of sediments in Smith's day. Strata had been segregated into four groupings, Primary, Secondary, Tertiary, and Quaternary, with the distinctions based primarily on the character of the rocks included within the strata. Particular emphasis was placed, in the classification, on the degree of deformation, as this seemed to be the most accurate criterion for judging the age of rocks. Thus the 18th-century geologist, confronted with a rock that was intensely folded and obviously recrystallized, simply placed it in the "Primary" along with all other rocks similarly deformed. If the rock was hardly more than unconsolidated sediment, still lying in a horizontal position with no sign of deformation, it was placed in the "Tertiary," and so forth.

More and more, in the years immediately preceding the first publication of Smith's work, geologists were realizing that their basis of subdivision was not a very dependable one. Some rocks, older than most of the Primary, were completely unaffected by heat and pressure, and had been no more deformed than rocks attributable to the Secondary or Tertiary. On the other hand, rocks of comparatively recent times had been involved in stupendous mountain-building episodes, and had been profoundly distorted and metamorphosed from their original form.

The tool for the erection of a sound framework for a geologic calendar was now at hand. William Smith, in propounding what has since been absorbed into the science as a basic law—The Law of Faunal Succession—had sown the seed for a harvest that his more learned contemporaries could reap in full. Now it was possible to "correlate" strata occurring in widely separated localities. Within the next few decades after the publication of Smith's original little chart, such correlations were being made throughout Europe, and even across the Atlantic into the new world. Major divisions of geologic time could be set up, characterized by distinctive assemblages of petrified animal or plant remains, and the same fossil assemblages could be found in Russia, England, the United States, or wherever the wanderlust of the geological pioneer carried him.

In 1815 Smith created another milestone in geological progress by his publication of the first geological map ever issued in the world, delineating the area of the formations identified in the British Isles

141

RENÉ LAENNEC (1781-1826), a French physician and teacher, was born in Brittany. His work as a regimental surgeon took him from Nantes to Paris, where he was appointed to the Necker Hospital. In 1822 Laennec became professor of medicine at the College de France. The invention of the stethoscope came around 1819 and thereafter he developed the technique of auscultation, indispensable to the diagnosis of diseases of the heart and lungs. This study published in the same year is entitled, De l'auscultation médiate, and it is from this work that our present knowledge of chest diseases is primarily obtained.

René Laennec

Invention of the stethoscope

IN 1816 I was consulted by a young woman presenting general symptoms of disease of the heart. Owing to her stoutness little information could be gathered by application of the hand and percussion. The patient's age and sex did not permit me to resort to . . . direct application of the ear to the chest.

I recalled a well-known acoustic phenomenon, namely, if you place your ear against one end of a wooden beam the scratch of a pin at the other extremity is most distinctly audible. It occurred to me that this physical property might serve a useful purpose in the case with which I was then dealing.

Taking a sheaf of paper, I rolled it into a very tight roll, one end of which I placed over the praecordial region, while I put my ear to the other, I was both surprised and gratified at being able to hear the beating of the heart with much greater clearness and distinctness than I had ever done before by direct application of my ear.

I at once saw that this means might become a useful method for studying not only the beating of the heart but likewise all movements capable of producing sound in the thoracic cavity, and that consequently it might serve for the investigation of respiration, the voice, rales, and even possibly the movements of a liquid effused into the pleural cavity or pericardium.

With this conviction, I at once began and have continued to the present time, a series of observations at the Hospital Necker. As a result I have obtained many new and certain signs, most of which are striking, easy of recognition, and calculated perhaps to render the diagnosis of nearly all complaints of the lungs, pleurae, and heart both more certain and more circumstantial than the surgical diagnosis obtained by use of the sound or by introduction of the finger . . .

Before proceeding with my subject I consider it my duty to record the various attempts that I have made to improve upon the exploring instrument I at present use; these attempts have proved almost entirely vain, and if I mention them it is in the hope that any other investigator seeking to perfect the instrument will strike out a fresh path.

The first instrument employed by me consisted of a cylinder or roll of paper 16 lines in diameter and one foot long, made of three quires of paper rolled very tightly round, and held in position with gummed paper and filed smooth at both ends. However tight the roll may be, there will always remain a tube three or four lines in diameter running up in the center, because the sheets of paper composing it can never be rolled completely on themselves.

This fortuitous circumstance gave rise, as will be seen, to an important observation upon my part: I found that for listening to the voice the tube is an indispensable factor. An entirely solid body is the best instrument that can be used for listening to the heart; such an instrument would indeed suffice also for hearing respiratory sounds and rales; yet these last two phenomena yield greater intensity of sound if a perforated cylinder is used, hollowed out at one end into a kind of funnel one and one-half inches in depth.

The densest bodies are not, as analogy would lead us to suppose, the best materials for constructing these instruments. Glass and metals, apart from their weight and sensation of cold that they impart in winter, are not such good carriers of the heartbeats and the sounds produced by breathing and rales, as are bodies of lesser density . . .

"The well-known acoustic phenomenon" Laennec mentions at the beginning of his description, was observed by him when he watched children playing in a Louvre garden. They had discovered that they could hear a pin scratch at one end of a seesaw plank if they pressed their ears to the other end

143

Substances of medium density, such as paper, wood, and cane, are those which have always appeared to me preferable to all others. This result may be in contradiction with an axiom of physics; nonetheless I consider it to be quite established.

I consequently employ at the present time a wooden cylinder with a tube three lines in diameter bored right down its axis; it is divisible into two parts by means of a screw and is thus more portable. One of the parts is hollowed out at its end into a wide funnel-shaped depression one and one-half inches deep leading into the central tube. A cylinder made like this is the instrument most suitable for exploring breathing sounds and rales.

Rales are abnormal, usually morbid, sounds which accompany the normal sounds of breathing

It is converted into a tube of uniform diameter with thick walls all the way, for exploring the voice and the heartbeats, by introducing into the funnel or bell a kind of stopper made of the same wood, fitting it quite closely; this is made best by means of a small brass tube running through it, entering a certain distance into the tubular space running through the length of the cylinder. This instrument is sufficient for all cases, although as I have already said, a perfectly solid body might perhaps be better for listening to the beating of the heart.

The dimensions indicated above are not altogether unimportant; if the diameter is larger it is not always possible to apply the stethoscope closely against all points of the chest; if the instrument is longer, it becomes difficult to hold it exactly in place; if it were shorter, the physician would often be obliged to adopt an uncomfortable position, which is to be avoided above all things if he desires to carry out accurate observations . . .

Suffice it to say for the moment that in all cases the stethoscope should be held like a pen, and that the hand must be placed quite close to the patient's chest in order to make sure that the instrument is properly applied.

"No discovery was ever made," wrote Logan Clendening, "which more clearly belongs to the man whose name is associated with it than Laennec's discovery of the stethoscope."

FARADAY sought to explain electromagnetic induction by the way iron filings arrange themselves, on a sheet of paper, in lines around a magnet. The space surrounding a magnet or electric conductor, he reasoned, must be filled with "lines" of magnetic force; an electric current results when a conductor cuts the lines of force. He further suggested that all space is pervaded with lines of magnetic force, their concentration and direction at any given point depending on the nearness and strength of a source (a magnet). He also said that space is filled with lines of force of other kinds: electric, heat and gravitational.

Michael Faraday

Inventor of the dynamo
by Leonard Engel

O NE DAY IN SEPTEMBER, 1831, Michael Faraday, successor to the immortal Sir Humphry Davy at the Royal Institution, wrote to his friend Richard Phillips: "I am busy just now again on electromagnetism, and think I have got hold of a good thing, but can't say. It may be a weed instead of a fish that, after all my labor, I may at last pull up."

It proved to be a fish, one of the biggest ever landed by science—the principle of the dynamo. Faraday had discovered that a moving magnet causes an electric current to flow in a wire placed in the field of the magnet. This is how we generate electricity today; an electric generator is essentially a coil of wire (called an armature) rotated between the poles of a set of magnets.

Almost exactly ten years before, Faraday had discovered how to obtain mechanical motion with the aid of an electric current—in other words, the principle of the electric motor. The new discovery completed the old. The two together laid the basis for the age of electricity —the vast network of generating plants that supply us with versatile electric power, the wonderful variety of electric motors and other electrical devices that serve us in countless ways.

Michael Faraday discovered not only the principles of the dynamo and the electric motor. Single-handed, he worked out almost all the basic laws governing the relationship between electricity and magnetism.

Faraday's brilliant advances and experiments in these fields were accepted slowly by his countrymen for he was, in contrast to his fellow scientists, uneducated

He evolved the concept of the electromagnetic field, the revolutionary idea that led to radio and relativity. He also worked out the laws of electrolysis; made important discoveries in the polarization of light and the diffusion of gases; liquefied many gases; prepared stainless steels almost a century before they came into use; and discovered benzene and other important carbon compounds.

In short, Faraday was one of the most remarkable experimenters in history, a person to whom the world owes an incalculable debt. Einstein has indicated that he considers Faraday an even greater scientist than Galileo.

Faraday was born September 22, 1791, a few miles from London. His father was a poor blacksmith from the north of England. He received little schooling. But his parents passed on two legacies that played a direct part in making him the foremost scientist of his age. One was a tremendous energy. The other was adherence to the Sandemanians, a small Scottish Presbyterian sect which frowned on wealth and worldly honor.

Faraday's lifelong devotion to the Sandemanian creed helped him to refuse honors (such as the presidency of the Royal Society) and huge lecturing and consulting fees that would have taken him away from his laboratory bench.

Also, the Sandemanians frowned on religious controversy and did not proselytize, a circumstance responsible at least in part for Faraday's famed modesty and willingness to let his experimental results speak for themselves.

Faraday, who was small in stature, looked like a New England Puritan and indeed was close to the Puritans in religion and spirit. Once he decided to become a scientist he went at it with ferocious determination. He taught himself by a process that was (in the phrase of a British biographer, J. G. Crowther) more like the training of an athlete than education.

Faraday was apprenticed to a London bookbinder at the age of 14. His interest in science was awakened by some of the books he had

Sir Humphrey Davy's laboratory.
Young Michael Faraday is shown
assisting the famous scientist

to bind and by some of the visitors to his master's shop. One of these, a Mr. Dance, presented Faraday with a set of tickets to a series of lectures by Davy. Faraday made a beautifully illustrated set of notes that filled 386 manuscript pages. He sent the notes (which may still be seen in the Royal Institution Library) to Davy with a letter asking for a job as a laboratory assistant.

Davy wrote a friendly reply and finally, some months later, took Faraday on. So, in 1812, at the age of 21, Faraday moved to the Royal Institution for the Diffusing of Knowledge. The Royal Institution, which had been founded in 1799 and was one of the world's earliest scientific institutes, was to be his home as well as his place of work for half a century.

Faraday's first years at the Royal Institution were distinguished by one of the classic journeys of science, a remarkable 18-month tour of Europe with Sir Humphry and Lady Davy. They received an enthusiastic welcome everywhere, even in France, with whom England was at war. Faraday did not do any research of his own until he was

147

Michael Faraday

Inventor of the dynamo

25 and his first important discovery—the principle on which the electric motor is based, was not made until he was past 30.

In 1820, the Danish electrical pioneer Oersted discovered that a current of electricity flowing in a wire turns a magnetic needle placed near the wire so that it is perpendicular to the wire. An English scientist, William Hyde Wollaston, suggested to Davy that this effect, which is due to the magnetic field around a flowing electric current, could be utilized to produce mechanical motion. But Wollaston had the wrong idea. He thought the wire could be made to turn on its own axis. His and Davy's experiment accordingly failed.

Faraday meanwhile studied Oersted's original experiments and came to a different conclusion. He thought the magnet ought to go around the wire or vice versa. A pair of brilliant experiments quickly proved him right. In one, he made a magnet floating in a bath of mercury go around an insulated wire standing in the mercury. In the other, he made a copper wire, one end of which was free to move, swing around a stationary magnet.

This is precisely what happens in an electric motor. When current is fed into the armature, the armature attempts to go around the magnets surrounding it. However, the current is fed in such a way, and the magnets are so arranged that the armature is forced to rotate instead of going around the magnets.

Science Digest

This first dynamo, built by Michael Faraday, is preserved by the Royal Society in London

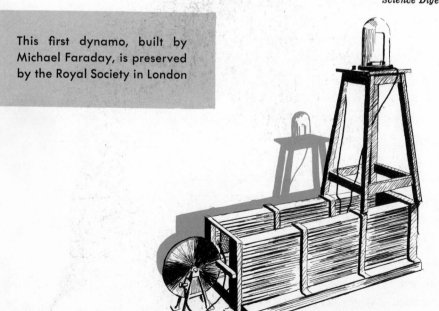

Practical electric motors might have been developed soon after Faraday's discovery of their principle. They were delayed by several circumstances. Faraday had no interest whatever in profiting personally from any of his discoveries; as soon as a discovery looked as though it might have commercial possibilities, he went on to something else.

Moreover, Faraday became involved in an acrimonious dispute with Wollaston and Davy which caused him to halt all work in electricity for a time. Among other things, this delayed the arrival of the other prerequisite of the electric motor—a practical source of electricity. The wet batteries then in use were clumsy and feeble; the principle of the dynamo was needed.

When Faraday announced his discoveries in electromagnetism and motion, Wollaston and Davy accused him of stealing their ideas. Faraday was able to convince other scientists and eventually Wollaston himself that he had not, but he seems never to have persuaded Davy. One result was that Davy cast the lone vote against Faraday when Faraday was nominated for England's top scholarly organization, the Royal Society. Another was that Faraday did not take up research on electricity again until 1831.

In the summer of that year, Faraday went back to a question that had first occurred to him when he heard of Oersted's experiments. If an electric current could produce magnetic effects, would magnetism produce an electric current?

Faraday first tried the simple experiment of placing a magnet near a copper wire. Of course, nothing happened. He then investigated the effect of an electric current floating in a wire (i.e., of the magnetic field around the wire) on a second wire. For this purpose, Faraday contrived what amounted to a crude transformer—an iron ring with two coils of insulated wire wound around it. One coil was connected to a battery, the other to a galvanometer.

As long as the first coil was connected to the battery, nothing happened. But at the instant the coil was connected or disconnected, the galvanometer showed a current flowing in the second coil.

Faraday was puzzled at first, but his keen intuition soon told him what was occurring. A magnetic field could indeed induce an electric current in a wire, but it had to be a *changing* magnetic field.

This led Faraday to the classic experiment he performed two months later. He wound a coil of insulated wire, connected to a galva-

149

nometer, on a hollow paper cylinder. As he thrust a magnet in and out of the cylinder, or moved the cylinder over the magnet (it made no difference which he did), the galvanometer registered the passage of an electric current in the coil of wire.

Eleven days later—on October 28, 1831—Faraday built the world's first generator. It consisted of a copper disk (the "coil") rotating between the poles of a large magnet. As Faraday turned the disk, a galvanometer registered the flow of a current in wires from the center and the edge of the disk. The Royal Society still has a model of Faraday's generator.

Faraday himself did nothing further to develop the generator as a practical source of electric power. His interest lay in a different direction. He wanted to know *why* a moving magnet induced an electric current in a conductor. It led him to what many scientists consider his greatest contribution—the theory of the electromagnetic field.

These modern generators are working
on the same principle discovered by Faraday

Westinghouse Electric Corp.

JOSEPH HENRY, one of America's most important physicists, was born in 1797. He began his career as a watchmaker's apprentice, and worked his way through the Albany Academy, to which school he returned to teach mathematics from 1826 to 1832. He was appointed professor of natural philosophy at Princeton in 1832, and remained at the post until his resignation in 1846. In that year he was elected the first secretary of the Smithsonian Institution, whose policies he guided until his death in Washington, D. C., on May 13, 1878. Henry's interests ranged from the fields of acoustics, signaling through fogs to meteorology.

Joseph Henry

Electrical experimenter

by Thomas Coulson

JOSEPH HENRY is a strangely neglected figure, and yet the story of his life contains many of those elements which endear a man to the American mind. His was a true story of the rise from poverty to—if not to riches at least to fame. Son of a day laborer in Albany, he was drifting aimlessly until the chance reading of a book guided him into a scientific career. At a time when America had very few professional scientists he engaged in electrical investigations which bore most fruitful results.

The difficulties he had to overcome were formidable. Working in the early years of the 19th century, when Albany was a frontier town, remote from the current of scientific thought and with only occasional information reaching him of what others were doing, he was laboring under difficulties which would have discouraged most men. He suffered from a chronic shortage of time, money and materials. Yet he attained a foremost position among the scientists of his day by his genius for experimentation, his inventive insight, his power of exact observation, and his keen sense of perspective and proportion.

What were the achievements upon which this claim to greatness rests?

There is not space to enumerate all Henry's discoveries and inventions, nor to describe fully his activities as an organizer of science, but let us glance at the most noteworthy. He began by converting the electromagnet from a toy into an instrument with enormous potentialities. This was the greatest single utilitarian electric invention of the period. Without the aid of this increase in the strength of electromagnetism it is doubtful whether Faraday would have succeeded in his experiments with electrical induction. The great English physicist had tried repeatedly to produce electricity from magnetism, but had always failed until he tried Henry's magnets.

The essence of Henry's success lay in his use for the first time of insulated wires, wound in coils of more than one layer. This form of construction is used universally for electromagnets today. Had he

Shown below is the reciprocating engine built by Joseph Henry with the aid of electromagnets and a commutator. Right, the first electromagnet constructed and used by Henry

Smithsonian Institution

done no more than this he would have been entitled to a place in the history of science. But it was only a beginning.

By demonstrating that the coils of a magnet could be made up of either one long wire or several short ones, he showed the proper relative proportions of magnet to battery for maximum effect. He pointed out that one arrangement was suitable for operating over long wires, while the other arrangement was best suited for local circuits. This was the first demonstration, made independently of Ohm's theory, of the necessity for properly matching the resistance of the different parts of an electrical circuit, a principle which is of primary importance in the design of circuits.

This was all performed during the first two years devoted to his investigation of electricity. The results he had obtained furnished the foundation upon which to erect that knowledge from which the electrical industry has grown.

Immediately beginning to apply his knowledge to the creation of practical things, he was the first to describe and to construct an electric motor using electromagnets and a commutator. His motor was reciprocal rather than rotational in motion, but he contributed the fundamental elements of permanent value, and served to stimulate interest in the problem of deriving mechanical power from electricity.

Every modern piece of machinery that uses electromagnets uses them in practically the same form as Henry's models of 1829

Henry then profited from his knowledge of circuit-matching to make the first practical electromagnetic telegraph with polarized armature, which made rapid signaling possible, and which has formed the basis of practically all subsequent commercial wire telegraphy. His receiver gave the first audible signal. I would ask you to observe that this was accomplished before Samuel Morse received his much better known inspiration. It is also worthy of observation that Morse was unable to make his system operate over a distance greater than about 40 feet until he was advised to study Henry's description of circuit matching.

Henry and Faraday independently discovered mutual induction and self-induction. Purely upon priority of publication Faraday is credited with the discovery of mutual induction. Nevertheless, if we examine carefully the work Henry was engaged upon at the time, we should do no violation to the truth if we concluded that Henry was in advance of Faraday with mutual induction but, because of a reluctance to publish an account of his results, he allowed the English scientist to forestall him. I do not wish to emphasize this point because the discovery was of a sufficiently momentous nature to furnish honor to both men, but I do lament that Henry's name is never mentioned in connection with this discovery.

However, there can be no doubt about the discovery of self-induction. Henry was undoubtedly in advance of his great rival in this field, and this is universally acknowledged by the adoption of his name as the unit of measure in self-induction—the *henry*.

Up to this point I have described Henry's achievement during three years while he was a teacher at the Albany Academy. The work had gained for him a reputation which secured the offer of a professorship at the College of New Jersey, as Princeton University was called in those days. The 14 years he spent at Princeton were the happiest of his life, and the most fruitful.

While at Princeton, Henry's interests grew. He held classes in physics, mathematics, chemistry, geology, mineralogy, astronomy and architecture. Here he also conducted experiments in many fields other than electricity

During this time he developed the magnetic relay which, I need hardly remind you, finds a multitude of uses in electrical engineering. Henry presented the idea of the relay to both Wheatstone in England and Morse in America, but neither acknowledged the debt which enabled them to overcome the obstacles preventing the transmission of impulses over long wires.

Both Faraday and Henry had employed a transformer structure in their first induction experiments, but it remained for Henry to discover that, by a proper proportioning of the coils, the voltage could be either stepped up or stepped down with this structure. This is the basis of the familiar transformer of today.

Other hardly less important discoveries made by Henry while at Princeton were non-inductive wirings, the relation of high-order induced currents, and electromagnetic shielding. There is however a series of investigations falling in this period which deserves more attention than it has received. This relates to the variation of induction between coils with separation, the action of induction at a distance, and the oscillatory nature of the discharge from a Leyden jar —all of which had an influential bearing upon the development of radio telegraphy and telephony.

While almost every branch of electricity is under debt to Henry, the alternating-current system now in general use, especially long-distance power distribution, is under a special obligation. The transformer is fundamental to the alternating-current system. Through its use it is possible to design generators at the most effective voltage, and then to step up the voltage to the most efficient level for use on the transmission lines, and again, at the distant point of these lines, step down the potential to the most efficient and convenient voltage for the distributing system.

I wish space permitted me to deal with some of Henry's other activities, notably his pioneer studies in the correlation of forces, which extended beyond the mere transformation of one force into another, as magnetism into electricity, or electricity into light. He was looking beyond this into a realm of nature where was to be found a unitarian force, the power or ability to do work, manifested in many ways.

But space must be reserved to speak of Henry as the organizer of science. This is difficult to evaluate, but it is probably just as significant as his scientific discoveries. He organized the Smithsonian Institution and was its secretary for 21 years. He was active in the formation of the National Academy of Sciences and the American Association for the Advancement of Science. Indeed, Henry did more to organize and correlate American science than any other man before or since his time. . . .

One of his first duties at the Institution was to set up a corps of volunteers for weather observations, and this eventually led to the establishment of the U.S. Weather Bureau

Those who knew him best have left a picture of a man of humble loves and great good will, warm in charity with the world. . . .

In this brief outline of Henry's work it has been possible only to indicate that we owe to him the developments which constitute the fundamentals of a complete magnetic telegraph system. The credit for this goes exclusively to Morse. If Henry had patented his ideas there could have been no Morse telegraphy. Yet Morse savagely attacked him. In his defense Henry modestly said: "My life has been principally devoted to science and my investigations in different branches of physics have given me some reputation in the line of original discovery. I have sought, however, no patent for invention and solicited no remuneration for my labors but have freely given the results to the world—expecting only in return to enjoy the consciousness of having added to the sum of human knowledge. The only reward I expected was the consciousness of having advanced science, the pleasure of discovering new truths, and the scientific reputation to which these labors entitle me."

AS A BOY, Friedrich Woehler (1800-1882) was encouraged by his father in many different fields. He decided on a medical career and after a year at Marburg University, Woehler went to Heidelberg in 1821, attracted by the reputation of the chemistry teacher, Leopold Gmelin. Woehler received his degree of Doctor of Medicine, Surgery, and Midwifery, but abandoned a medical career in favor of research when he was invited to work in the laboratory of Jons Jakob Berzelius, the world-famous Swedish chemist. Woehler spent the remainder of his long life in Sweden. From 1836 until his death he was professor of chemistry in the medical faculty of University of Gottingen.

Friedrich Woehler

Founder of organic chemistry
by Ernest Borek

A CENTURY and a quarter ago one great roadblock in the path to knowledge was the principle of vitalism which dominated scientific thought until the middle of the 19th century. Scientists had explored with fruitful zest the nonliving world, but they halted with awe and impotence before a living thing. The believers in vitalism thought that the cell membrane shrouded mysterious vital force and "sensitive spirits." It was an unassailable belief that not only could we not fathom these mysteries, but that we should never be able to duplicate by any method a single product of such vital forces. An uncrossable chasm was supposed to separate the realm of the living, organic world from the realm of the nonliving, inorganic world.

Then, in 1828, a young man of 28 unwittingly bridged that chasm. He made something in the chemical laboratory which, until that time, had been made only in the body of a living thing. This achievement was the "atom bomb" of the 19th century. And its influence in shaping our lives is far greater than the influence of atomic energy will be.

Had there been science writers on the newspapers of that day they could very well have unfurled all the cliches of their present-day counterparts about the achievement. But, oddly, not only were the man and his feat unknown to his contemporaries, he is practically unknown even today. The generals of the Napoleonic era—Blucher, Ney, Bernadotte—are known to many, but their contemporary, Friedrich Woehler, who was a giant of intellect and influence compared to them, is known only to chemists.

Friedrich Woehler was a student of medicine at Heidelberg in the early 1820's. His chemistry teacher, Gmelin, was one of those rare teachers who not only dispensed knowledge but "shaped souls." Under his guidance Woehler left medicine and became a chemist. He more than justified his teacher's faith, for, in addition to the great discovery which shook the foundation of vitalism, we owe to Woehler many other discoveries in chemistry. After absorbing all that Heidelberg could offer, he went to Sweden to work with Berzelius, the greatest contemporary master of chemistry.

It was Berzelius who discovered three elements and devised our modern system of chemical symbols and formula writing

There Woehler discovered, quite by accident, a method of making urea, a substance theretofore produced only by the cells of living creatures. So contrary to current ideas was this achievement that he published it only after numerous repetitions, four years later. How did he learn the secret of the sensitive spirits? How did he make urea?

Urea is a substance found as a waste product in the urine of some animals. It can be cajoled out in the form of pure white crystals by the knowing hands of the chemist. Like all other pure compounds, urea has characteristic attributes which distinguish it from any other substance. Sugar and salt are two different pure compounds which superficially look alike. But the tongue tells them apart with unfailing ease. Their different impact on our discerning little taste buds is but one of many differences between salt and sugar. The chemist has discovered scores of other differences. The elements of which they are composed, the temperature at which they melt, certain optical properties of the crystals, these are some of the distinguishing lines in the fingerprint of a compound, by means of which the chemist can recognize a particular compound among the multitudes.

Urea happens to be made of four different elements. One atom of carbon, one of oxygen, two of nitrogen, and four of hydrogen make up a urea molecule. These atoms are attached to each other in a definite pattern, a pattern unique to each substance. The force which

157

Friedrich Woehler
Founder of organic chemistry

binds these atoms into the distinctive pattern of urea (or any other substance) is the energy in the electrons of those atoms.

A chemical union between atoms is a light, superficial affair. Two atoms meet, some of their outer electrons become entangled and a temporary union is formed. The nucleus of the atom is completely unaffected by a chemical union. The energy involved in the making or breaking of such a union is minuscule compared to the vast energy locked within the nucleus of the atom—the monstrous nuclear, or atomic, energy.

Although his manufacture of urea lay in the organic-chemistry domain, the bulk of Woehler's work was done in the field of inorganic chemistry. His various texts were widely influential; and the Catalogue of the Royal Society *lists 276 scientific memoirs prepared by Woehler independently, and 43 more written in collaboration with others*

Until Woehler succeeded in *making* it, urea was thought to be fashioned only in a living animal by unknown, awesome, animated spirits. The spirits whimsically flung out their product into the urine for reasons no human could fathom.

Woehler had no intention of making urea in a test tube. He was studying a simple, undramatic chemical reaction. He wanted to make a new inorganic compound, ammonium cyanate. He went through a variety of manipulations which were expected to yield the new substance. As the final step, he boiled away the water and some white crystals were left behind. But they were not the new inorganic salt that he had expected; they were the very same urea which animals excrete!

It so happens that in ammonium cyanate, the substance Woehler had set out to make, there are the same elements in the same proportions as in urea. The difference is in the *pattern* the atoms form. The pattern of ammonium cyanate was disrupted by the heat of the boiling water and the atoms rearranged themselves to form urea. (The changing of chemical structures by heat is not unusual; indeed it is an everyday household feat—a boiled egg is quite different from an uncooked one.)

Simple? It looks simple now, more than a century and a quarter later, when animated spirits have become scientific antiques, and the manufacture of synthetic vitamins is a big industry. Thus, only in our hindsight, which sharpens with the elapsed years, does it look simple.

The importance of the finding was not lost to Woehler or his contemporaries. While he wrote very modestly of his achievement in his four-page technical communication, he let himself go when writing to his mentor, Berzelius. "I must now tell you," he wrote, "that I can make urea without calling on my kidneys, and indeed, without the aid of any animal, be it man or dog."

The homage of history was paid by Sir Frederick Gowland Hopkins, Nobel Prize winner, on the centenary of the discovery: "The intrinsic historic importance of Woehler's synthesis can hardly be exaggerated. So long as the belief held ground that substances formed in the plant or animal could never be made in the laboratory, there could be no encouragement for those who instinctively hoped that chemistry might join hands with biology. The very outermost defences of vitalism seemed unassailable."

Though the barrier between organic and inorganic chemistry was demolished by Woehler, the terms have been retained, but with new meanings. Organic chemistry now embraces the chemistry of the compounds of carbon. This element is uniquely fecund in forming compounds. Close to half a million different compounds of carbon have been made by organic chemists. And new ones, by the dozen, are being added daily.

The compounds prepared before 1930 are briefly described in a "handbook" of some 60 volumes, of about a thousand pages each. In those pages are hidden veritable mines of drugs, perfumes and plastics. It is impossible to predict what uses a new compound may have. Sulfanilamide, DDT, four members of the vitamin B group, and many other drugs lay for years on the shelf of organic chemistry before their potency, in nutrition and medicine, was discovered.

To inorganic chemistry is relegated the study of the compounds of the other elements. All of these together number only a paltry 25,000.

Encouraged by Woehler's success, chemists threw themselves on the problem of the products and the constituents of the living cell. With ravenous zest they started to tear cells apart, and today they still have not been sated; they are still at it. Hundreds of compounds which had been pried out from the cell are duplicated in the laboratory after Woehler's fashion.

These successes changed medicine, changed nutrition, changed our way of life. Are you eating vitamin-enriched bread? Were you given large doses of vitamin K before an operation to stop excessive hemorrhage? Are you receiving injections of hormones? Has the life of a dear one been saved by penicillin? For all these bounties, thank Woehler and the generations of chemists his deed encouraged.

Woehler's researches dealt with almost every element known during his lifetime. In 1827-28 he isolated metallic aluminum and beryllium, and later isolated yttrium, boron and silicon, and titanium. He discovered calcium carbide and demonstrated that it could be used to prepare acetylene. With his life-long friend, Justus von Liebig, the German chemist, Woehler made important investigations of benzaldehyde, and cyanic and uric acid

PAUL EMILE BOTTA, the distinguished French archeologist, diplomat and traveler, was born in 1802. After a voyage around the world, which included a visit to western America during his youth, he served as physician to Mehemet Ali (and collected zoological specimens) on an expedition from Egypt to Sennaar. In 1837, after Botta's appointment as French consul at Alexandria, he journeyed to Arabia; when he returned he recorded his discoveries in his Relation d'un voyage dans le Yémen. *Botta lived in Jerusalem as French consul-general from 1847 to 1857, and held the same position at Tripoli from 1857 until his death in 1870.*

Paul Emile Botta

The discovery of Nineveh
by C. W. Ceram

FLAT WAS THE LAND between the Euphrates and Tigris Rivers, but here and there mysterious mounds rose out of the plain. Dust storms swirled about these protuberances, piling the black earth into steep dunes, which grew steadily for a hundred years, only to be dispersed in the course of another five hundred.

The Bedouins who rested by these mounds, letting their camels graze on the meager fodder growing at the base, had no idea what they might contain. Believers in Allah, and in Mohammed, his prophet, they knew nothing of the Biblical passages describing their arid land. A question was needed, a powerful intimation, to set in motion the solution of the mounds' layered secrets. This and an attack by an energetic Frenchman who knew how to make bold use of pick and shovel.

As a young man Paul Emile Botta had already made a trip around the world. In 1830 he entered the service of Mohammed Ali as a physician, and in this capacity also accompanied the Egyptian commission to Sennar. In 1833 the French government made him consul in Alexandria, from which point he made a trip into Yemen, the results of which he comprehensively recorded in a book. In 1840 he was appointed consular agent in Mosul, on the upper Tigris. Evenings, at twilight, when Botta had fled the suffocating heat of the bazaars to refresh himself on horseback excursions out into the countryside, he would see the strange mounds that dotted the landscape everywhere.

Englishmen and Frenchmen, much more often than Germans, Russians, and Italians, have combined an interest in science and the arts with practical affairs. Often, in adventurous fashion, they have been shining representatives of their nationalities in foreign parts and are remembered as men who knew how to combine a high respect for the political necessities with scientific and artistic labors. Recent examples of this type of personality are Paul Claudel and André Malraux, the French authors, and Colonel T. E. Lawrence, the English soldier.

Botta was such a man. As a physician he was interested in natural science and as a diplomat he knew how to make the most of his social connections. He was everything, it would seem, but an archeologist. What he did bring to his future task was a knowledge of native tongues, and an ability, developed during his extensive travels, to establish friendly relations with the followers of the Prophet. He also had a fine constitution and a boundless capacity for work, which even the murderous climate of Yemen and the swampy Nile flatlands could not dent.

Botta set to work without any plan or basic hypothesis to guide him. Vague hope, mingled with curiosity, carried him along. And when he was successful, no one was more surprised than he.

Evening after evening, having closed up his office, with wonderful persistence he reconnoitered the landscape about Mosul. He went from house to house, from hut to hut, always asking the same questions: Have you any antiquities for sale? Old pots? An old vase, perhaps? Where did you get the bricks for building this outhouse? Where did you get these clay fragments with the strange characters on them?

Botta bought everything he could lay hands on. But when he asked the sellers to show him the place where the pieces came from, they shrugged their shoulders, explaining that Allah was great and that such things were strewn about everywhere. One need only look to find them.

Botta saw that he was getting nowhere by quizzing the natives.

Although Botta was not the first to notice these strange mounds nor the first to suspect that ruins lay beneath them, it was partly through his persistence that archeology began in that region

Paul Emile Botta
The discovery of Nineveh

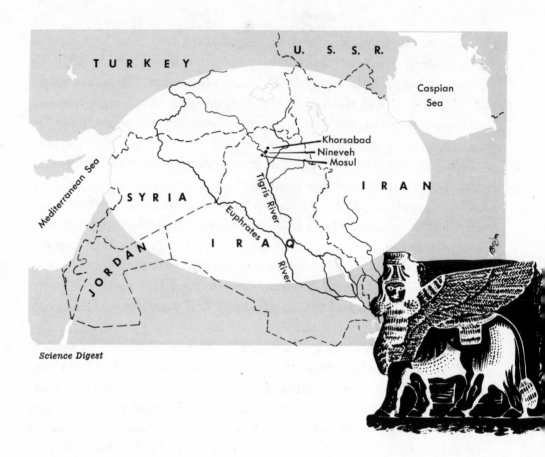

Science Digest

He decided to try his hand with the spade at the nearest mound of any size, the one at Kuyunjik.

One must imagine what it meant to persist in such apparently fruitless activity; what it meant, particularly, when there was nothing to spur on the would-be digger but the ambiguous notion that the mound *might* contain something worth the effort of excavation; what it meant to go on day after day, week after week, month after month, without finding anything more rewarding than a few battered bricks covered with signs that nobody could read, or a few sculptured torsos, so badly broken that the original form was quite unrecognizable.

A whole year long!

Should we wonder, therefore, when Botta, after the year had run out, during which innumerable false leads had been brought to him by the natives, at first dismissed a talkative Arab who, in colorful language, reported a mound containing a rich store of all the things that Botta was looking for? The Arab gabbled on, ever more importunately, about how he came from a distant village, how he had heard about Botta's search, how he loved the French and wanted to help them. Was it bricks with inscriptions that Botta wanted? There were masses of them where he lived in Khorsabad, right near his native village. He ought to know, for he had built his own stove out of these same bricks, and everybody else in his village had done the same since time immemorial.

When Botta found he could not rid himself of the Arab, he sent a couple of his workmen to look over the alleged site, some nine or ten miles away.

By sending off this little expedition Botta was eventually to immortalize his name in the history of archeology. The identity of the Arab informant is forgotten, lost in the drift of the years. But Botta is still remembered as the first to disclose the remains of a culture that had flowered for almost 2,000 years, and for more than two millennia and a half had slumbered under the black earth between the two rivers, forgotten by men.

A week later an excited messenger came back to report to his master. Hardly had they turned the first spadeful of earth, the man said, when walls came to light. These walls, when freed of the worst of the dirt that clogged them, proved to be richly carved. There were all kinds of pictures, reliefs, terrible stone animals.

Botta rode over to the site posthaste. A few hours later he was squatting in a pit, drawing the most curious figures imaginable— bearded men, winged animals, figures unlike any that he had seen in Egypt, and certainly unlike any sculptures familiar to European eyes. Shortly afterwards he moved his crew from Kuyunjik to the new site, where he put them to work with pick and shovel. And soon Botta no longer doubted that he had discovered, if not all of Nineveh, certainly one of the most splendid palaces of the Assyrian kings.

The moment came when, no longer able to keep this conviction to himself, he sent the news to Paris, and so out into the world. "I believe," he wrote with pride, and the newspapers made headlines of it, "that I am the first to discover sculptures that can be truly identified with the period when Nineveh was at its height."

The discovery of the first Assyrian palace was not only a newspaper sensation. Egypt had always been thought of as the cradle of civilization, for nowhere else could the history of mankind be traced back so far. Hitherto only the Bible had had anything pertinent to say about the land between the two rivers. The sparse evidence found in

The mound of Kuyunjik yielded nothing to Botta's determined hand but his successor, Layard, found a wealth of archeological material—statues, pottery and inscriptions telling the full story of ancient Nineveh

163

the ancient writers was taken more seriously than the Biblical sources. The facts offered by these early writers were not entirely unbelievable, yet often they contradicted one another and could not be made to agree with Biblical dates.

Botta's finds, in consequence, amounted to a demonstration that a culture as old as the Egyptian or even older had once flourished in Mesopotamia—older if one cared to give credence to Biblical accounts. It had risen in might and splendor, only to sink, under fire and sword, into oblivion.

Nineveh had been the capital of Assyria for only ninety years before the Medes captured, looted and destroyed the city in 612 B.C.

France was fired by Botta's revelations. Aid was mobilized on the most generous scale to enable Botta to continue with his work. He dug for three years, from 1843 to 1846. He fought the climate, sickness, the opposition of the natives, and the interference of the pasha, the despotic Turkish governor of the country. This greedy official could think of only one explanation for Botta's tireless excavations: the Frenchman must be looking for gold.

The pasha took Botta's Arab workmen away from him and threatened them with whippings and imprisonment to get them to tell him Botta's secret. He ringed the hill of Khorsabad with guards, he wrote complaining letters to Constantinople. But Botta was not the sort to be intimidated. His diplomatic experience now came in handy: he countered intrigue with intrigue. The result was that the pasha gave the Frenchman official permission to continue with his project, but unofficially he forbade all natives, on pain of dire punishment, to have anything to do with the Frank. Botta's diggings, he said, were nothing but a pretext for building a fortress to be used in depriving the Mesopotamian people of their freedom.

Undeterred, Botta pressed on with his work.

The palace was laid bare, rising up from mighty terraces. Archeologists who had rushed to the site on reading Botta's original report of his find recognized the structure as the palace of King Sargon, the one mentioned in the prophecies of Isaiah. It was, in fact, a summer palace that had stood on the outskirts of Nineveh, a sort of Versailles, a gigantic Sans Souci built in the year 709 B.C., after the conquest of Babylon. Wall after wall emerged from the rubble, courtyards with richly ornamented portals took shape, public reception rooms, corridors, private apartments, a tripartite seraglio, and the remains of a terraced tower.

The number of sculptures and reliefs was staggering. At one

Nineveh, once the capital of Assyria. In the distance is one of the two mounds bordering the city. It was this mound that Botta excavated, finding the fabulous palace of King Sargon

swoop the mysterious Assyrian people were lifted out of the abyss of the past.

Here were their reliefs, their household implements, their weapons; here too, they could be visualized in the domestic round, at war, on the hunt.

The sculptures, however, which in many cases had been made of highly destructible alabaster, fell apart under the hot desert sun after being removed from the protective covering of debris and earth. The French government then commissioned Eugene Napoleon Flandin to help Botta, and he went at once to the Middle East. Flandin was a draftsman of note, who in the past had gone with an archeological expedition that explored Persian sites, and later had written books about his experiences, containing very excellent drawings of ancient sculptures.

Flandin became for Botta what Vivant Denon had been for Napoleon's Egyptian commission. But whereas Denon had drawn

The discovery and excavation of Nineveh was, of course, Botta's outstanding contribution. But he supplemented it with two important works: Mémoire de l'écriture cunéiforme Assyrienne, *an analysis of the cuneiform writing of the Assyrians—and the great* Monuments de Ninive, *a five-volume study of the monuments of Nineveh*

enduring structures, Flandin had to make hurried records of material that was falling apart under his eyes.

Botta succeeded in loading a whole series of sculptures on rafts. But the Tigris, here at its upper course, was a fast-flowing and tempestuous mountain stream. The rafts whirled about, spun like tops. They tipped to one side and the stone gods and kings of Assyria, newly resurrected from oblivion, sank once more out of sight.

Botta refused to be discouraged. He sent a new load down river, this time taking all imaginable precautions, and the trip was a success. At the river mouth the precious pieces of sculpture were loaded aboard an ocean-going vessel, and in due course the first Assyrian carvings arrived on European shores. A few months later they were on exhibition in the Louvre.

Botta himself continued to work on a large frieze, until eventually a commission of nine archeologists took the task off his hands. One member of the commission was Burnouf, soon to be known as one of the most important French archeologists—a quarter of a century later he became Heinrich Schliemann's oft-cited "learned friend." Another was a young Englishman named Austen Layard, whose later fame was to eclipse Botta's.

Yet Botta ought not to be forgotten. He was the trail-breaker in Assyria. Botta's account of Nineveh: *Monuments de Ninive decouverts et descrits par Botta, mesures et dessines par Flandin,* is a classic of archeological literature.

The city of Nineveh was originally surrounded by great walls enclosing an area about three miles long and, at the broadest point, one mile wide. Fifteen gates permitted entrance into the city which, aside from dwellings, contained very beautiful parks and open areas. Two mounds, one of which is shown on page 165, formed immense strongholds against attack from the surrounding plains, and were joined by a part of the western city wall.

SEVERAL world conferences on work for the blind have helped to spread Braille to India, Iran and Iraq, Saudi Arabia, Ceylon and other parts of Asia and even to Africa. Some governments make arrangements to have all apparatus distributed free to their blind. As soon as the readers of Braille become sufficiently numerous, large libraries will be opened for them in Asia and Africa. It is high time for Louis Braille's genius to be recognized throughout the earth, and for the story to be told of the godlike courage and heart of gold with which he built a large, firm stairway for millions of sense-crippled human beings to climb from hopeless darkness to the Mind Eternal.

Louis Braille

Light bearer to the blind
by Helen Keller

A HUNDRED YEARS AGO in Coupvray, a little French village about 25 miles from Paris, Louis Braille died—a complete human being, though blind, and great because he had greatly used his loss of sight to liberate his afflicted fellow creatures. He had both lived and died in the glorious light of a victorious spirit and a brilliant, inventive intellect. The purpose of this article is to lay my tribute on the shrine which he occupies forever in the hearts of captives of the dark for whom he held aloft "lamps with hope's young fire to fill."

Braille was, I believe, among the forerunners of unimagined changes in society and the views which cement it. For he wrought his will through an invention so to mold the world of the blind that today their spirit and mind are different. Their outlook upon life is different because a blind man dared to assert his manhood and to establish for them a practical system of writing and reading that they could use for educational purposes.

Louis was born in 1809 while the turmoil of revolution was sweeping over France. He was in the thick of events when Napoleon imposed levies of bread, cows, mares and hay upon the countryside for the Grand Army after its terrible defeat in Russia, and the people were assessed for money. Simon René, Louis' father, paid a tax of 340 francs. Later, the Russian grenadiers came through Coupvray, and Simon René was forced to give up his cow. Afterward, there was an invasion of Prussian soldiers, and he was compelled to provide billeting for them for 74 days. Louis could not help sensing the hardships of the people around him or hearing their excited political discussions.

At the age of three, Louis accidentally pierced his eye with a sharp instrument in the shop of his father, who was a harnessmaker, and as a result he never beheld the light of day again. There is very little known regarding the effects of his blindness upon Louis as a small child. But, judging from the brilliancy of his mind displayed later at school, I picture him as an exceptionally bright little boy, full of curiosity concerning everything he could touch. Besides, he was blessed with affectionate parents, and I am sure that he responded to their love as a plant to sunshine.

With the loss of sight, the other sense organs of the body are developed to an extremely high degree. Even echoes play an important part

It is a fact that he attended the village school with seeing children, where he was recognized as a pupil of unusual promise, and it is easy to surmise how he sensed an atmosphere charged with social ferment and unpredictable events. No doubt he caught something of the white-hot energy that was stirring in the souls and minds of the French people. Possibly, it was owing to this circumstance that arrangements were made for his enrollment as a pupil at the Institution des Jeunes Aveugles de Paris.

Certainly, the driving force of a new France—and, as it proved, of world change—was aroused in Louis before his 13th year when his father took him to the institution, and it was never extinguished throughout his life. Despite his horror of violence, he believed in the republic and its new implications, and after he was appointed as a professor at the institution, he actively applied the freedom proclaimed in the Rights of Man to his blind fellows who had not known before how to use the initiative and self-determination that are essential to individual development. His invention of a dot system as a tool for their education was a means by which their intellectual release was effected.

I have read all the facts about Louis' outlook on the world I could secure, and I find no statement of his "philosophy of life." However, when he was a professor at the institution, he taught his pupils Braille as a means to their own intellectual development, nurtured their love and pursuit of knowledge and trained them to be skillful and efficient, either as workers or as musicians. He was a modern educator in the best sense—he recognized the right and the need of the blind to evolve personalities as natural and resourceful as those of the seeing. He seems never to have thought of himself as a creature set apart from seeing humanity.

The blind were then only just emerging from the degradation which had pursued them down the ages. Although the pupils at the Institution des Jeunes Aveugles de Paris received affectionate care and the best possible instruction, yet as a whole the blind were still avoided and regarded as victims of divine wrath.

At the institution, various characters in relief had been attempted in the hope that the blind could use them for reading and writing. Valentin Haüy, the founder of the Institution des Jeunes Aveugles, had devised an embossed type resembling ordinary capitals. Unfortunately, however, his system did not meet adequately the physiological requirements of the reader's finger. As a result, the characters were considerably modified and other new types were brought forth on the principle that the blind and the seeing should employ the same sort of printed type as far as possible. Still, the number of readers remained discouragingly small, and obviously without books the sightless could not be educated.

Movable leaden type, pins inserted in cushions and large wooden letters were other earlier methods of teaching the blind to read

Charles Barbier, an army official who had been much occupied with various modes of communication and of correspondence, invented a method in which words were represented by signs composed of dots arranged in different positions and punched on paper with a simple contrivance.

The base of the Barbier system was 12 dots and he thought that from it all sorts of combinations might be made for all purposes. But it presented grave drawbacks. It occupied much space and was too cumbersome for the nerve centers of the finger to seize. Besides, Barbier did not follow the rules of orthography, his code was phonetic, and therein lay an obstacle for the pupils and a threat to their chance of attaining high scholarship.

It was Louis Braille who, with the neat French faculty of adaptation, reduced the base of 12 dots to 6 and demonstrated that 6 dots were sufficient for the alphabet and marks of punctuation, mathematics and music. Thus, his rapidly flowering genius from that amazing seed of ingenuity brought forth man's greatest achievement for the blind.

After his appointment as professor at the institution, he modified and perfected his system for the writing of music, and by that step he placed the musical blind on a footing of equality with the seeing. Under the benign directorship of M. Pignier, he taught the students in Braille the subjects of grammar, geography, history, mathematics and music. His splendid powers of teaching delighted M. Pignier and inspired confidence. Finally, he brought out a written explanation of his ingenious procedure of point writing. The edition was embossed in 1829 and displayed at the Exposition of Industrial Products in 1834. There was a second Braille edition of Louis' pamphlet in 1837.

The Braille system is now being used all over the world. It has even been translated into Chinese

He was now sure of his triumph, but he remained humble and absorbed in his work. To escape interruptions he devoted himself to his experiments during the early morning hours and sometimes far into the night. The mental picture of him carrying paper, slate, stiletto and other tools of labor to his bedroom and falling asleep in their midst moves me inexpressibly. He was literally wearing himself out. He was a prey to pulmonary tuberculosis and at times he had a presentiment of his early death. He never murmured, however. When a hemorrhage overtook him he went home with the warmhearted wishes of the institution for a holiday of weeks or months or even years.

On his return to the institution, he took up his work again with brave cheer, braced his pupils "in the dark hours and crooked passages," and maintained a gentle, yet firm discipline among the children.

It seemed impossible that in the peace and benevolent shelter of the Institution de Jeunes Aveugles anything could occur to destroy Louis Braille's happiness. Yet, a sorrow befell him more cruel than blindness had ever been.

His devoted friend, M. Pignier, was dismissed from the institution in 1840 and the new director, M. Dufau, was hostile to Louis Braille's system. He honestly believed that the use of an alphabet engineered by the blind would segregate them more completely than they already were, and he knew that seeing teachers feared the loss of their positions if it was rendered possible for those without sight to teach the pupils by means of the Braille procedure. After Louis came back from one of his enforced vacations in 1843, he found that Dufau had changed the dimensions of the Valentin Haüy embossed letters and burned all the institution's old books. Unwittingly, he had prepared his own Waterloo, but for the time being it looked as if Louis had been defeated.

American Foundation for the Blind

Considering the mental travail he had undergone, it is a wonder that he did not succumb. But he was not a fighter by temperament, and, Christlike, he suffered in silence. Serenely, he continued his classes and waited for the day of his vindication.

There was an intelligent man, John Gaudet, acting as assistant director at the institution, who at first sided with Dufau in the dot-alphabet controversy. But he was observant and soon realized the immense advantages of Louis' procedure of writing and reading. He published a 15-page pamphlet entitled *"Account of the System of Raised Dots for Use by the Blind,"* and in 1844 he read it aloud at the opening of the new buildings of the institution which had been moved from Victor Street to commodious quarters on the Boulevard des Invalides, where it still stands. In the pamphlet, Gaudet described the tactile systems of Barbier and Braille and paid tribute to Louis' talent. A demonstration was given of the facility and pleasure with which the embossed-dot type could be read by little blind children, and its success was so pronounced, so undeniable, that Dufau accepted it as the official mode of instruction.

Secure at last in the knowledge that his supreme service to the blind was accomplished, Louis resumed his task of improving his Braille musical notation, but his failing body prevented him from perfecting it, and he reluctantly let others steer to port the ship he had so faithfully commanded. Nevertheless, his soul was at peace. As he lay in the infirmary a month before his death, he said to a friend, "Oh, unsearchable mystery of the human heart! I am convinced that my mission on earth is finished." Thus passed from earth one of the bravest, purest revelations of genuine angelhood.

The unwearied activity of his clear, scientific mind, his calmness and forbearance, his inventive abilities as a teacher, the wealth of his heart expended in uncounted secret gifts out of his scanty savings to the needy, both blind and seeing, are a priceless legacy.

Chess, dominoes, cards and other games have been adapted to Braille. An arithmetic board, which can solve the most complicated mathematical problems, is also now in use

Another legacy is the beams which have been spreading ever since Louis Braille's death from the searchlight he kindled. One of those rays fell upon me when I was a little girl, only just escaped from the dungeon of deaf-blindness. By one of the small ironies of life it was not the system Louis Braille had originally conceived but a mixed version called American Braille.

Later, on receiving some books from England, I was delighted with the well-arranged dots of the alphabet and other excellent qualities that made it a pleasure for me to read European Braille. Years later, I studied at Radcliffe College with the aid of European Braille books, not only in English, but also French, German and Greek. The world around me shone afresh with treasures of poetry and thought on philosophy, history and literature in other lands. Enraptured I sensed my membership in the human race anew and welcomed the

> "congress of the great, the wise,
> The hearing eyes, the seeing eyes"

that brought me inspiration out of every clime and age.

This was the attitude which my teacher Anne Sullivan adopted toward me. She never let me be infected with the idea that I was different from others. She treated me just like any seeing and hearing child, and that is why my life has been a full, satisfying one.

AS A BOY Charles Darwin (1809-1882) was more interested in watching birds and collecting beetles and butterflies than in reading his Greek and Latin. In 1825 he began the study of medicine at Edinburgh, but dropped it after two years. He then went to Cambridge and received a degree in the ministry. In that year he was given the post of naturalist on H.M.S. Beagle, about to begin a five-year charting and chronometric voyage to South America and Australia. At various stops made during the voyage Darwin collected specimens and filled his notebooks with the observations which, together with further years of investigation and study, resulted in the Origin of Species.

Charles Darwin

The origin of species

IF UNDER CHANGING CONDITIONS of life, organic beings present individual differences in almost every part of their structure, and this cannot be disputed; if there be, owing to their geometrical rate of increase, a severe struggle for life at some age, season, or year, and this certainly cannot be disputed; then, considering the infinite complexity of the relations of all organic beings to each other and to their conditions of life, causing an infinite diversity in structure, constitution, and habits, to be advantageous to them, it would be a most extraordinary fact if no variations had ever occurred useful to each being's own welfare, in the same manner as so many variations have occurred useful to man.

But, if variations useful to any organic being ever do occur, assuredly individuals thus characterized will have the best chance of being preserved in the struggle for life; and from the strong principle of inheritance, these will tend to produce offspring similarly characterized.

This principle of preservation, or the survival of the fittest, I have called Natural Selection. It leads to the improvement of each creature

173

in relation to its organic and inorganic conditions of life; and consequently, in most cases, to what must be regarded as an advance in organization. Nevertheless, low and simple forms will long endure if well fitted for their simple conditions of life.

Natural selection, on the principle of qualities being inherited at corresponding ages, can modify the egg, seed, or young, as easily as the adult. Amongst many animals, sexual selection will have given its aid to ordinary selection, by assuring to the most vigorous and best adapted males the greatest number of offspring. Sexual selection will also give characters useful to the males alone, in their struggles or rivalry with other males; and these characters will be transmitted to one sex or to both sexes, according to the form of inheritance which prevails.

Whether natural selection has really thus acted in adapting the various forms of life to their several conditions and stations, must be judged by the general tenor and balance of evidence given in the following chapters. [Of the book, *The Origin of Species*.] But we have already seen how it entails extinction and how largely extinction has acted in the world's history, geology plainly declares.

Natural selection also leads to divergence of character; for the more organic beings diverge in structure, habits, and constitution, by so much the more can a large number be supported on the area,— of which we see proof by looking to the inhabitants of any small spot, and to the productions naturalized in foreign lands.

Therefore, during the modification of the descendants of any one species, and during the incessant struggle of all species to increase in numbers, the more diversified the descendants become, the better will be their chance of success in the battle for life. Thus the small differences distinguishing varieties of the same species, steadily tend to increase, till they equal the greater differences between species of the same genus, or even of distinct genera.

We have seen that it is the common, the widely diffused and widely ranging species, belonging to the larger genera within each class, which vary most; and these tend to transmit to their modified offspring that superiority which now makes them dominant in their own countries. Natural selection, as has just been remarked, leads to divergence of character and to much extinction of the less improved and intermediate forms of life. On these principles, the nature of the affinities, and generally well-defined distinctions between the innu-

The first edition of Origin of Species, a printing of 1,250 copies, sold out on the day it was published, November 24, 1859

merable organic beings in each class throughout the world, may be explained.

It is a truly wonderful fact—the wonder of which we are apt to overlook from familiarity—that all animals and all plants throughout all time and space should be related to each other in groups, subordinate to groups, in the manner which we everywhere behold—namely, varieties of the same species most closely related, species of the same unequally related, forming section and sub-genera, species of distinct genera much less closely related, and genera related in different degrees, forming sub-families, families, orders, sub-classes and classes. The several subordinate groups in any class cannot be ranked in a single life, but seem clustered round points, and these round other points, and so on in almost endless cycles.

If species had been independently created, no explanation would have been possible of this kind of classification; but it is explained

Charles Darwin seated in his study. His controversial book, the *Origin of Species,* was and still is one of the most influential contributions ever made by any individual to man and biological science

through inheritance and the complex action of natural selection, entailing extinction and divergence of character. . . .

The affinities of all the beings of the same class have sometimes been represented by a great tree. I believe this simile largely speaks the truth. The green and budding twigs may represent existing species; and those produced during former years may represent the long succession of extinct species.

At each period of growth all the growing twigs have tried to branch out on all sides, and to overtop and kill the surrounding twigs and branches, in the same manner as species and groups of species have at all times overmastered other species in the great battle for life. The limbs divided into great branches, and these into lesser and lesser branches, were themselves once, when the tree was young, budding twigs, and this connection of the former and present buds by ramifying branches may well represent the classification of all extinct and living species in groups subordinate to groups.

Of the many twigs which flourished when the tree was a mere bush, only two or three, now grown into great branches, yet survive and bear the other branches; so with the species which lived during long-past geological periods, very few have left living and modified descendants. From the first growth of the tree, many a limb and branch has decayed and dropped off; and these fallen branches of various sizes may represent those whole orders, families, and genera which have now no living representatives, and which are known to us only in a fossil state.

As we here and there see a thin straggling branch springing from a fork low down in a tree, and which by some chance has been favored and is still alive on its summit, so we occasionally see an animal like the Ornithorhynchus or Lepidosiren, which in some small degree connects by its affinities two large branches of life, and which has apparently been saved from fatal competition by having inhabited a protected station.

As buds give rise by growth to fresh buds, and these, if vigorous, branch out and overtop on all sides many a feebler branch, so by generation I believe it has been with the great Tree of Life, which fills with its dead and broken branches the crust of the earth, and covers the surface with its ever-branching and beautiful ramifications.

Darwin by no means was the first to conceive the theory of evolution but he proved it so convincingly that it could no longer be doubted. An interesting aspect is that Darwin thought of all possible arguments against his theory and then set out to prove them wrong in Origin of Species

FROM EARLY boyhood, William Morton (1819-1868) wanted to be a doctor. But low finances kept him out of medical school and he resolved to become a dentist first, then to study medicine and become a doctor. He was graduated from Baltimore College of Dental Surgery in 1842, married the next year, and began dental practice in Boston in 1844. Shortly afterwards, Morton began to conduct experiments with ether on insects, animals and finally on a man. The success of his experiments enabled him to demonstrate the value of ether in a surgical operation. A patent controversy prevented him from gaining any financial reward and he died in poverty.

William Morton

Founder of anesthesia

The administration of ether

ALTHOUGH VARIOUS publications have appeared since the new application of sulphuric ether was discovered which have made it evident that it can be used, both safely and effectually, for the relief of much of the suffering to which the human race is liable, I believe that a manual containing an account of the mode of administering it, the effect which it produces, the symptoms of insensibility, the difficulties and dangers attending its use, and the best means of obviating and removing these, as far as possible, is still a desideratum.

This is particularly the case with those who have not had an opportunity to witness its administration but who may wish to make use of it in their own practice.

To supply this want, and to avoid the necessity of replying to the letters frequently addressed to me . . . the following pages have been written.

To those who have used the ether, many of the directions may appear tediously minute; but to those who have not they will afford desirable information.

In the first place it is of the utmost consequence that the ether which is used should be not only free from all impurities, but as highly concentrated as possible; as some of these impurities would prove injurious if taken into the system, and as, of course, the stronger the ether the sooner the patient comes under its influence. Unrectified sulphuric ether contains, as impurities, alcohol, water, sulphurous acid, and oil of wine; and is unfit for use internally.

In order to make it fit for inhalation unrectified sulphuric ether must be redistilled and washed, and then dried with chloride of calcium. This will free it from the impurities above mentioned; and render it more concentrated than the original article.

The next point I have to treat of is the best mode of administering ether. The earliest experiments were mostly made by pouring ether upon cloths and inhaling it from them. The results obtained in this way were somewhat uncertain and not always satisfactory, and this mode of administering it was, before long, exchanged for that by means of an apparatus which rendered the experiments more uniformly successful.

Some alterations and improvements were afterward made in this apparatus, but, substantially, it remained the same as long as it continued in use; and, as many persons may read these pages who have never seen the apparatus, or one like it, a few words by way of description will not, perhaps, be unacceptable.

The apparatus first used consisted of a glass vessel about six inches square, with rounded corners; one opening, two inches in diameter, was left on the top, through which a sponge was inserted and the ether poured, and another, an inch and a half in diameter, on one side for the admission of external air. On the side opposite the last-named opening was a glass tube, two inches in diameter and an inch in length, terminating in a metal mouthpiece three inches long, and of the same caliber as the glass tube. This mouthpiece was provided with two valves, one covering a circular opening, three quarters of an inch in diameter, on the top, and the other extending across it. These valves were so arranged that, when the patient filled his lungs, the upper valve shut down, closing the aperture in the top of the mouthpiece, while the one across the mouthpiece opened and allowed the ethereal vapor, mixed with atmospheric air, to pass into the lungs; and, when

A Boston chemist, Dr. Charles Jackson, hearing of Morton's search for something to relieve pain in tooth extractions, suggested sulphuric ether to the young dentist and showed him the proper method of inhalation

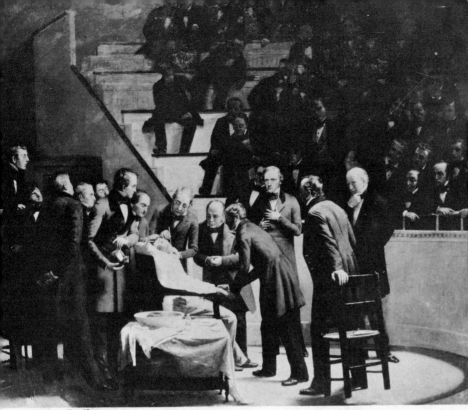

A young dentist, Dr. William Morton, demonstrating the use of ether as an anesthetic to a group of eminent surgeons at the Massachusetts General Hospital on Oct. 16, 1846

he emptied his lungs, the pressure of the expired air closed the valve across the tube, while the same pressure opened the upper valve and allowed the vapor, which had been once breathed, to pass into the room instead of returning into the reservoir. Thus, at each inspiration, the patient had a fresh supply of air thoroughly charged with the vapor of ether, which vapor was continually given off by the sponge. . . .

When a surgical operation is to be performed, the inhalation should be steadily continued for three minutes without speaking to the patient. If at the end of this time, the pulse is quickened and the muscles relaxed, so that the head has a tendency to fall on one side, the patient should be told, in a loud, distinct tone, to open his eyes; and if he does *not* do so, the operation should be immediately commenced.

If he does open his eyes, even in a slow and languid manner, he should be directed to close them, and the inhalation should be continued two minutes longer, when the same question may be repeated; and it will usually be found that, by this time, the patient is unconscious.

Should this not occur, however, the surgeon should place his hand over about one half of the sponge, so as to prevent loss of ether by evaporation, and continue the inhalation until 10 minutes have elapsed from the time when the patient first began to breathe it, calling upon him to open his eyes at intervals of about one minute each.

If, at the end of 10 minutes, he still continues to open his eyes when directed to do so, the inhalation should be discontinued and not resumed again for at *least* five minutes. At the end of that time two ounces more of ether should be poured upon the sponge, and the inhaling resumed as before; but, if, after inhaling a second time for 10 minutes, it does not produce its effect, an interval of *10* minutes must be allowed to the patient, and then, the ether having been again renewed, the inhaling may be resumed once more. If at the end of the third trial of inhaling ether the patient still remains unaffected by it, the operation had better be deferred until another day; but I can hardly suppose that this will ever happen where the ether is pure and highly concentrated, and has been administered in the manner above described.

Dr. Morton's triumph

The following eyewitness account of William Morton's historic demonstration of the use of ether as a general anesthetic appeared in The Semicentennial of Anesthesia, *issued by the Massachusetts General Hospital in 1897*

THE DAY ARRIVED; the time appointed was noted on the dial when the patient was led into the operating room (of the Massachusetts General Hospital, in Boston) and Dr. Warren (the senior surgeon) and a board of the most eminent surgeons in the state were gathered around the sufferer.

"All is ready—the stillness oppressive."

It had been announced "that a test of some preparation was to be made for which the *astonishing* claim had been made that it would render the person operated upon free from pain." These are the words of Dr. Warren that broke the stillness.

The writer of this account, Washington Ayer, was a young medical student and one of the many interested observers in the auditorium during this famous demonstration

Those present were incredulous, and, as Dr. Morton had not arrived at the time appointed and 15 minutes had passed, Dr. Warren said with significant meaning, "I presume he is otherwise engaged."

This was followed with a "derisive laugh," and Dr. Warren grasped his knife and was about to proceed with the operation. At that moment Dr. Morton entered a side door, when Dr. Warren turned to him and in a strong voice said, "Well, sir, your patient is ready." In a few minutes he was ready for the surgeon's knife, when Dr. Morton said, "Y*our* patient is ready, sir."

Here the most sublime scene ever witnessed in the operating room was presented, when the patient placed himself voluntarily upon the table, which was to become the altar of future fame. Not that he did so for the purpose of advancing the science of medicine, nor for the good of his fellow men, for the act itself was purely a personal and selfish one. He was about to assist in solving a new and important problem of therapeutics, whose benefits were to be given to the whole civilized world, yet wholly unconscious of the sublimity of the occasion. . . .

That was a supreme moment for a most wonderful discovery, and, had the patient died under the operation, science would have waited long to discover the hypnotic effects of some other remedy of equal potency and safety, and it may be properly questioned whether chloroform would have come into use as it has at the present time.

The heroic bravery of the man who voluntarily placed himself upon the table, a subject for the surgeon's knife, should be recorded and his name enrolled upon parchment, which should be hung upon the walls of the surgical amphitheater in which the operation was performed. His name was Gilbert Abbott.

The operation was for a congenital tumor on the left side of the neck, extending along the jaw to the maxillary gland and into the mouth, embracing a margin of the tongue. The operation was successful; and when the patient recovered he declared he had suffered no pain.

Dr. Warren turned to those present and said, "Gentlemen, this is no humbug."

Sir Humphry Davy was probably one of the first to discover anesthesia while experimenting with nitrous oxide (laughing gas). Faraday also wrote about its abilities to kill pain but, generally, anesthetics remained a medical curiosity until Morton's demonstration

"Were we to imagine ourselves suspended," said Daetigues, the celebrated French surgeon, "in timeless space over an abyss out of which the sounds of the revolving earth rose to our ears, we should hear naught but an elemental roar of pain, uttered as with one voice by suffering mankind." The credit for quieting that elemental roar was claimed by many men but the honor for the introduction of anesthesia is given to the man who first publicly demonstrated it to the medical profession and gave it to the world—a struggling 27-year-old dentist named William Morton.

THE HEREDITARY units which Mendel's experiments revealed in peas have been found in all species of plants and animals that have been investigated. The evidence that Mendel's laws of heredity apply to human beings is apparent every day. Each individual is a mixture of characteristics sculptured by dominant and recessive genes, and by many cooperative genes which work to a common end. Blue-eyed children of brown-eyed parents; father and daughter with a blaze of white hair on their foreheads; the baby whose blood must be replaced at birth because of the Rh factor; the child with a predisposition to rheumatic fever: these are only a few examples of the working of Mendel's law.

Abbot Mendel

Founder of genetics

by Robert C. Cook

THE HEREDITY RIDDLE was solved in 1865 by Gregor Mendel, abbot of the Augustinian monastery at Brühn (now Brno in Czechoslovakia). He presented his findings to the Natural Sciences Society of Brühn, and they were published in 1866 in the *Proceedings* of the society, which were widely circulated to libraries throughout the world. There on library shelves his report gathered dust for a third of a century.

The world did not learn of his discovery until 1900, 34 years after he had reported it. Meanwhile, Mendel had died in 1884, a disappointed man.

Born in 1822 of peasant parents, young Mendel's one ambition was to rise to the exalted position of village schoolmaster in his native hamlet of Heinzdorf. His parents had neither money nor influence, but his mother, Rosina, made heroic sacrifices to enable him to complete his education. Unfortunately, his health failed, ending any hope that he could achieve his ambition.

The sponsorship of one of his teachers led to an invitation to join the Augustinian order at Brno, and in 1843 he entered the monastery as a novice. There his teaching ambitions were partly realized; he taught for several years in the Brno schools, but he never got a teacher's certificate. His two attempts to pass the examination were defeated when he failed his favorite subject, natural history. Yet his interest in science and in teaching did not wane. He was one of the founders, in 1862, of the Natural Sciences Society.

As years passed, Mendel achieved modest distinction, becoming abbot of the monastery and leading citizen of Brno. His work as abbot occupied only part of his mind. Mendel was a born biologist, and his heart was in his hobbies. He had a keen eye and a passion for detailed records. Through all his life he collected facts about the world in which he lived the way other people collect postage stamps.

Years after his death, when worldwide fame came suddenly, bales of records in his precise hand were found in the monastery attic. For many years he had recorded the time of the rising and the setting of the sun, the daily temperature, and the direction of the wind. He studied the life of the bees in the monastery hives in a way that would have done credit to a Fabre or a Maeterlinck.

The greatest interest of Abbot Gregor Mendel's life was his monastery garden. There he watched, year after year, the germination, growth and flowering of many kinds of plants. There, on less than half an acre, he made the simple, conclusive experiments with peas which revealed the basic laws of heredity.

What Mendel found from his peas about the transmission of hereditary differences from one generation to the next, laid bare the secret of the evolutionary process. When he reported his discovery, he undoubtedly expected that it would be widely acclaimed. The silence and lack of interest which actually ensued were a bitter disappointment; not a soul who heard or read Mendel's paper seemed to have grasped his theory, although he had presented it logically and lucidly.

During his entire lifetime, Mendel published only one scientific paper about his experiments with peas.

Sixteen years after Mendel was in his grave, he became famous overnight as the man who had united mathematics and experimental biology to found the science of genetics. In 1899, Hugo De Vries, a Dutchman; Karl Correns, a German, and Erich Tschermak, an Austrian, were carrying out independent researches in heredity. When they began to work up their theses, all three stumbled by accident on

Fabre, a French entomologist, was a contemporary of Mendel. His life work consisted of studying insects, their habits and life histories. Fabre's life, by his own choice, was a secluded one—the better for his work, which was all based on direct observations. His principal subjects were spiders, wasps, beetles and grasshoppers

Mendel's long-neglected report. They were so amazed to discover this detailed theory of heredity, based on ingenious and convincing experiments, that they all rushed into print almost simultaneously with their discovery.

That Mendel succeeded in solving the puzzle of heredity where so many before and after him had failed was no lucky accident. He had reflected for many years on the mystery of heredity, and had read the works of all the earlier experimenters. He deliberately set out to discover how inherited differences were transmitted from one generation to the next, examining his problem from every angle; and he made his plans with care.

Carl Nageli, one of the most noted botanists of that time, when informed by Mendel of his work, advised the monk to quit wasting his time with peas and start investigations of hawkweed. Thus Mendel sadly turned his back on his pea experiments

The many distinct varieties of garden peas afforded a rich reservoir of purebred strains differing in many inherited characteristics. Since the pea plant is an annual, a new generation can be grown each year—even two or three generations, in a greenhouse. There were giant varieties and dwarf varieties; varieties with green seeds and others with yellow seeds. Some varieties had white flowers, others had violet-red flowers. Hence he found available a large assortment of clear-cut differences.

Another important consideration in Mendel's choice was that the sex physiology of the pea flower made it ideal for his purposes. This species is classified by botanists as "perfect-flowered," which means that each flower contains both male and female sex elements. The anthers, or stamens, bear the male sex cells, the pollen. When the female element, pistil or stigma, becomes mature and receptive, a pollen grain placed on it grows down to its base to fertilize the female ovary. There fusion of the male and female gametes, or sex cells, takes place to initiate the development of a new individual.

Ordinarily the pea flower fertilizes itself, but its structure is such that experimental crosses are rather easily made by removing the pollen-bearing stamens from the bud before the flower opens, and then, when the pistil is mature, putting the pollen of another selected plant on the stigma to produce the hybrid. Accidental contamination with unwanted pollen is avoided by tying over the emasculated flower a paper bag with a wad of cotton around the stem, to exclude pollen-bearing insects.

Mendel chose varieties showing seven clear-cut differences for his experiments. Among these were two varieties of peas with a dramatic difference in stature; one was a giant and the other a dwarf. He found that when bred by themselves, the tall strain never grew less than six to seven feet tall, while the dwarfs never reached a height of more than two feet. There were no intermediates. Mendel concentrated his attention on this clear-cut "either-or" stature difference, tall vs. dwarf, and he ignored everything else.

He crossed the tall and dwarf varieties, putting pollen from a dwarf plant on the stigma of a tall plant. The resulting hybrid thus had a dwarf father and a giant mother. He also made the cross the other way, using tall pollen on the flower of a dwarf mother plant. He repeated this process ten times, so that he would have a quantity of seed.

The next year he planted these seeds, and the first hybrid generation plants which grew from them all resembled the tall-parent variety: there were no dwarfs and no intermediates. As a matter of fact these hybrids were actually somewhat taller than their parents— a phenomenon known as "hybrid vigor." The dwarf parentage had apparently completely disappeared. Whether the father was a giant or a dwarf made no difference, the progeny all resembled the giant parent.

Next, Mendel allowed these tall hybrid plants to self-fertilize themselves naturally. He saved the seeds, which he planted the following year. Now he found in his second hybrid generation of 1,064 plants that 787 were tall and 277 were short. After skipping a generation, the dwarf characteristic reappeared unmodified. Again there were no intermediates. The distinction between tallness and dwarfness was clear and definite, with no blending of the dwarf and the giant tendencies.

Mendel was so disillusioned in later life that he would not even discuss genetics with anyone

Mendel was puzzled, but he went on with his experiments, using the same techniques of self-fertilization. When he examined the plants of the third hybrid generation the following year he noted another significant fact: seed from self-fertilized dwarf plants produced only dwarf plants. Seed from some of the self-fertilized tall plants produced only tall progeny; other tall plants produced both tall and dwarf offspring, as had the tall plants of the previous generation.

When Mendel analyzed the numerical relationships of tall and dwarf plants in the children of the second and third generation, he noticed another significant fact. Among the plants able to produce both tall and dwarf plants, he found a consistent preponderance of tall plants. There were, on the average, about three giants to one dwarf. Pondering over the significance of this consistent three-to-one relationship gave Mendel the key to the heredity mystery.

Mendel conceived that alternative characteristics like tallness or shortness are determined by *heredity-atoms* within the living cell. These atoms he called "units"; today we call them "genes"—and their existence has been confirmed under the microscope.

Tallness and shortness were alternative forms of the same genetic unit. Such a pair of units is called "allelomorphs" by geneticists—or "alleles" for short.

These gene-units, Mendel said, were transmitted from one generation to the next in the sex cells. The male gametes, or sex cells, carried one set of genes; the female gametes carried another set.

Hence every plant (or animal) had a dual heredity with respect to these gene-units. One of each pair of genes came from the father and one of each pair from the mother. Mendel conceived the *total heredity* of a plant or animal to be represented by a great many different gene-pairs.

When new gametes were formed prior to the reproduction of another generation, the paired units again separated, so that the gametes again carried only one complete set of genes. When two of these simple gametes united at fertilization or conception, a new individual would be created, which again had two complete sets of genes.

Geneticists called the fertilized egg cell and the resulting individual a "zygote" from the Greek word for "yoke," since the genes were acting as a team.

When Mendel first crossed his tall and dwarf peas, he produced a hybrid which carried alleles for both tallness and dwarfness. Instead of blending and showing an intermediate stature, the offspring were just as tall as the tall parent. Mendel said that tallness was "dominant," and since shortness had been masked in its presence, he called shortness "recessive" to tallness.

Mendel's system of gene labeling has also stood the test of time. The dominant tall alleles of the gene for stature, he designated by a capital letter—**T**; the corresponding recessive short allele by the lower-case **t**. He pointed out that there are only three possible combinations of allele pairs: pure tall plants had the genetic constitution **TT** ("genotype," the geneticists call it). Pure short plants had the genotype **tt**. The tall-short hybrid plants (which were all tall) had the genotype **Tt**.

A great deal of Mendel's work was based on experiments conducted by German scientists on cell structure and other elements concerning life. These experiments took place between 1800 and the time of the Abbot's famous study of pea plants

The two pure forms with respect to tallness and dwarfness (**TT** and **tt**) are called "homozygous." This merely means a zygote with similar alleles.

The hybrid (**Tt**) produced by a union of different alleles is called "heterozygous." This terminology is the basic vocabulary of genetics.

Mathematically, the distribution and recombination of gametes, which is the basis for the regularities Mendel noted in his pea hybrids, is governed by the same laws of chance that determine how often two heads or two tails will be tossed when two pennies are flipped.

If heads correspond to the dominant allele, and tails to the recessive, there are obviously three possible combinations of heads and tails: two heads, one head and one tail, and two tails. These correspond to the three possible combinations of two alleles, **TT**, **Tt** and **tt**.

According to the theory of probability, the three combinations will occur on the average in a ratio approximately ¼ two-head tosses; ½ head-tail tosses; and ¼ two-tail tosses.

By tossing two pennies a hundred times and recording the combinations actually obtained it is found that the average frequency of the three categories closely approaches the theoretical one of 1 **TT**: 2 **Tt**: 1 **tt** distribution. If only a few tosses are made, chance deviation may alter considerably the theoretical ratio of 1 : 2 : 1.

The basic genetic ratio is therefore 1 **TT**: 2 **Tt**: 1 **tt**, for these are the frequencies with which the three combinations of alleles will occur in the second generation of a cross such as Mendel made. The three-to-one ratio that Mendel obtained is obviously the result of dominance, for the **TT** and **Tt** genotypes are tall and can be distinguished only by progeny-testing the tall plants in the next generation. When that was done, Mendel confirmed his postulation that the pure-breeding **TT** plants approximately equalled in number the dwarf **tt** plants.

When mated with **tt** plants, the **Tt** talls produced a ratio of one tall to one short in their progeny, as expected according to theory.

Mendel made his crosses both ways and got the same results, thus demonstrating conclusively that each parent contributes half of the heredity to the child. He tried seven different pairs of alleles and got the same results. He made crosses involving two pairs of alleles and got the expected distribution among his hybrids.

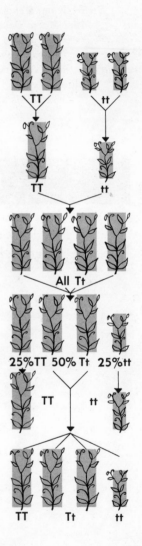

*LOUIS PASTEUR, the son of a tanner,
was born at Dôle, Franche-Comté, in France,
on December 27, 1822. He studied at Arbois
and at the Royal College of Besancon. His
early dedication to chemistry was inspired by
the lectures of J. B. Dumas at the Sorbonne.
In 1849 he was appointed professor of
chemistry at the Faculté of Science at
Strasburg and shortly afterwards married
Mlle. Marie Laurent. Five years later,
secure in his position as a leader of French
science, Pasteur was appointed professor of
chemistry and dean of the Faculté des Sciences
at Lille. Pasteur died in 1895, honored by
scientists throughout the world.*

Louis Pasteur

The prevention of rabies

AFTER MAKING almost innumerable experiments, I have discovered a prophylactic method which is practical and prompt, and which has already in dogs afforded me results sufficiently numerous, certain, and successful, to warrant my having confidence in its general applicability to all animals, and even to man himself.

This method depends essentially on the following facts:

The inoculation of the infective spinal cord of a dog suffering from ordinary rabies under the dura mater of a rabbit always produces rabies after a period of incubation having a mean duration of about 15 days.

If, by the above method of inoculation, the virus of the first rabbit is passed into a second, and that of the second into a third, and so on, in series, a more and more striking tendency is soon manifested toward a diminution of the duration of the incubation period of rabies in the rabbits successively inoculated.

The virus of rabies at a constant degree of virulence is contained in the spinal cords of these rabbits throughout their whole extent.

If portions, a few centimeters long, are removed from these spinal cords, with every possible precaution to preserve their purity, and are then suspended in dry air, the virulence slowly disappears, until at last it entirely vanishes. The time within which this extinction of virulence is brought about varies a little with the thickness of the morsels of spinal cord, but chiefly with the external temperature. The lower the temperature the longer is the virulence preserved. These results form the central scientific point in the method.

These facts being established, a dog may be rendered refractory to rabies in a relatively short time in the following way:

Every day morsels of fresh infective spinal cord from a rabbit which has died of rabies, developed after an incubation period of seven days, are suspended in a series of flasks, the air in which is kept dry by placing fragments of potash at the bottom of the flask. Every day also a dog is inoculated under the skin with a. . . . syringeful of sterilized broth, in which a small fragment of one of the spinal cords has been broken up, commencing with a spinal cord far enough removed in order of time from the day of the operation to render it certain that

Rabies is transmitted to man by the saliva of an infected animal entering a wound or cut in the skin— in most instances caused by the animal itself. In about 90 percent of the cases rabies is communicated to man by dogs

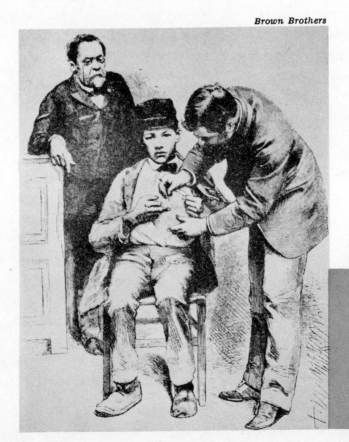

Louis Pasteur supervises the inoculation of a young boy for hydrophobia. The procedure consists of introducing half a syringeful of a diseased rabbit's spinal cord into the body

the cord was not at all virulent. (This date had been ascertained by previous experiments.) On the following days the same operation is performed with more recent cords, separated from each other by an interval of two days, until at last a very virulent cord, which has only been in the flask for two days, is used.

The dog has now been rendered refractory to rabies. It may be inoculated with the virus of rabies under the skin, or even after trephining, on the surface of the brain, without any subsequent development of rabies.

The symptoms of rabies in man are something terrible and frightening to observe. There is an uncontrollable thirst followed by a choking condition whenever an attempt to swallow occurs. Hysteria is intermixed with periods of unusual calm and convulsions are frequent. The afflicted person is constantly tortured by a secretion accumulating in his mouth and is seen continually spitting this fluid out. Difficulties in breathing are also experienced. Before death, all the symptoms have stopped and the ability to swallow returns

Never having once failed when using this method, I had in my possession 50 dogs, of all ages and of every race, refractory to rabies, when three individuals from Alsace unexpectedly presented themselves at my laboratory, on Monday, the sixth of last July (1885).

Théodore Vone, grocer, of Meissengott, near Schlestadt, bitten in the arm, July 4, by his own dog, which had gone mad.

Joseph Meister, aged nine years, also bitten on July 4, at eight o'clock in the morning, by the same dog. This child had been knocked over by the dog and presented numerous bites, on the hands, legs, and thighs, some of them so deep as to render walking difficult. The principal bites had been cauterized at eight o'clock in the evening of July 4, only 12 hours after the accident, with phenic acid, by Dr. Weber, of Villé.

The third person, who had not been bitten, was the mother of little Joseph Meister.

At the examination of the dog, after its death by the hand of its master, the stomach was found full of hay, straw, and scraps of wood. The dog was certainly rabid. Joseph Meister had been pulled out from under him covered with foam and blood.

Monsieur Vone had some severe contusions on the arm, but he assured me that his shirt had not been pierced by the dog's fangs. As he had nothing to fear, I told him that he could return to Alsace the same day, which he did. But I kept young Meister and his mother with me.

The weekly meeting of the Académie des Sciences took place on July 6. At it I met our colleague, Dr. Vulpian, to whom I related what had just happened. Monsieur Vulpian, and Dr. Grancher, professor in the Faculté de Médecine, had the goodness to come and see little Joseph Meister at once, and to take note of the condition and the number of his wounds. There were no less than 14.

The opinion of our learned colleague, and of Dr. Grancher, was that, owing to the severity and the number of the bites, Joseph Meister was almost certain to take rabies, I then communicated to Monsieur Vulpian and to Monsieur Grancher the new results which I had obtained from the study of rabies since the address which I had given at Copenhagen a year earlier.

The death of this child appearing to be inevitable, I decided, not without lively and sore anxiety, as may well be believed, to try upon Joseph Meister the method which I had found constantly successful with dogs. . . .

Consequently, on July 6, at eight o'clock in the evening, 60 hours after the bites on July 4, and in the presence of Drs. Vulpian and Grancher, young Meister was inoculated under a fold of skin raised in the right hypochondrium, with half a syringeful of the spinal cord of a rabbit, which had died of rabies on June 21. It had been preserved since then, that is to say, 15 days, in a flask of dry air.

In the following days fresh inoculations were made. I thus made 13 inoculations, and prolonged the treatment to 10 days. I shall say later on that a smaller number of inoculations would have been sufficient. But it will be understood how, in the first attempt, I would act with a very special circumspection. . . .

On the last days, therefore, I had inoculated Joseph Meister with the most virulent virus of rabies, that, namely, of the dog, reinforced by passing a great number of times from rabbit to rabbit, a virus which produces rabies after seven days' incubation in these animals, after eight or ten days in dogs. . . .

Joseph Meister, therefore, has escaped not only the rabies, which would have been caused by the bites he received, but also the rabies with which I have inoculated him in order to test the immunity produced by the treatment, a rabies more virulent than ordinary canine rabies.

The final inoculation with very virulent virus has this further advantage, that it puts a period to the apprehensions which arise as to the consequences of the bites. If rabies could occur it would declare itself more quickly after a more virulent virus than after the virus of the bites. Since the middle of August I have looked forward with confidence to the future good health of Joseph Meister. At the present time, three months and three weeks have elapsed since the accident; his state of health leaves nothing to be desired. . . .

With the success of the inoculation of Joseph Meister, the Institut Pasteur was organized in 1888 and thousands threatened by hydrophobia have been treated. The mortality rate has been reduced to about one percent

Louis Pasteur

The prevention of rabies

The germ theory

THE SCIENCES gain by mutual support. When, as the result of my first communications on the fermentations in 1857-1858, it appeared that the ferments, properly so-called, are living beings, that the germs of microscopic organisms abound in the surface of all objects, in the air and in water; that the theory of spontaneous generation is chimerical; that wines, beer, vinegar, the blood, urine and all the fluids of the body undergo none of their usual changes in pure air, both Medicine and Surgery received fresh stimulation. . . .

Our researches of last year left the etiology of the putrid disease,

Fisher Scientific Company

Although many of his researches enriched "pure" chemistry and biology, Pasteur is remembered for his practical solutions of the technological and medical problems of his time

or septicemia, in a much less advanced condition than that of anthrax. We had demonstrated the probability that septicemia depends upon the presence and growth of a microscopic body, but the absolute proof of this important conclusion was not reached.

To demonstrate experimentally that a microscopic organism actually is the cause of a disease and the agent of contagion, I know no other way, in the present state of Science, than to subject the *microbe* (the new and happy term introduced by M. Sedillot) to the method of cultivation out of the body. It may be noted that in 12 successive cultures, each one of only 10 cubic centimeters volume, the original drop will be diluted as if placed in a volume of fluid equal to the total volume of the earth.

It is just this form of test to which M. Joubert and I subjected the anthrax bacterium. Having cultivated it a great number of times in a sterile fluid, each culture being started with a minute drop from the preceding, we then demonstrated that the product of the last culture was capable of further development and of acting in the animal tissues by producing anthrax with all its symptoms. Such is—as we believe— the indisputable proof that *anthrax is a bacterial disease. . . .*

If it is a terrifying thought that life is at the mercy of the multiplication of these minute bodies, it is a consoling hope that Science will not always remain powerless before such enemies, since for example at the very beginning of the study we find that simple exposure to air is sufficient at times to destroy them. . . .

Summarizing—it appears that it is possible to produce at will, purulent infections with no elements of putrescence, putrescent purulent infections, anthracoid purulent infections, and finally combinations of these types of lesions varying according to the proportions of the mixtures of the specific organisms made to act on the living tissues.

These are the principal facts I have to communicate to the Academy in my name and in the names of my collaborators, Messrs. Joubert and Chamberland. Some weeks ago (Session of the 11th of March last) a member of the Section of Medicine and Surgery, M. Sedillot, after long meditation on the lessons of a brilliant career, did not hesitate to assert that the successes as well as the failures of Surgery find a rational explanation in the principles upon which the germ theory is based, and that this theory would found a new Surgery—already begun by a celebrated English surgeon, Dr. Lister, who was among the first to understand its fertility.

Pasteur chose to remain poor and lead a life of simplicity even though the money values of his discoveries would have made him a tremendously rich man

193

JOSEPH LISTER, English surgeon, was born near London on April 5, 1827. Botany and zoology were his earliest interests. At 17 he became a medical student in the University College of London, and at 25 he was appointed a Fellow of the Royal College of Surgeons. In 1853 Lister went to the University of Edinburgh where he became resident house surgeon under the famous Professor James Syme, whose daughter he married in 1856. He became President of the Royal Society in 1895, was raised to the peerage two years later, and retired from active practice, though he continued his research. He died on February 10, 1912.

Joseph Lister

"On the antiseptic principle"

IN THE COURSE of an extended investigation into the nature of inflammation, and the healthy and morbid conditions of the blood in relation to it, I arrived several years ago at the conclusion that the essential cause of suppuration (forming of pus) in wounds is decomposition, brought about by the influence of the atmosphere upon blood or serum retained within them, and, in the case of contused wounds, upon portions of tissue destroyed by the violence of the injury. . . .

When it had been shown by the researches of Pasteur that the septic properties of the atmosphere depended not on the oxygen, or any gaseous constituent, but on minute organisms suspended in it, which owed their energy to their vitality, it occurred to me that decomposition in the injured part might be avoided without excluding the air by applying as a dressing some material capable of destroying the life of the floating particles. Upon this principle I have based a practice of which I will now attempt to give a short account.

The material which I have employed is carbolic or phenic acid, a volatile organic compound, which appears to exercise a peculiarly destructive influence upon low forms of life, and hence is the most powerful antiseptic with which we are at present acquainted. . . .

In conducting the treatment, the first object must be the destruction of any septic germs which may have been introduced into the wounds, either at the moment of the accident or during the time which has since elapsed. This is done by introducing the acid of full strength into all accessible recesses of the wound by means of a piece of rag held in dressing forceps and dipped into the liquid . . .

The next object to be kept in view is to guard effectually against the spreading of decomposition into the wound along the stream of blood and serum which oozes out during the first few days after the accident, when the acid originally applied has been washed out or dissipated by absorption and evaporation. . . .

(Difficulties have) been overcome by employing a paste composed of common whiting (carbonate of lime) mixed with a solution of one part of carbolic acid in four parts of boiled linseed oil so as to form a firm putty. This application contains the acid in too dilute a form to excoriate the skin, which it may be made to cover to any extent that may be thought desirable, while its substance serves as a reservoir of the antiseptic material. . . .

If a perfectly healthy granulating sore be well washed and covered with a plate of clean metal, such as block tin, fitting its surface pretty accurately, and overlapping the surrounding skin an inch or so in every direction and retained in position by adhesive plaster and a bandage, it will be found, on removing it after 24 or 48 hours, that little or nothing that can be called pus is present. . . .

Here the clean metallic surface presents no recesses like those of porous lint for the septic germs to develop in, the fluid exuding from the surface of the granulations has flowed away undecomposed, and the result is the absence of suppuration.

This simple experiment illustrates the important fact that granulations have no inherent tendency to form pus, but do so only when subjected to preternatural stimulus. Further, it shows that the mere contact of a foreign body does not of itself stimulate granulations to suppurate; whereas the presence of decomposing organic matter does. . . .

I left behind me in Glasgow a boy, 13 years of age, who between three and four weeks previously, met with a most severe injury to the left arm, which he got entangled in a machine at a fair. There was a

Carbolic acid came to Lister's attention when he discovered it was used to disinfect sewage. He later developed a spray from the acid to be used to cleanse the air in an operating room

wound six inches long and three inches broad, and the skin was very extensively undermined beyond its limits, while the soft parts were generally so much lacerated that a pair of dressing forceps introduced at the wound and pushed directly inward appeared beneath the skin at the opposite aspect of the limb.

From this wound several tags of muscle were hanging, and among them was one consisting of about three inches of the triceps in almost its entire thickness; while the lower fragment of the bone, which was broken high up, was protruding four inches and a half, stripped of muscle, the skin being tucked in under it.

Lister developed many new operative techniques and introduced a number of new surgical instruments. His spectacular success in performing amputations other doctors dared not attempt made him the outstanding surgeon of Europe

Without the assistance of the antiseptic treatment I should certainly have thought of nothing else but amputation at the shoulder joint; but as the radial pulse could be felt and the fingers had sensation I did not hesitate to try to save the limb and adopted the plan of treatment above described, wrapping the arm from the shoulder to below the elbow in the antiseptic application, the whole interior of the wound, together with the protruding bone, having previously been freely treated with strong carbolic acid.

About the tenth day the discharge, which up to that time had been only sanious and serous, showed a slight admixture of slimy pus; and this increased till (a few days before I left) it amounted to about three drams in 24 hours. But the boy continued as he had been after the second day, free from unfavorable symptoms, with pulse, tongue, appetite, and sleep natural and strength increasing, while the limb remained as it had been from the first, free from swelling, redness, or pain.

I therefore persevered with the antiseptic dressing; and before I left the discharge was already somewhat less, while the bone was becoming firm. I think it likely that, in that boy's case, I should have found merely a superficial sore had I taken off all the dressings at the end of the three weeks; though, considering the extent of the injury, I thought it prudent to let the month expire before disturbing the rag next the skin. But I feel sure that if I had resorted to ordinary dressing when the pus first appeared the progress of the case would have been exceedingly different.

The next class of cases to which I have applied the antiseptic treatment is that of abscesses. Here also the results have been extremely satisfactory and in beautiful harmony with the pathological principles indicated above. . . .

All that is requisite is to guard against the introduction of living atmospheric germs from without, at the same time that free opportunity is afforded for the escape of the discharge from within. . . .

Ordinary contused wounds are, of course, amenable to the same treatment as compound fractures, which are a complicated variety of them. . . .

If the severest forms of contused and lacerated wounds heal thus kindly under the antiseptic treatment, it is obvious that its application to simple incised wounds must be merely a matter of detail. . . .

There is, however, one point more that I cannot but advert to, viz., the influence of this mode of treatment upon the general healthiness of a hospital. Previously to its introduction the two large wards in which most of my cases of accident and of operation are treated, were among the unhealthiest in the whole surgical division of the Glasgow Royal Infirmary, in consequence apparently of those wards being unfavorably placed with reference to the supply of fresh air; and I have felt ashamed when recording the results of my practice to have so often to allude to hospital gangrene or pyemia.

It was interesting, though melancholy, to observe that whenever all or nearly all the beds contained cases with open sores, these grievous complications were pretty sure to show themselves; so that I came to welcome simple fractures, though in themselves of little interest either for myself or the students, because their presence diminished the proportion of open sores among the (hospital) patients.

But since the antiseptic treatment has been brought into full operation, and wounds and abscesses no longer poison the atmosphere with putrid exhalations, my wards, though in other respects under precisely the same circumstances as before, have completely changed their character; so that during the last nine months not a single instance of pyemia, hospital gangrene, or erysipelas has occurred in them.

As there appears to be no doubt regarding the cause of this change, the importance of the fact can hardly be exaggerated.

It was here, in the high mortality wards of the Infirmary at Glasgow, that Lister began to suspect that septic diseases were caused by "living ferments" in wounds themselves and not by spontaneously generated forces or the oxygen in the air

ERNST MACH was born in Turas, Austria, in 1838, the son of a poor school teacher. As a boy he showed a keen interest in the various physics experiments conducted by his father, and it wasn't long before he was doing them himself. Mathematics also interested him and by the time he was 18 he had enrolled in the University of Vienna. Graduating from that institution with high honors, Mach quickly engaged in postgraduate work at Gratz, and by 1867 had been appointed professor of physics at Prague University. It was while at Prague that he became interested in the shock-wave theory and began experiments in that field. Mach died in 1916.

Ernst Mach

Past the sound barrier
by Bill Bullock

ALMOST 15 YEARS before the Wright brothers made history on the sand dunes at Kitty Hawk, N. C., a young German professor of physics at Prague University began experimenting with the ratio of the speed of flow of gases and the speed of sound.

His name was Ernst Mach, and he never saw an airplane that would fly faster than 100 m.p.h. He has been dead now about four decades, but his name is in daily use all over the world as a common term used to express the speed of fast jet-propelled aircraft and rockets.

In his later years the good professor had expressed hope that the world would some day pay tribute to him as a physicist and philosopher. He would probably be bitterly disappointed to know that very few people even heard of him until the coming of the jet.

Mach's early experiments with the speed of sound were very crude. They were carried out with the help of a cannon borrowed from the Royal Navy. Mach had a theory that projectiles moving rapidly through a fluid formed a sort of cone which produced shock waves. To prove this, he set up condenser plates in a darkened area and attached them to batteries. Close by the plates he placed sensitized glass photographic plates. By firing the cannon shells past the condenser plates at different muzzle velocities, he actually caused the shells to take their own photographs as the sparks caused by the shells passing the condenser plates registered on the photographic plates. A careful analysis of these crude pictures proved that Mach was right, and that shock waves did exist.

From these experiments came the term "Mach angle," and scientists throughout the civilized world used the term in their papers and experiments until just prior to World War II when the term "Mach number" was adopted by engineers working on the development of high-speed propeller-driven airplanes.

With the coming of the fast jet fighters, aircraft engineers began to attach much more importance to Prof. Mach's experiments.

In designing and testing high-speed jet airplanes—and propeller-driven airplanes—that fly at speeds approaching the speed of sound, it becomes increasingly important that accurate computations of stresses be made. As an airplane approaches the so-called "sonic barrier" strange things begin to happen. The air which normally flows smoothly over the surface of the wing begins to pile up and form a

Notice the gradual increase of shock waves in these pictures, taken of models in a transonic tunnel, as speed is increased from Mach .98 to Mach 1.02 to Mach 1.06 and to Mach 1.09

NACA

solid barrier. This condition causes severe buffeting of the aircraft, and in some cases has caused complete disintegration! As the aircraft attempts to crash the barrier, much difficulty is experienced with the controls.

Gene Mays, veteran Douglas Aircraft Co. test pilot, who flew many of the early tests on the Navy *Skyrocket,* and was the first human to ever fly faster than sound at sea level, reported that the airplane had a tendency to roll to the right and left, and that the controls were extremely hard to move. Once through the dreaded barrier, however, things were smooth and there was practically no noise save that of the jet exhaust which seemed to be miles behind him.

Without becoming involved in a lot of long-haired mathematics, the term "Mach number" simply means the ratio between the speed of flight and the speed of sound. This means that Mach 1 would be flight at the speed of sound, Mach 2 would be flight at twice the speed of sound, and Mach .5 would be flight at half the speed of sound. Supersonic research airplanes flying at high altitudes have exceeded Mach 2 many times in test flights. The speed of sound has been established at 761 m.p.h. at sea level with the temperature at 59° F. Temperature and density of the air, however, cause this figure to vary. An airplane flying at near 35,000 feet, where the temperature remains a constant 65° F., would approach the speed of sound almost 100 m.p.h. sooner than at sea level, according to theoretical calculations.

At a sustained flight at Mach 3 aerodynamic heating could raise the temperature of a missile's surface to more than 600 degrees Fahrenheit

Mach was a very vigorous and outspoken man. He cared little for office or position, and often engaged in red-hot arguments with his associates on many technical subjects.

A character named Lenin, who at the time was throwing his weight around Russia a lot, once engaged in a heated argument with Mach over a question on philosophy. As usual, Mach won out, and the great Lenin retired to Russia.

The Russians never forgot the incident, for today they use the term "Bairstow number," after the celebrated English scientist Leonard Bairstow, to express the speeds of their jet fighter planes! This term may change any day now since the Russians have adopted the "we did everything first" policy.

The common term "Mach number" will become more and more important and take on greater significance as our engineers strive for greater things in aviation. Maybe the good professor would be just a little proud after all.

ON THE NIGHT of March 24, 1882, distinguished German scientists gathered at the Berlin Physiological Society for their monthly meeting. The scheduled speaker, Robert Koch, began quietly. He had identified the cause of tuberculosis. It was a rod-like bacillus which he had found in every patient he had examined who had died of the disease. He had recovered the germ, grown it in pure culture and when he injected it into laboratory animals the animals got tuberculosis. Finally he had recovered the bacillus from the infected animals and with it caused tuberculosis in still other animals. There could be no doubt that the rod-like bacillus was the cause of the white plague.

Robert Koch

Strategist in man's war on disease
by Leonard Engel

THE YEARS BETWEEN 1882 and 1900 were a uniquely exciting time in man's war on disease. Scarcely a month passed without discovery of the cause of another age-old foe of the human race. In 1883, the diphtheria and cholera germs were identified; in 1884, the microbe responsible for lockjaw; in 1886, the cause of pneumonia—the pneumococcus; in 1887, the undulant-fever germ; in 1894, *Pasteurella pestis*, the germ of bubonic plague; later in the nineties, the microbes of botulism and bacillary dysentery.

In 1865, the immortal Pasteur had proved that germs could cause disease in animals and suggested that they might also be responsible for disease in man. At first, no one believed; then everyone did. Men with microscopes were soon finding "disease microbes" everywhere. But their efforts began to bear real fruit only after a meeting of the Berlin Physiological Society in 1882 at which Koch announced his discovery of the tuberculosis germ.

It was not only that Koch had uncovered the cause of tuberculosis. His exquisite proof that the tubercle bacillus was the criminal supplied what microbe hunters had lacked until then: a technique for showing, beyond any possible doubt, that a given kind of germ—and only that kind among the infinitely many that may be found in the human body at any moment—is responsible for a particular disease.

Find the germ in all patients with the disease; recover it and grow it in pure culture; produce the disease in animals with the cultured germs; recover *them* and produce the disease again—these four rules provided a sure guide for selecting the particular microbes responsible for infectious disease. Armed with Koch's postulates (as the four rules have come to be called), the microbe hunters had figuratively but to tap their microscope barrels, and a flood of discoveries gushed forth.

It was no accident that Koch worked out sound rules for identifying disease microbes; he was a coolly analytical, painstaking man. It was a fortunate accident, though, that turned him toward microbe hunting. Koch was born in a small town in northwestern Germany on December 11, 1843. In medical school and as an intern in Hamburg, he dreamed of adventure in Africa and Central Asia. Instead, he married and settled down to practice in a succession of deadly East German villages. To assuage his boredom, his wife, on his 28th birthday, gave him a microscope. With the microscope, Koch was soon off on adventures more remarkable than any he would ever have had in Tibet or Timbuktu.

While studying medicine at Gottingen, Koch was influenced by Jacob Henle who in a book on contagions had said, "Before microscopic forms can be regarded as the cause of contagion in man, they must be found constantly in the contagious material, they must be isolated from it, and their strength tested."

In moments snatched from delivering babies and tending sick children and farmers, Koch turned his microscope on everything around him. He not only taught himself how to use his new instrument, but invented several methods that are still in use, such as the "hanging drop" technique for isolating a single variety of microbe. The reward for his patience and ingenuity was the discovery, in 1876, of *Bacillus anthracis*, the cause of anthrax, and of a practical technique for ridding farms of this scourge.

When he had finally convinced himself of the guilt of *B. anthracis*, Koch packed up his slides and animals and set out for the University of Breslau to show his evidence to the great bacteriologist, Prof. Cohn, who had written him encouraging letters. Cohn and his friend and colleague Cohnheim were convinced and immediately recognized in the obscure country doctor one of the greatest microbe hunters of them all. The hullabaloo they set up led, a few years later, to Koch's appointment to the Imperial Health Office in Berlin.

The first task Koch set himself in his new laboratory, with its undreamed of wealth of apparatus, was not the discovery of other disease microbes, but of a way to grow bacteria in pure culture. Many germ hunters were already dimly aware that pure cultures were needed to complete the proof that a particular microbe causes a particular disease. But how obtain them? Despite the utmost care, the liquid "soups" then used for growing bacteria soon became hopelessly contaminated with all sorts of germs from the air.

One day Koch noticed differently colored spots on a piece of boiled potato on his laboratory bench. Curiously, he put a slice of the potato under his microscope. Each spot turned out to be a pure colony of a different kind of microbe! Evidently, the microbes had stayed where they landed on the potato, with each giving rise to a distinct, uncontaminated ring of daughter microbes. Koch saw at once that pure cultures could be grown on solid nutrients.

Up to this time liquid gelatin had been used for cultivating bacteria. Koch discovered that by altering the proportions the gelatin would harden and provide a better medium for bacteria cultures

Now he was ready for what was to be one of the supreme adventures of all time—tracking down the tuberculosis germ. A French experimenter, Villemin, had proved that tuberculosis was infectious by injecting tuberculous material from human patients into animals. But no one had ever seen the tuberculosis microbe.

Koch started by trying all known dyes and stains on tubercles dissected out of patients dead of consumption in Berlin hospitals. None brought out the elusive bacterium. He and his faithful assistants Gaffky and Loeffler (later to become famous germ hunters in their own right) then concocted a bewildering assortment of dyes and stains of their own. One worked and one day, the slender killer floated into Koch's lens.

This was only a beginning. The bacillus had to be isolated and cultured—no mean feat, for the tuberculosis microbe proved to have a super-finicky appetite. To grow it, Koch had to invent a special nutrient medium, jellied blood serum. Now, the artificially grown bacilli had to be injected into laboratory animals—a deadly dangerous business, for a slip of the syringe might put the lethal stuff into Koch's finger instead. Koch inoculated hundreds of animals of a score of species; all known to be susceptible to the human variety of tuberculosis promptly came down with the disease.

Koch was still not satisfied. Tuberculosis is ordinarily contracted by breathing the germs, not by inoculation. So, in the garden behind the laboratory, Koch rigged a closed box into which he could spray, through a pipe from his laboratory, tuberculosis microbes. Guinea pigs and other tuberculosis-susceptible animals placed in the box and subjected to the spray likewise contracted the disease. At last, the case against the tubercle bacillus was complete.

Koch's discovery of the cause of tuberculosis made his laboratory a Mecca of world science overnight. Within days, it was crowded with scientists from all over Europe; in weeks, with scientists from all over the world—all come to learn how the shy little man with the mousy beard and disinfectant-blackened hands hunted microbes. Unexpectedly, the triumph also brought Koch the other kind of adventure he craved.

Until Koch's discovery of the tuberculosis germ, the white plague had been the cause of one of every seven deaths in the world

Early in 1883, a cholera epidemic flashed out of India across the Middle East to Egypt. Germany and France both saw in the outbreak an opportunity not only to benefit mankind, but to gain national prestige. Germany dispatched Koch, and France, two of Pasteur's most brilliant assistants, Roux and Thuillier, on official missions to track down the cause of cholera. The strange race that ensued (heightened by an old dispute between Koch and Pasteur over Pasteur's anthrax vaccine) was won by Koch. In India, he unearthed proof that cholera was caused by a comma-shaped inhabitant of polluted water, *Vibrio comma*.

Koch was greeted on his return like a conquering general. He received Germany's highest decoration from the hands of the Kaiser himself. This moment was the high point of his career. He still had 27 years of useful work before him: in 1886, he and an American, J. E. Weeks, would independently discover the Koch-Weeks bacillus, which is responsible for pink eye; and on two trips to South Africa, he would find practical means of combating rinderpest, the dread South African cattle disease. But he was not to have another triumph comparable to his earlier discoveries. In fact, his reputation was somewhat tarnished by his mistaken announcement, in 1890, of a cure for tuberculosis in tuberculin, an extract of the tubercle bacillus useful in diagnosing the white plague but not in treating it.

But his place in science is secure. In the 10 years between his 28th birthday, when his wife gave him the microscope, and that night at the Berlin Physiological Society, he did enough for many lifetimes. He not only tracked down some of man's greatest enemies himself, but showed others how to stalk those that remained. He, together with Pasteur, laid the basis for the conquest of infectious disease—perhaps the 19th century's finest achievement.

THE DATE of the discovery of X rays was November 8, 1895. Roentgen, working with a Crookes' tube covered by a shield of black cardboard, had been passing a current through the tube. He noticed a peculiar black line across a piece of barium platinocyanide paper. "The effect," Roentgen said, "was one which could only be produced . . . by the passing of light. No light could come from the tube because the shield which covered it was impervious to any light known. . . ." Assuming that the effect must have come from the tube, he tested it and in a few minutes there was no doubt about it—rays were coming from the tube which had a luminous effect upon the paper. It was clearly something new.

Wilhelm Roentgen

The X ray
by William P. Schenk

PHYSICISTS all over the world, back in 1895, were pretty much agreed that the great work had all been done. Some of them mourned publicly that no discoveries of truly major importance were likely to be made in the future. But then they did not know that a Professor Roentgen, working alone in a modest laboratory in Germany, had begun a series of experiments with a crude induction coil, a pear-shaped bulb from which the air had been removed, and a sheet of paper painted with certain metallic salts. And Professor Roentgen did not know that his work was destined to reveal a force of nature—never before suspected—that would almost overnight revolutionize medicine and technology, and become an instrument for deeper probing of the structure of matter.

Wilhelm Konrad Roentgen was born on March 27, 1845, in the old-world town of Lennep in the German Rhineland. He was an only child, son of a well-to-do cloth merchant and manufacturer. When he was only three, the family escaped the revolutionary disturbances that shook its homeland, moved to Holland, and settled in the town of Apeldoorn. Here the boy learned his first lessons, attended boarding school, and suffered a childhood illness that cost him the sight of one eye.

In 1862, Roentgen entered the Utrecht Technical School, having shown no inclination to follow in his father's footsteps, but having already demonstrated a high degree of mechanical aptitude. From this school, while still in his teens, Roentgen was expelled for his refusal to name the student who had caricatured one of the teachers.

X rays today have found many uses, not only in medical practice but also in the industrial fields where proper inspection of metallic parts is impossible without "the wonder rays"

Roentgen's father, however, was able to arrange for a special examination, which, if Wilhelm passed it, would take the place of his high school work and admit him to the University of Utrecht. Unfortunately, the examiner happened to be one of the members of the board that had expelled Roentgen from the Technical School, and his prejudice against the young man, it is said, resulted in Roentgen's failing the examination. Although he was unable to enter the University of Utrecht as a regular student, Roentgen was allowed to attend certain lectures there for two semesters.

Roentgen's erratic career as a student was by no means over. He next applied for admission to the Polytechnical School in Zurich, and, possibly a little to his own surprise, was accepted. But the lake and mountain setting of the famous Swiss school tempted Roentgen more irresistibly than its classrooms and lecture halls. Tall and slender, usually dressed in the best and latest fashion, he was more popular with his many student friends than with the professors of the engineering courses in which he was supposed to specialize.

He was a leader of boating parties and mountainside climbs and became a frequent visitor to the local inn kept by Gottfried Ludwig. Before long he fell in love with Anna Bertha, the innkeeper's daughter, and they became engaged. After a period during which Anna Bertha lived with Roentgen's mother to learn the style of cooking most pleasing to her future husband, the pair were married on January 19, 1872.

Roentgen found himself when he was twenty-four, or rather, August Kundt, a brilliant experimental physicist at the Polytechnical School, took him in hand. He sensed the young man's dissatisfaction with engineering, fired him with his own enthusiasm for the classic beauty of physics, and urged him to try that science as his career. And he invited Roentgen to come into his laboratory as his assistant. Fortunately for himself, and for the millions of people who were to benefit from his eventual success, Roentgen accepted Kundt's offer.

The laboratory was stimulating to Roentgen. He acquired the known principles of physics in an amazingly short time, and spent half his nights reading the journals' reports of its latest advances. It was inevitable that Kundt took him with him when he was called to the University of Strassburg. There Roentgen worked on the ratio of the heats of gases, measured the heat-conductivity of crystals, and experimented on the absorption of heat rays in water vapor, and on the electromagnetic rotation of the planes of polarization in gases.

Roentgen was a master-worker with apparatus he constructed with precision skill. He made himself a sought-after researcher and teacher within ten years. His first professorship came from the Hessian University of Giesen when he was thirty-four; and even Von Helmholtz (who invented the ophthalmoscope) was among the distinguished group who recommended him. When he was forty-three Roentgen became professor of physics at the University of Wurzburg, and director of its newly established Physical Institute. And it was there, in his fiftieth year, that Roentgen discovered the X ray.

Roentgen officially announced his discovery in a paper, *On a New Kind of Rays,* read to members of the Wurzburg Physical Medical Society on January 23, 1896. The 4,000-word milestone in the history of science began as follows:

"If the discharge of a fairly large induction coil be made to pass through a Hittorf vacuum tube, or through a Lenard tube, a Crookes' tube, or other similar apparatus, which has been sufficiently exhausted, the tube being covered with thin, black cardboard which fits it with tolerable closeness, and if the whole apparatus be placed in a completely darkened room, there is observed at each discharge a bright illumination of a paper screen covered with barium platinocyanide, placed in the vicinity of the induction coil, the fluorescence thus produced being entirely independent of the fact whether the coated or the plain surface is turned toward the discharge tube. This fluorescence is visible even when the paper screen is at a distance of two meters from the apparatus.

"It is easy to prove that the cause of the fluorescence proceeds from the discharge apparatus, and not from any other point in the conducting circuit."

"We soon discover," the paper went on, "that all bodies are transparent to the agent, though in very different degrees. I proceed to give a few examples: Paper is very transparent; behind a bound book of

The discovery of X rays belongs entirely to Roentgen but Crookes has been credited with being the first man to actually produce X rays although he did not realize it at the time

about one thousand pages I saw the fluorescent screen light up brightly, the printer's ink offering scarcely a noticeable hindrance. In the same way the fluorescence appeared behind a double pack of cards. . . . Sheets of hard rubber several centimeters thick still permit the rays to pass through them." And in a footnote at this point the author said, "For brevity's sake I shall use the expression rays, and to distinguish them from others of this name, I shall call them 'X rays.' "

Further on in his paper Roentgen pointed out, "If the hand be held between the discharge tube and the screen, the darker shadow of the bones is seen within the slightly dark shadow image of the hand itself."

Armed Forces Institute of Pathology

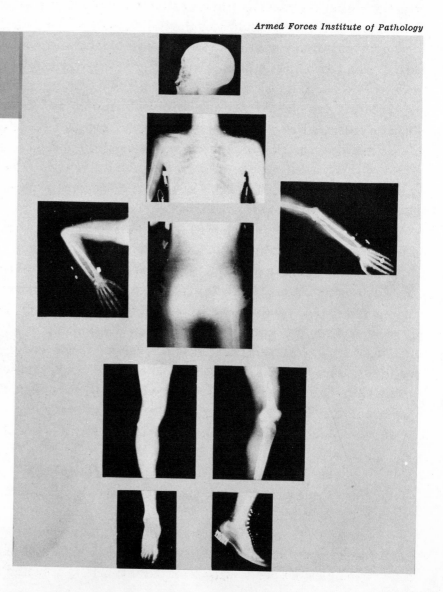

X-ray studies of human subjects made three months after the discovery of X rays by Roentgen

"Of special significance in many respects," Roentgen went on, "is the fact that photographic dry plates are sensitive to the X rays. We are, therefore, in a condition to determine more definitely many phenomena, and so the more easily to avoid deception; wherever it has been possible, therefore, I have controlled, by means of photography, every important observation which I have made with the eye by means of the fluorescent screen."

And toward the end of his paper, the world's first radiologist said, "The justification for calling by the name 'rays' the agent which proceeds from the walls of the discharge apparatus, I derive in part from the entirely regular formation of shadows, which are seen when more or less transparent bodies are brought between the apparatus and the fluorescent screen (or the photographic plate).

"I have observed, and in part photographed, many shadow pictures of this kind, the production of which has a particular charm. I possess, for instance, photographs of the shadow of the profile of a door which separates the rooms in which, on one side, the discharge apparatus was placed, on the other the photographic plate; the shadow of the bones of the hand; the shadow of a covered wire wrapped on a wooden spool; of a.set of weights enclosed in a box; of a compass in which the magnetic needle is entirely enclosed by metal; of a piece of metal whose lack of homogeneity becomes noticeable by means of the X rays, et cetera."

Like the atom bomb, half a century later, the X ray was a complete surprise to an unprepared world. It *was* a new kind of magic, and in their reaction to the premature and garbled reports from Wurzburg, people jumped to the wrong conclusions from all directions.

An English firm immediately advertised "X-ray-proof" underclothing for women. Assemblyman Reed, of Somerset County, N. J., introduced a bill into the House at Trenton, prohibiting the use of X rays in opera glasses in theaters. Cartoonists and versifiers suddenly had a made-to-order theme. One newspaper gleefully printed this example:

X-actly So!

The Roentgen Rays, the Roentgen Rays
What is this craze?
The town's ablaze
With the new phase
Of X ray's ways.

After reading his paper Roentgen prepared to give demonstrations to the still dubious audience. Using the chairman of the meeting as a subject, Roentgen turned on his X-ray machine and the bones of the subject's hands stood out clearly. The audience was spellbound and immediately voted to name the new discovery "Roentgen rays" in honor of their discoverer

Wilhelm Roentgen
The X ray

I'm full of daze,
Shock and amaze;
For nowadays
I hear they'll gaze
Thro' cloak and gown—and even stays
These naughty, naughty Roentgen Rays.

These stories reached such ridiculous heights that the London Pall Mall Gazette said, "We are sick of the Roentgen rays. Perhaps the best thing would be for all civilized nations to combine to burn all the Roentgen rays, to execute all the discoverers, and to corner all the equipment in the world and to whelm it in the middle of the ocean. Let the fish contemplate each other's bones if they like, but not us."

Thomas Edison received a request for "a pound of X rays" to be sent "as soon as possible." One student reported that his dog became hungry when X rays were used to project the shadow of a bone upon his brain. There were fakers who could turn a handful of change into a bushel basket full of gold with the X ray—quacks who could take X-ray pictures of the human soul. The X ray was an overnight world-wide sensation—until the novelty wore off.

Scientists all over the world soon repeated Roentgen's experiments, confirmed them, and set to work on the problems they posed and the new avenues of research they opened up; in a generation they developed the X ray into one of man's most valuable and versatile tools.

After the X-ray discovery, Roentgen returned to his study of the properties of crystals, their electrical conductivity and heat expansion. In 1900, at the special request of the Bavarian government, he joined the Philosophical Faculty of the University of Munich. There, continuing meanwhile with his own researches, he organized the work of that university's Physical Institute. In 1901 he was awarded the first Nobel Prize for Physics; he bequeathed the prize money to the University of Wurzburg. Germany's kaiser decorated him with the Prussian Order of the Crown. And when the University of Wurzburg gave him an honorary Doctor of Medicine degree, the students honored Roentgen with a torchlight procession.

Roentgen's beloved wife died in 1919 after a lingering illness; he had no happiness the rest of his life. In 1920 he retired from active teaching, but continued to work in the two laboratory rooms that were put at his disposal until shortly before his death. In 1922 he made his last Alpine climb, saying, "I still prefer to leave the well-worn path and clamber over bramble and stone. If I should ever be missing, don't search for me on the main road." He died on February 10, 1923, of cancer, an illness he diagnosed himself.

GEORGE WESTINGHOUSE *patented his famous air brake in 1869, and organized the Westinghouse Air Brake Co. in July of that year. But that was only the beginning of the part he played in the development of American technology. By 1886, Westinghouse had perfected electric-signal control for railroads, and revolutionized electric-power production. Before he died, in 1914, Westinghouse harnessed Niagara Falls, striking the keynote of a new era in hydroelectric power; pioneered the electrification of railroads; and guided the development of the steam turbine. He also built dynamos for the rapid transit systems of New York City and London, England.*

George Westinghouse

Inventor—engineer—builder
by Dorothy Rickard

A TALL, WELL-BUILT young man of 22 drew the last bill from his wallet to tip Dan Tate, an engineer on the Panhandle Railroad.

Then, turning, he ran back to join railroad officials and guests in the last coach of the special train which was to test his air brake in a trial run from Pittsburgh, Pa., to Steubenville, Ohio.

As the train steamed out of the Pittsburgh yards the youth sat silent. The test must be a success. He had poured all of his own money into his invention. Still more serious, he had borrowed additional funds from friends to promote it.

His heart began to sink as his mind ran back over past failures.

Always considered a dreamer by members of his family, George Westinghouse was of little use in his father's machine shop. Each time he was given a job to do, he left it partly finished in order to tinker with some toy machine of his own invention.

The eighth of ten children in the Westinghouse family, George was born in Central Bridge, N. Y., on October 6, 1846. His father, originally a Vermont farmer, moved to Schenectady some years after George was born. Here the father became an inventor and manufacturer of farm machinery. And it was here, too, that George received most of his education.

His school teachers thought him "dull and backward." He was asked to leave Union College, at the age of 19, after he had confessed to its president that he would "like college very well, if I had time to give my mind to my studies."

He had even failed in his first runaway attempt to join the Union Army during the Civil War, and was hauled back by his father.

Later his parents gave their permission for their son to join the cavalry. But that, too, proved to be a failure, for George, wanting to be an officer, was promised a commission if he could bring in 50 recruits.

After combing the countryside around his boyhood home in Central Bridge, he reported to his commander with 17 recruits and renewed his pleas for a commission.

His superior officer rejected him with a "Too bad, my boy, but you can't turn 17 into 50." George became a corporal until he transferred to the Navy.

Even during the time the young inventor was searching for a railroad interested enough to give his air brake a trial, one railroad official sent the young man out of his office labeling him and his invention as "crazy."

Not everything in George Westinghouse's past life had been a failure. Once, when he was 13, his father had refused to let him go on a pleasure trip with some other boys until he had cut a pile of metal pipe into equal lengths.

"This is hard work," his father said, "and will probably take all your spare time during the rest of the week."

Before noon, however, the job was done. George had rigged up a combination tool which, attached to a power machine, fed and cut the pipe automatically in a few hours.

Perhaps his most astonishing youthful achievement was a small rotary engine which he designed and built without counsel or prompting. For this invention he received his first patent three weeks after his 19th birthday.

It was not the perfect solution of rotary power for which the world waited. That would come later. But it demonstrated that young Westinghouse was thinking in fundamentals. He was on the right track.

In spite of being labeled a "dull and backward" student, George Westinghouse went on to astound both his teachers and the world with his achievements— employing tens of thousands of engineers, craftsmen, and technicians and creating innumerable new occupations. Moreover, he was to leave the world a better, safer place in which to live

But his empty wallet, on that April day in 1869 when the air brake was tested, must have induced thoughts of his previous defeats, rather than his successes. He scarcely had time to brood, for the train, which passed through Grant's Hill tunnel and emerged on the other side of Pittsburgh, suddenly came to a violent and unscheduled halt.

Railroad officials and guests on the train were thrown into an undignified heap. Indignantly they regained their feet and, turning to the young inventor, demanded to know what had gone wrong.

Not waiting to offer an explanation, George Westinghouse dashed forward to where Dan Tate sat in the cab. Had the engine jumped the track? Had it struck something?

Once he had reached the head of the train there was no need to ask. On the tracks, not four feet from the cowcatcher, lay a drayman, thrown there by his horse.

Tate, seeing the horse rear in fright at sight of the approaching engine, had nervously reached for the handle of his newfangled air brake, knowing it was the only chance he had of saving the drayman's life. The brake held and the train ground to a stop a few feet from the drayman's wagon. It was a great moment in the annals of railroad history.

When Dan Tate reached for the engineer's brake-valve handle, the old manual brake was doomed

Up to this time, each car in a train had been braked separately—trainmen rushed from car to car tightening hand brakes—and usually, even though disaster loomed ahead, a speeding train traveled from a half mile to a mile before it could be stopped.

The first practical application of the Westinghouse air brake had proved a highly dramatic success and within the month the young inventor received his first air-brake patent.

The Westinghouse invention, by enabling the engineer to control all brakes instantly from the cab, literally revolutionized the speed, comfort and economy of rail transportation and has justly been called the "most important safety device ever known."

It carried the railroads far towards becoming the safest form of of public transportation in use in the world today. Within five years more than 2,000 American locomotives and 6,500 cars had been equipped with the Westinghouse air brake.

Many foreign railroads had also put it into use. Orders came from England, China, Japan, Burma and many of the countries of

213

Europe. And George Westinghouse was well on his way to becoming one of America's greatest inventors.

Westinghouse's services to the railroads, however, had just begun—103 further air-brake patents would be issued to him during the next 40 years. He would solve the knotty problems of applying the air brake to longer and still longer trains as rail traffic increased. He would develop the ingenious friction draft gear to save wear and tear on rolling stock and its contents.

The air brake, while it marked the real beginning of his inventive career, wasn't his first development, however. His first patent, on the rotary steam engine, was one of ten patents granted to Westinghouse before he was 30. It was his second invention, a railroad-car replacer, that set him on the path of inventive genius.

George had been working in his father's machine shop since his failure at Union College. Occasionally, the elder Westinghouse would entrust his son to represent him on trips involving company business. It was while returning to his home in Schenectady on one such trip that his train was held up for two hours while two derailed cars of a preceding train were put back on the rails.

George and a fellow traveler whiled away the time watching the railroad crew as it grappled with one car, then the other, painfully prying each one back, inch by inch, until it could finally be jacked over into place on the rails.

As the work neared its end, George remarked, "That was a poorly handled job."

"I suppose so," his companion admitted, "but it couldn't be helped."

"Yes, it could," the young inventor remarked. "They could have done the whole thing in 15 minutes by clamping a pair of rails to the track and running them off at an angle so they would come up even against the wheels of the derailed car. Then, by hitching an engine to the car, they could shunt it back into place."

"Why don't you make a car replacer like that and sell it to the railroads?" his acquaintance jokingly inquired.

"That's a good idea," George replied seriously. "I'll do it."

Full of his new idea, George Westinghouse was unable to sleep that night until he had thought out the details of his invention. The next morning he made his drawings, and as soon as he had prepared his model he carried it to his father.

"He was not a military hero," wrote Westinghouse's biographer, Francis E. Leupp, "though he tasted war; he was not a statesman, though counting presidents and kings among his friends; he was master of no magic arts, yet his clever hands, responsive to a fertile mind, were always busy converting prophecy into history."

The older Westinghouse examined it with care then, turning to his son, he said, "It seems to be a workable idea. But think of the money it would cost to patent, manufacture and market it. And where's that money coming from?"

"I thought you would lend it to me," George said.

"My son, if I've learned one thing in this world, it's not to stick my nose into something I know nothing about," Mr. Westinghouse replied. Then seeing the downcast look on his son's face, he added, "You'll have to make my share a very small one."

Encouraged by his father's promise, George made the rounds of some of the wealthy men of Schenectady. Most of them laughed at him, but among them he found two men willing to risk $5,000 each on the new invention.

Business was brisk for a time in the new car replacer shop. But the market was soon saturated, for the life of a replacer seemed to be endless, and George's business partners became dissatisfied with the constantly diminishing returns on their investment.

In a showdown among the three men, the partnership was dissolved, and George, although he owned the patents to the car replacer, found himself without anyone to manufacture it.

Hearing of a new steel plant in Pittsburgh which might take over production of the replacer, Westinghouse set off for that city. Here he struck a much more favorable agreement with a Pittsburgh manufacturer, who hired him as the replacer's salesman.

Although Westinghouse was to develop alternating current, the turbine generator, the marine turbine, the system for transmitting natural gas through pipes, the automatic, central telephone-exchange system, and many other modern devices, he would return again and again through the years to unraveling the many difficult problems facing transportation.

There were 40,000 miles of railroad track in the United States when Westinghouse introduced the air brake. Eleven years later that mileage had doubled. Moreover, trains were traveling faster, and city railroad yards had expanded into vast and complex networks of rails.

Westinghouse moved with energy and vision. He merged leading concerns in the field into the great Union Switch and Signal Co. Applying his own powers of invention to the problem, he secured patent after patent on fundamental electromagnetic equipment.

Using, as one scientist expressed it, "compressed air for the heavy

About this time George also invented a reversible steel railway frog—which made it possible for a train to pass from one track to another

work, electricity to pull the trigger," he gradually developed a system of power signaling and interlocking that laid the foundations of the general practice which still serves our vast rail systems.

A beautiful logic runs through the Westinghouse career. Transportation and alternating current had become the two major preoccupations of his life, and now, in 1905, he was to bring them together in one work of engineering—the single-phase, main-line electric locomotive.

He had not originated the idea of moving trains and cars by electricity. Men had experimented with it before he was born. And electric street cars were in operation when he entered the field in 1889.

But his contributions had already been notable. In 1890 he had brought out a single-reduction-gear motor for direct current which caused sweeping changes in trolley-car development.

He had made the first major application of alternating current to a railway system by building the huge AC generators for the Manhattan Elevated and the New York subway.

These systems, however, used rotary converters to supply direct current to the motors of the cars, and what Westinghouse wanted was a complete alternating-current system—one that would permit more economical conversion and distribution of power.

On May 16, 1905, his new electric locomotive made its first trial run, fulfilling Westinghouse's expectations.

During his lifetime George Westinghouse received patents on 361 inventions—an average of one invention every six weeks for 48 years. He founded 60 companies, among them the Westinghouse Electric Corp., the Westinghouse Air Brake Co. and the Union Switch and Signal Co.

THOMAS EDISON took out some 2000 patents but many ideas he gave to the public without patenting. Still others he kept as trade secrets. His mind and hands were so fertile that no one has ever fully described all they produced. The electric light, the phonograph, silent and talking motion pictures—these alone would have put him among the elect of science and technology. But he also devised the duplicating machine, first practical loud speaker, electro-magnetic brake, nickel-iron storage battery and innumerable other contrivances. Edison invented not only an astonishing multitude of devices, but a machine for making inventions— the modern technical research laboratory.

Thomas A. Edison

American wizard of the industrial age
by Leonard Engel

IT IS NATURAL that a man who accomplished so much should have become a subject for legends, such as the tale that he had to go to work early because his parents were poor. They weren't. Tom was born February 11, 1847, in Milan, Ohio, where his father was a successful shingle manufacturer. When he was seven, the family moved to Port Huron, Mich., where his father became a prosperous grain and lumber dealer. Young Tom went to work as a newsboy and "candy butcher" on the Grand Trunk Ry. before his 13th birthday because he needed money for the well-stocked laboratory he already had in his cellar.

It is true, though, that he did poorly in school and that he was educated largely by his mother and by reading at home. In his case, this was fortunate. It helped make him extremely opinionated—but it also contributed to his originality.

Edison made his first real invention as a youth of 19. It was a device for recording votes in Congress. Congress wasn't interested. "Young man," a candid member of the House of Representatives told

217

him, "the last thing a congressman wants is to have his every vote recorded."

Edison learned the lesson well. Thereafter he made sure that there was a market for everything he turned his hand to. His judgment in this regard was extraordinary.

Henry Ford—with Harvey Firestone, the rubber manufacturer, a camping and fishing crony of Edison in later years—tells of an electric-utility industry conference in 1896 attended by Edison. The assembled leaders of the infant industry enthusiastically predicted big sales of electricity for charging the batteries of electric automobiles. Someone mentioned that Ford, who was there as chief engineer of the Detroit Edison Co., had just built a gasoline auto.

Edison asked some questions, then said, "Young man, that's the thing. Electric cars will never do. They must keep near to power stations. The storage battery is too heavy. Steam cars won't do either. You have the thing. Keep at it."

In 1876, Edison moved to Menlo Park, N. J., from nearby Newark, where he had had a laboratory set up with the proceeds from the first invention he sold, a stock ticker.

Interior view of Edison's Menlo Park laboratory taken in 1880. Notice the incandescent lights and the phonograph (left). The organ at the rear was used for Edison's experiments on sound

General Electric Company

Not long after settling in Menlo Park, Edison handed John Kruesi, one of his chief assistants, a sketch of a machine with instructions to have it made up in a local shop. The machine consisted essentially of a long, spirally grooved cylinder turned by a crank; on each side of the cylinder was a small tube with a parchment diaphragm and needle at the inner end. Kruesi couldn't imagine what the contraption was for.

A few days later, Kruesi brought back the completed model. Edison carefully wrapped the long cylinder in tinfoil and adjusted one of the small tubes so that a needle rested on the tin foil over a groove in the cylinder. Then Edison turned the crank and recited "Mary had a little lamb" into the other end of the small tube. When he placed the other needle in the groove and turned the crank again, the words "Mary had a little lamb" came back out of the machine to an astonished laboratory crew.

The invention of the phonograph was as simple as that. Edison had got the idea 10 years before. As a telegraph operator, he had used an embossing machine to record Morse code messages for "playing back" through a telegraph sounder and transcribing when convenient. It occurred to him that he could use the same principle for recording sound. He later also turned the telegraph recording idea into another important device—the automatic telegraph repeater.

The phonograph was one of Edison's favorite inventions, partly because of his deafness. Tradition has it that Edison lost his hearing as the result of a cuff on the ear from a train conductor when spilled chemicals set fire to the baggage car in which Edison, as a young newsboy, made his headquarters and had a laboratory.

According to Edison himself, the damage to his hearing occurred when a trainman saved his life by pulling him aboard a moving train by the ears; Edison had slipped in climbing onto the train and was about to go under the wheels.

At any rate, the loss of his hearing, Edison used to say, not only saved him a great deal of distraction, but helped with the phonograph. Like many hard-of-hearing persons, Edison had trouble understanding *S* sounds, which are also difficult to reproduce. He labored over the phonograph until it reproduced "specie" and similar sibilant words well enough for him to understand. "When this was done," he said, "I knew that everything else could be done."

Edison returned to the phonograph again and again in later life; at the time of his death, he held more than 100 patents on improve-

Edison was granted a patent for his phonograph just two months after his application without the aid of a single reference. The following year he predicted 10 important uses for his invention

ments on it. And without the phonograph, there would have been no electric light. For it was the phonograph that made him a national figure and enabled him to obtain the financial backing he needed for development of the incandescent lamp, his next project.

A few years before, William Wallace, Charles F. Brush and other pioneers had developed the arc light, based on the brilliant arc formed when an electric current is passed between carbon electrodes placed a short distance apart. Arc lights were already seen in the main squares of Cleveland, New York and other cities. The arc light, however, was a big lamp, suitable only for street or auditorium lighting; there was (and is) no such thing as a little arc light for home use. Partly at the suggestion of a chemist friend, Dr. George W. Barker, Edison determined to find some way of making a home-size electric light.

Edison had already done a little experimenting with electricity for lighting. This, plus further experiments, soon convinced him that the answer lay in an observation of Sir Humphry Davy nearly three-quarters of a century before. This was that carbon rods and metallic wires could be made to glow by forcing a powerful current through them. Edison recognized, though, that turning Davy's observation into a practical lighting device would be a formidable task. Accordingly, Edison first raised $300,000—a huge sum for those days for backing an invention as yet unmade—by forming the Edison Electric Light Co.

Now the great work really got under way. Edison quickly found that the incandescent filament could not be made to work effectively in the open air. All of the materials he tried were consumed by oxidation within a few seconds at most. The filament would have to be enclosed in a glass envelope from which the air had been removed.

His first experiments with vacuum bulbs, however, were unsuccessful. His best lamp, which had a platinum-iridium filament, burned for only a few minutes. The difficulty was in the vacuum pumps then available; they left a considerable quantity of air in the bulb. Moreover, a certain amount of air was absorbed and held in the structure of the filament itself.

Edison discovered that the absorbed air could be "boiled out" of the filament by passing a small current through the filament and heating it while the bulb was being pumped out. In addition, about this

Thomas Edison at the White House with his tin-foil phonograph, invented in 1877. The phonograph, one of his favorite inventions, brought world recognition to the "Wizard of Menlo Park"

time, he obtained a new and vastly improved type of pump. He built lamps that showed that he was on the right track at last.

Then came the famous search for the right filament material. Literally tens of thousands of different materials were tried. On October 21, 1879—the official birth date of the incandescent electric lamp—a bulb with a carbonized cotton sewing thread filament stayed lit for 40 hours.

Still the hunt went on. A small army was sent out from the Menlo Park beehive to explore the corners of the earth for fibers that would outdo cotton. A species of bamboo from Japan proved to be what was wanted; carbonized bamboo fibers were the basis of the electric light until metallurgists, two decades later, learned how to draw fine wires from brittle metals like tantalum and tungsten.

The development of a practical lamp was not the end of Edison's work with lighting, any more than it was the end of his career. To bring light into homes, electric generating stations, a transmission system, electric meters, a score of other subsidiary contrivances were needed. Edison went on to design or invent them all: a suitable dynamo, switchgear, an appropriate type of underground cable, the first electric meter. By 1882, central-station power plants and lighting systems were operating in New York and London.

In the course of further work on the electric-light bulb, Edison made another discovery that was also to have revolutionary social consequences—the "Edison effect," the basis of the radio tube.

One day in 1883, a glass blower in Edison's laboratory sealed an extra electrode into the nose of a light bulb. Edison found that a current could be detected in the wire from the extra electrode when the wire was connected to the positive terminal of a battery, but not to the negative terminal. In other words, current could flow in only one direction through the vacuum between filament and electrode—in modern terminology, from filament to plate.

Two decades later, the British electrical engineer, Sir John Flem-

Working parts of Edison's motion-picture camera used in 1894 for the production of "Black Maria." Edison's early pictures were accompanied by synchronized sound from a phonograph record

Thomas Alva Edison Foundation Museum

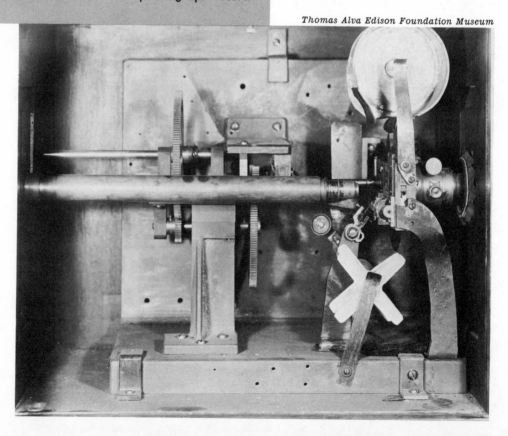

ing used the Edison effect in the "Fleming valve," as a detector for radio signals. In 1906 De Forest added a grid to control the flow of current from filament to plate and made the modern radio tube—that could serve as amplifier, signal generator and what have you.

In the meantime, Edison was off on a track that had an equal impact on our lives. He had been interested for some time in photography as a means of doing for sight what the phonograph had done for sound.

He followed carefully the early experiments of Eadweard Muybridge and others in photographing motion. These experiments were frustrated by the heavy glass photographic plates then in use. In 1889, however, Eastman brought out roll film.

Edison saw at once that it was the solution of the motion picture problem. Within five years, Edison and one of his chief aides, William Kennedy Laurie Dickson, had perfected the intermittent-motion principle (with the film stopping for a brief instant as it comes to the shutter), a practical motion-picture camera, and the first practical viewing device, the kinetoscope.

And more, Edison created the "star" system of the movies, by bringing famous Broadway personalities to his laboratory to act in the first movies. He also successfully synchronized movie and phonograph to make the first talking pictures, although commercial talkies had to wait until the development of modern amplifying equipment.

Edison also did quite a bit of experimenting with X rays the year after their discovery was announced. He developed the fluoroscope but did not patent it because of its medical importance

During all these years, Edison worked at a furious pace. Invention, he liked to remind visitors to his laboratory, was 2 percent inspiration and 98 percent perspiration. He often worked several days through; he averaged about four or five hours of sleep a night. In later years, he slackened his pace somewhat. But he still worked uncommonly hard and accomplished uncommonly much.

During the Twenties, for example, he became interested in finding a rubber-yielding plant that could be grown in the United States. More than 15,000 plants were tested at an experiment station he set up in Florida. He never found a plant that could compete with the tropical rubber tree.

But when the United States launched a domestic natural-rubber program after Pearl Harbor as a backstop against failure of the synthetic-rubber program, the plant chosen was the guayule of the Southwest—found years before by Edison to be the best of native American rubber-yielding plants.

A VIGOROUS MAN, Bell spent time in many other fields that had always interested him. He conducted experiments in sheep-breeding; he invented the photophone which saddled light rays to carry sound for short distances; he worked out an induction balance to locate bullets and other metallic objects lodged in the body; he proposed a vacuum jacket that was a forerunner of the modern iron lung; he founded the magazine Science, *which became the organ of the American Association for the Advancement of Science. After 1895, Bell was mainly busy with his experiments on flight. He made and flew a variety of man-lifting kites.*

Alexander Graham Bell

Words through a wire
by William P. Schenk

THE RESONANCE of a hollowed log booming in the jungle—the diaphragms of animal skin beaten with bones—sometimes he thought of these even on sweetheart walks in New England.

From the ancient acoustics of Vitruvius to the latest tone theory of Von Helmholtz, his notebooks bulged with facts, and with questions, about the caprice and the constancy of Sound.

He performed and re-performed all the classic demonstrations, then he mounted a dead man's ear and coaxed its delicate drum to vibrate a needle of hay against smoked glass to "picture" the highs and lows of his voice as he talked into it.

Like his grandfather and his father before him—but probing deeper than they—he understood the flesh-and-blood mechanism of man's gift of speech, and the nerve-and-bone architecture of his sense of hearing, and was devoting his life to the rescue of the dumb, the stutterers, and the deaf-born. And he learned lessons from them. They were part of the extraordinary background that made him the perfectly prepared man when Opportunity (so busy at the portals of inventors in those days) in the form of a tiny metallic sound, chirped at his attic door. At 109 Court Street, in Boston.

In that gas-lit garret, in his 28th year, working as usual with his acid jars, magnets, and wires, Alexander Graham Bell was trying to perfect a mechanism he called a "harmonic telegraph." And there, during the afternoon of June 2, 1875, he seized upon the faint twang of a bit of steel spring as the key to the secret of "sending" the human voice through a length of wire, and, figuratively, held in his hand the more than 75 million telephones in the world today.

In 1877, two years after the invention, there were 2,600 telephones in use in the United States

Bell, as described by his mechanical assistant, co-worker, and lifelong friend, Thomas A. Watson, was, at this time, "a tall, slender, quick-motioned man with pale face, black side whiskers, and drooping mustache, big nose and high sloping forehead crowned with bushy, jet black hair." He was, in his own words, "in actual want." And he was very much in love, and wanted to get married.

Like many others in the early 70s, Bell realized what fame and fortune would come to the man who could devise a way of sending more than one Morse message at the same time over a single telegraph wire—a technique urgently required by a commercially and

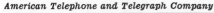

A scale model of the first successful telephone built by Alexander Graham Bell. It was with a duplicate of this instrument that Bell first transmitted speech sounds electrically in 1875

geographically mushrooming United States. If he could perfect his "harmonic telegraph" system, Bell thought he could send six or eight messages simultaneously.

To solve the problem, he had designed, and had Watson make, a succession of instruments which utilized tuning forks, and later, sensitive steel reeds set above the electromagnets of his telegraph transmitters and receivers, so that they vibrated in sympathetic harmony.

Bell, clumsy with his hands, hired Watson, an experienced electrician, on a part-time basis to construct the instruments that he designed. Later, when Bell offered the young electrician full-time work, it was turned down for Watson did not want to give up his $18-a-week job

"Theoretically," Watson wrote, "when a transmitter sent its electrical whine into the line wire, its own faithful receiver spring at the distant station would wriggle sympathetically but all the others on the same line would remain coldly quiescent." But, Watson said farther on, "Try our best, we could not make that thing work rightly, and Bell came as near to being discouraged as I ever knew him to be."

It was then that the little steel reed whispered its momentous hint.

"Things were badly out of tune that afternoon in that hot garret," Watson recalled, "not only the instruments, but, I fancy, my enthusiasm and my temper, though Bell was as energetic as ever. I had charge of the transmitters as usual, setting them squealing one after the other, while Bell was retuning the receiver springs one by one, pressing them against his ear. . . .

"One of the transmitter springs I was attending to stopped vibrating and I plucked it to start it again. It didn't start and I kept on plucking it, when suddenly I heard a shout from Bell in the next room, and then out he came with a rush, demanding, 'What did you do then? Don't change anything. Let me see.'

"I showed him. It was very simple. The contact screw was screwed down so far that it made permanent contact with the spring, so that when I snapped the spring the circuit had remained unbroken while that strip of magnetized steel by its vibration over the pole of its magnet was generating that marvelous conception of Bell's—a current of electricity that varied in intensity precisely as the air was varying in density within hearing distance of that spring.

"That undulatory current had passed through the connecting wire to the distant receiver which, fortunately, was a mechanism that could transform that current back into an extremely faint echo of the sound of the vibrating spring that had generated it, but what was still more fortunate, the right man had that mechanism at his ear during the fleeting moment, and instantly recognized the transcendent importance of that faint sound thus electrically transmitted. The shout I heard and his excited rush into my room were the result of that recognition. The speaking telephone was born at that moment."

The two men spent the rest of the afternoon verifying the discovery, repeating it with differently tuned reeds. Before they parted that night Bell told Watson how to make the first telephone instrument. "I was to mount a small drumhead of gold-beater's skin," Watson wrote, "over one of the receivers, join the center of the drumhead to the free end of the receiver spring and arrange a mouthpiece over the drumhead to talk into."

When the membrane was set in motion by the speaker's voice, it would make the spring vibrate over the pole of the magnet in the receiver. This would set up in the circuit an undulatory current that was a copy of the waves in the air caused by the voice. Watson had the device ready the next day, and it worked. It transmitted only voice *sounds*—not a sentence of speech, or even understandable words.

Alexander Bell at the New York end of the circuit to Chicago. This line, opened in 1892, 7 years after the invention of the telephone, was a feature of the Columbian Exposition ceremonies

Bell's patent for his telephone was filed just two hours before another experimenter along the same lines, Elisha Gray, filed his claim in the U. S. Patent Office

But if it was inarticulate, and if it stuttered, the first telephone was yet the child of a professional speech teacher concerned with helping people who stuttered. And by now Bell had that knowledge of electricity old Joseph Henry, dean of American scientists, had tersely told him to *get* when Bell had asked his advice at the Smithsonian the year before.

So, the articulate words were not long in coming—and they came in a complete, intelligible sentence—on the evening of March 10, 1876.

How many transmitters did Bell design; how many receivers did Watson fashion? Night after night, through the summer of 1875, they experimented, made refinements, used longer wires. Both men took rooms at the same boarding house—in the attic at 5 Exeter Street, Boston. And they worked on through the fall and winter, brought the telephone out of its voice-powered, magnetic-induction phase to the galvanic-battery stage.

On March 10 Watson had completed yet another instrument according to Bell's design, and had brought it with him, "intending," he said, "to spend the night with Bell testing it."

This was Bell's liquid transmitter. It consisted of a short wire attached directly to a voice-operated diaphragm dipped into a metal cup of sulphuric acid diluted with water. The cup with its conducting liquid and the wire formed part of the electrical circuit containing also a battery and a tuned reed receiving apparatus. As the diaphragm vibrated, the wire would move up and down in the liquid. This caused the resistance of the circuit to change and made the current vary to conform with every undulation of the sound waves directed upon the diaphragm.

On that evening of March 10, the men lost no time connecting the new transmitter to the battery and to the one-way wire strung out through the hallway that connected their rooms. Bell stood at one end of the line bent over the new transmitter on the littered table in his workroom. Watson went to the other end of the line and stood at the bureau in Bell's bedroom. He put the receiving instrument to his ear. An instant later he was amazed to hear Bell cry out—"Mr. Watson, come here, I want you!"

Watson ran to Bell's room—not out of concern for whatever trouble Bell was in—but to shout out his excitement at the words that had seemed literally, to *jump* out of the receiver. "Mr. Bell," he gasped, "I heard every word you said distinctly!" Then he saw the overturned

American Telephone and Telegraph Company

battery and the acid Bell had upset over the bench and on his clothes. But that was nothing. For the first intelligible sentence had traveled over wire for the first time.

And Bell was soon telling his lecture audiences, "It is conceivable that cables of telephone wires could be laid underground or suspended overhead, communicating with private dwellings, counting houses, shops, manufactories. . . . Not only so, but I believe in the future, wires will unite different cities, and a man in one part of the country may communicate by word of mouth with another in a distant place."

ALEXANDER GRAHAM BELL was born on March 3, 1847, in Edinburgh, Scotland. His grandfather and his father—whose characters and devotion to their own work influenced him so profoundly, and made them the spiritual godfathers of the telephone—were descended from a long line of Scottish shoemakers. His mother, Eliza Grace Symonds, the daughter of a Royal Navy surgeon, was a sensitive musician and portrait painter whose own hearing loss when Bell reached his twelfth year, brought deafness very close to him, gave him a sweet kindliness that made him a beloved teacher, and that never, even after he achieved his own eminence, allowed him to refuse his time to the young inventors who wanted his help.

His grandfather, the white-haired Alexander Bell, was a specialist with a large practice in the correction of speech defects—what people then called a "corrector of defective utterance." But he had glamor. He lived in London, had been on the stage, and gave public readings from Shakespeare's plays. Bell's father, Alexander Melville Bell, was the world-famous inventor of "Visible Speech," a code of symbols to guide the action of the throat, tongue and lips in the shaping of various sounds. It was devised as a key to the pronunciation of words in all languages, but had become even more valuable in teaching the deaf to speak.

Alexander Graham Bell was the author of many scientific pieces. In one of these he dealt with the formation of a deaf variety in the human race

Though at first his native musical ability turned young Alexander toward a career as a pianist, he sooned followed in the footsteps of his father and grandfather. As a boy he helped make a model skull fitted with a rubber vocal apparatus and a bellows that could squawk an imitation of "Ma-ma, Ma-ma." And he trained his Skye terrier to growl steadily while he manipulated its vocal cords and opened and shut its jaws trying to make it say "How do you do."

By the time he was 15, Bell was his father's assistant in his visible speech demonstrations, and at Weston House, a boys' school near Edinburgh, traded music and elocution lessons for instruction in other subjects. He continued his formal education at the University of Edinburgh, and later specialized in the anatomy of the vocal apparatus at University College, London. When he was 22, a fully qualified speech teacher, his father took him into partnership, and in 1870, fearful of the tuberculosis from which a younger brother had died, the Bell family crossed the ocean and settled in Ontario.

A year later, in April, 1871, young Bell was living in Boston, where Sarah Fuller, principal of a school for the deaf had asked him to teach his father's visible Speech system to her teachers. He was very successful there and at the Clarke School for the Deaf in Northampton and the American Asylum in Hartford. In October, 1872, he opened his own school of "Vocal Physiology and Mechanics of Speech" in Boston.

His announcement read in part, "For the correction of stammering and other defects of utterance and for practical instruction in visible speech, conducted by Alexander Graham Bell, member of the Philological Society of London."

At this school Bell instructed deaf children in order to demonstrate his teaching methods; in 1873 he transferred his classes to Boston University, where he had been appointed professor of vocal physiology.

It was in Boston that Bell met the two men who financed his pioneer work with the telephone: Gardiner Greene Hubbard, a Boston lawyer whose daughter had lost her hearing through scarlet fever when she was four (and whom Bell married in July, 1877), and Thomas Sanders, a wealthy leather merchant of Salem, whose son, born deaf, was one of Bell's private pupils.

"While Hubbard's faith was in the multiple telegraph," wrote Bell's biographer, Catherine Mackenzie, "Sanders' unbounded faith was in Bell." In any case, their protégé began to write the specifications for his first telephone patent in September of 1875, and filed his application on February 14, 1876. And though there followed what has been called "the most extensive patent litigation in history," Bell's claims were completely upheld by the U. S. Supreme Court.

After his invention of the telephone, Bell spent the last part of his life in Washington, D. C., and at his summer home, Beinn Bhreagh (Beautiful Mountain), in Nova Scotia. He proudly became a citizen of the United States in 1882.

He continued his work in behalf of the deaf, peering into the nature and causes of deafness, and made an embracing study of its heredity. He gave $300,000 to found the American Association to Promote the Teaching of Speech to the Deaf, and set up a research laboratory to work for the deaf.

Alexander Graham Bell died at his summer home on August 2, 1922—and the 14,347,000 telephones then in operation in the United States were silent for two minutes during the funeral service of the man who had called them into being—the man who had so splendidly followed his own advice to others: "Don't keep forever on the public road, going only where others have gone. Leave the beaten track occasionally and dive into the woods."

Bell and his backers undertook to promote the telephone business themselves. They started out by renting telephones to individuals in pairs for local transmission which, at its best, was extremely poor. A single iron wire with grounded return circuits served as a connection between the two phones

WILLIAM OSLER *was born at Bond Head, Ontario, on July 12, 1849. Following a year of divinity studies, he completed two years of study at the Toronto Medical School, and then transferred to McGill University in Montreal. There he won a prize with his thesis and received his M.D. in 1872. After two years' study in Europe, Osler returned to Ontario and was appointed professor of medicine at McGill. In 1884 he came to the United States, and until 1889 served as professor of clinical medicine at the University of Pennsylvania. For the next five years he occupied the chair of medicine at Johns Hopkins University. The following year he returned to England. He died in 1919.*

William Osler

Selections from his writings

OSLER REVISED hospital procedures, raised the standards of nursing, and fought physicians' too liberal use of medicine. He made his own contributions to the science of medicine—on blood platelets, heart infections, malaria, chorea, cerebral palsies in children, and diseases of the blood and spleen. But he was primarily a teacher—one of the greatest teachers of his time. Class after class of medical students entered their professional work trained in Osler's methods of studying disease in relation to the patient's background and environment as a whole—and inspired by the humanitarian principles he taught and lived by.

The following extracts from Osler's philosophy are taken from a number of his numerous addresses and writings.

There are two great types of leaders: one, the great reformer, the dreamer of dreams who, with aspirations completely in the van of his generation, lives often in wrath and disputations, passes through fiery ordeals, is misunderstood, and too often despised and rejected by his generation. The other, a very different type, is the leader who sees ahead of his generation, but who has the sense to walk and work in it. While not such a potent element in progress, he lives a happier life, and is more likely to see the fulfilment of his plans.

Measure as we may the progress of the world—materially, in the advantages of steam, electricity, and other mechanical appliances; sociologically, in the great improvement in the conditions of life; intellectually, in the diffusion of education; morally, in a possibly higher standard of ethics—there is no one measure which can compare with the decrease of physical suffering in man, woman, and child, when stricken by disease or accident. This is the one fact of supreme personal import to every one of us. This is the Promethean gift of the century to man.

Of the altruistic instincts veneration is not the most highly developed at the present day; but I hold strongly with the statement that it is the sign of a dry age when the great men of the past are held in light esteem.

As clinical observers we study the experiments which Nature makes upon our fellow creatures. These experiments, however, in striking contrast to those of the laboratory, lack exactness, possessing as they do a variability at once a despair and a delight—the despair of those who look for nothing but fixed laws in an art which is still deep in the sloughs of empiricism; the delight of those who find in it an expression of a universal law transcending, even scorning, the petty accuracy of test-tube and balance, the law that in man, "the measure of all things," mutability, variability, mobility, are the very marrow of his being.

As a schoolboy at Dundas, Ontario, the youngster who was destined to become known as "The Great Physician" locked a flock of geese in the classroom and was expelled. Later at Trinity College School at Weston, Ont., when he was sixteen, the lad who was to have scholarships, wards, and hospitals named after him, was one of eight boys fined a dollar each for "fumigating" a matron whom they had locked in a closet

Biology touches the problem of life at every point, and may claim, as no other science, completeness of view and a comprehensiveness which pertains to it alone. To all whose daily work lies in her manifestations the value of a deep insight into her relations cannot be overestimated. The study of biology trains the mind in accurate methods of reasoning, and gives to a man clearer points of view, and an attitude of mind more serviceable in the working-day world than that given by other sciences, or even by the humanities.

The student must be allowed full freedom in his work, undisturbed by the utilitarian spirit of the Philistine, who cries, *Cui bono?* and distrusts pure science. The present remarkable position in applied science and in industrial trades of all sorts has been made possible by men who did pioneer work in chemistry, in physics, in biology, and in physiology, without a thought in their researches of any practical application. The members of this higher group of productive students are rarely understood by the common spirits, who appreciate as little their unselfish devotion as their unworldly neglect of the practical side of the problems.

Breathes here a man with soul so dead that it does not glow at the thought of what the men of his blood have done and suffered to make his country what it is? There is room, plenty of room, for proper pride of land and birth. What I inveigh against is a cursed spirit of intolerance, conceived in distrust and bred in ignorance, that makes the mental attitude perennially antagonistic, even bitterly antagonistic, to everything foreign, that subordinates everywhere the race to the nation, forgetting the higher claims of human brotherhood.

The art of detachment, the virtue of method, and the quality of thoroughness may make you students, in the true sense of the word, successful practitioners, or even great investigators, but your characters may still lack that which can alone give permanence to powers—the grace of humility.

Things cannot always go your way. Learn to accept in silence the minor aggravations, cultivate the gift of taciturnity and consume your own smoke with an extra draught of hard work, so that those about you may not be annoyed with the dust and soot of your complaints. More than any other the practitioner of medicine may illustrate the second great lesson, that we are here not to get all we can out of life for ourselves, but to try to make the lives of others happier.

Nothing will sustain you more potently in your humdrum routine, as perhaps it may be thought, than the power to recognize the true poetry of life—the poetry of the commonplace, of the ordinary man, of the plain, toil-worn woman, with their loves and their joys, their sorrows and their griefs. The comedy, too, of life will be spread be-

In 1892 Osler wrote his famous textbook, Principles and Practice of Medicine

During World War I, Osler was a tireless advisor to British military hospitals, and a crusader for vaccination of the troops

fore you, and nobody laughs more often than the doctor at the pranks Puck plays upon the Titanias and the Bottoms among his patients. The humorous side is really almost as frequently turned towards him as the tragic. Lift up one hand to heaven and thank your stars if they have given you the proper sense to enable you to appreciate the inconceivably droll situations in which we catch our fellow creatures.

The speedy success which often comes from the cultivation of a specialty is a strong incentive to young men to adopt early a particular line of work. How frequently are we consulted by sucklings in our ranks as to the most likely branch in which to succeed, or a student, with the brazen assurance which only ignorance can give, announces that he intends to be a gynaecologist or an oculist. No more dangerous members of our profession exist than those born into it, so to speak, as specialists. Without any broad foundation in physiology or pathology, and ignorant of the great processes of disease, no amount of technical skill can hide from the keen eyes of colleagues defects which too often require the arts of the charlatan to screen from the public.

To study the phenomena of disease without books is to sail an uncharted sea, while to study books without patients is not to go to sea at all.

The patient's faith in a doctor is universal, but what of a doctor's faith? Osler wrote, "... we doctors have always been a simple, trusting folk! Did we not believe Galen implicitly for 1,500 years and Hippocrates for more than 2,000? In the matter of treatment the placid faith of the simple believer, not the fighting faith of the aggressive doubter, has ever been our besetting sin."

Emulating the persistence and care of Darwin, we must collect facts with open-minded watchfulness, unbiased by crotchets or notions; fact on fact, instance on instance, experiment on experiment; facts which fitly jointed together by some master who grasps the idea of their relationship, may establish a general principle.

Would you know the signs by which in man or institution you may recognize old fogeyism? There are three: first, a state of blissful happiness and contentment with things as they are; secondly, a supreme conviction that the condition of other people and other institutions is one of pitiable inferiority; and thirdly, a fear of change, which not alone perplexes but appals.

We recognize today the limitations of the art; we know better the diseases curable by medicine, and those which yield to exercise and fresh air; we have learned to realize the intricacy of the processes of disease, and have refused to deceive ourselves with half-knowledge, preferring to wait for the day instead of groping blindly in the dark or losing our way in the twilight. The list of diseases which we can positively cure is an ever increasing one; the number of diseases the course of which we can modify favorably is a growing one; the number of incurable diseases . . . is diminishing.

"I have had three personal ideals . . . to do the day's work well and not to bother about tomorrow . . . to act the Golden Rule . . . toward my professional brethren and towards the patients committed to my care . . . to cultivate such a measure of equanimity as would enable me to bear success with humility. . . ."
Sir William Osler

Walter Bagehot tells us that the pain of a new idea is one of the greatest pains to human nature. "It is, as people say, so upsetting; it makes you think that, after all, your favorite notions may be wrong, your firmest beliefs ill-founded; it is certain that till now there was no place allotted in your mind to the new and startling inhabitant; and now that it has conquered an entrance, you do not at once see which of your old ideas it will not turn out, with which of them it can be reconciled, and with which it is at essential enmity." It is on this account that the man who expresses a new idea is very apt to be abused and ill-treated. All this is common among common men, but there is something much worse which has been illustrated over and over again in history. How eminent soever a man may become in science, he is very apt to carry with him errors which were in vogue when he was young—errors that darken his understanding, and make him incapable of accepting even the most obvious truths.

Thousands of germs are needed for the transmission of an individual of any species. In the case of the salmon only one in a thousand is fertilized, and of these not one in a thousand reaches maturity. So it is with books—a thousand or more are needed to secure the transmission of a single one of our very limited stock of ideas. Were all the eggs of the salmon to reach maturity the sea could not contain this one species, while the world itself could not contain the books that would be written did even one in a thousand transmit a fertile idea.

ONE DAY in the 1880's, Paul Ehrlich injected a bit of the dye methylene blue into the ear vein of a fine white rabbit. He watched the dye as it spread slowly through the animal's blood stream, then picked out and colored its nerve endings blue, but touched no other of the rabbit's tissues. "The dye," he reasoned, "singles out just one tissue in the rabbit's body and has no effect on other tissues. Why not chemical agents that single out murderous microbes and have no effect on any tissues of the patient's body?" The wonder drugs do just that. Of course, half a century was to pass before the wonder drugs' arrival, but the age of chemotherapy was born that day in 1880.

Paul Ehrlich

Inventor of chemotherapy
by Leonard Engel

IT IS A FAVORITE myth that great scientists labor in obscurity for years, then astound their colleagues with a historic discovery. More often, great scientists show their outstanding genius early and make many discoveries in the course of their careers. Such was the case with Paul Ehrlich. We honor him today as the inventor of chemotherapy and the discoverer of the first laboratory-produced disease-fighting chemical agent. However, the Nobel Prize, which he received in 1908, was awarded him not for salvarsan (the anti-syphilis drug was not announced until 1910), but for his discoveries in immunity to disease.

Ehrlich devised our basic methods for measuring the potency of vaccines. He also showed that when a person becomes immune to an infectious disease, a specific substance is formed in his blood for neutralizing the cause of that disease. He showed that the neutralizing reaction, moreover, is a chemical reaction; neutralizing substances (or antibodies, as we now call them) halt invading germs by latching onto them chemically and inactivating them in a way not unlike the neutralization of acid by alkali. His clear picture of the "immune reaction" paved the way for blood tests for disease. Such tests as the Wassermann test for syphilis depend on the presence of neutralizing antibodies; if they are present, the patient has or has had the disease.

Paul Ehrlich was born of a well-to-do Jewish family in a small town in southeastern Germany in 1854. As a boy, he was interested in science, mathematics and ancient languages; to the end of his days he loved to coin bellicose slogans in Latin whenever he got into an argument, which was often.

Ehrlich's boyhood hero was an older cousin, Karl Weigert. Weigert was one of the scientists who found that dyes could be used to make the details of tissues and microbes stand out under the microscope. Through Weigert, Ehrlich acquired a lifelong interest in dyes and stains. He experimented with them in a home laboratory while a high school student. In medical school, instead of the assigned laboratory exercises, he performed tests on more dyes. (As was then the custom in Germany, Ehrlich spent a year or two at each of three medical schools, finally receiving his degree from the last.) He was an indifferent student in the many subjects that bored him. But before he had his medical diploma, he had made the capital discovery that there are many types of white cells in the blood, which can be told apart by the dyes that stain them.

An important advancement toward chemotherapy was the research conducted by Ehrlich on the staining of living tissues. Previously medical men had been able to stain only dead tissues, thus restricting their observations to nonliving cells

Young Dr. Ehrlich went to Berlin as an assistant in Charité Hospital. Here his beloved dyes led him to two other important discoveries: a simple urine test for typhoid fever and a method of staining the tuberculosis bacillus, still in use, with little variation, today.

The rabbit experiment and the idea for chemotherapy came soon afterward, while working in the institute of Robert Koch, the immortal discoverer of the tubercle bacillus. Before he could begin a real hunt for chemical agents to cure disease, however, he came down with tuberculosis and had to take a two-year rest cure in Egypt. And for 10 years after his return, he was too busy with his work on vaccines and immunity to undertake more than an occasional (and unsuccessful) experiment in chemotherapy.

But he was discovering many things that would serve him well when the great search for a "magic bullet" finally began. He worked out the concept of the Minimum Lethal Dose, the amount of a drug or toxin that would kill a stated percentage of a given number of laboratory animals in 24 hours, the method by which we still measure the toxicity of drugs. He invented the "therapeutic index," the ratio between the poisonous and curative doses; the index tells researchers whether a drug is safe enough for practical medical use. And he was storing up, in that prodigious memory of his, an unmatched accumulation of information on dyes and other chemicals. Ehrlich read nearly everything that came his way, and remembered practically every comma of what he read.

The search for a "magic bullet" got under way in 1901. Two years before, Ehrlich had moved from Berlin to Frankfurt-am-Main. In Frankfurt, he would be near Germany's great dye plants and their battalions of master chemists who were busily concocting ever more dyes. Besides, the Berlin universities were filled with men who scoffed at the idea of chemotherapy. The prevailing idea then—remember, this was still in the early morning of scientific medicine—was that any possible germ-killing chemical would harm the patient more than the disease microbe. Ehrlich wasn't afraid to argue with the supporters of this view; he was long a familiar figure in cafes and scientific meetings, getting up and waving his inevitable cigar excitedly as he sought to drive home a point. But in Frankfurt he would get more done.

In a French scientific journal, Ehrlich read of the discovery that mal de caderas, a paralytic disease of horses, is caused by a large protozoan parasite named *Trypanosoma equinum,* and that 100 percent of mice inoculated with *T. equinum* die within four days. Here, said Ehrlich to himself, is a perfect subject for experiments on disease-fighting chemical agents. The trypanosome is large and easy to observe. We know many dyes with which it can be killed and stained, so we have an idea of what chemicals to start with. And the trypanosome kills *all* mice into which it is injected. If even one mouse is saved, we will know that we have something worth following up.

Ehrlich and a little Japanese doctor, Kiyoshi Shiga (discoverer of the germ responsible for bacillary dysentery), who joined Ehrlich in Frankfurt, set to work. They tried over 500 dyes. Not one saved a single mouse from the lethal trypanosome. Then Ehrlich and Shiga tested a new class of dyes called the benzopurpurin dyes. Ehrlich decided that the benzopurpurin colors were not spreading through the animals swiftly enough. So he figured out a way to alter them chemically to make them a little more soluble and got one of the dye-plant chemists to prepare samples.

The term "magic bullet" came from this statement made by Paul Ehrlich: "We must learn to make magic bullets which, like those of the ancient fable, cannot miss their mark, and will destroy only the pathogenic agents against which they are aimed."

One day, Dr. Shiga injected one of the modified dyes, trypan red, into half a group of inoculated mice. A week later, some of those that had received the new dye were alive and recovering, whereas all that had not were dead. Paul Ehrlich had found a chemical that had saved the life of a mouse.

He was still an long way, though, from a chemical to save the life of a man. When tested in guinea pigs and rats, and in other trypanosome diseases such as dread African sleeping sickness, trypan red had no effect at all. But, in failing, Ehrlich had made yet another discovery which was to contribute to his eventual success and which is basic to the search for new drugs today. This was the principle of variation: if a chemical gives any indication of curative power at all, try all possible variations of it. Change one atom in its molecule and test it, change another and test again; one of the variants might be more potent or safer than the parent compound.

Not long afterward, sitting in the one chair in his laboratory not piled high with books and journals, Ehrlich read of atoxyl, an arsenical drug intended for sleeping sickness. When tested on patients, it had made many blind or deaf; despite its name which meant "not poisonous," it was extremely poisonous. But atoxyl had kept many mice infected with sleeping sickness alive for months, whereas mice usually succumb in days. Ehrlich would modify atoxyl to make it both safer and more potent, though the chemists who had invented it

Bettmann Archive

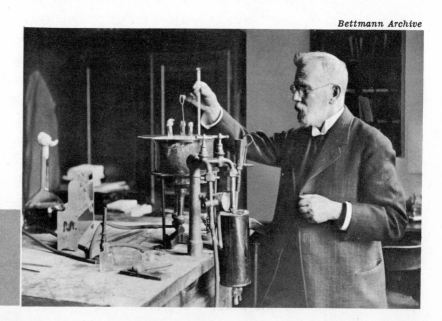

The science of chemotherapy was founded in this laboratory by Dr. Ehrlich's work on salvarsan

insisted that it could not be altered in any way without destroying its properties.

Working alone in his laboratory with hardly more equipment than a Bunsen burner and a few flasks and test tubes, Ehrlich proved that atoxyl could be modified by modifying it. Then he set the chemists in Georg-Speyer House, the research institute built for him by the widow of a rich Frankfurt banker, to work.

The chemists turned out variations on atoxyl by the score. Some were more dangerous than the original drug, some cured mice of mal de caderas but then gave the animals anemia or jaundice or made them dance for the rest of their lives. None could be considered really useful until No. 606 came along. The latter, dioxy-diamino-arseno-benzol-dihydrochloride, the 606th atoxyl derivative synthesized by the chief Speyer House chemist, A. Bertheim, and his associates, cured mal de caderas. And it was safe; it harmed not a cell in the mouse's body.

Mal de caderas is not a disease of man. So what to do with 606? Certain arsenical drugs had been known for several years to have some effect on syphilis. So Ehrlich decided to test 606 on the disease of the evil name.

The first tests, performed on rabbits, which are as susceptible to syphilis as man, were unsuccessful. The shrewd, persistent Ehrlich, however, was not satisfied that the associate who had performed the tests had carried them out carefully. So the next time the tests were repeated by a careful Japanese physician, Sakachiro Hata, who had just joined Ehrlich. The tests were an unquestioned success. Salvarsan (as Ehrlich named the drug) cured rabbits of syphilis as it cured mice of mal de caderas. Tests in Frankfurt hospitals soon showed that it was a potent remedy for syphilis in man as well.

After ushering in the age of chemotherapy, Ehrlich's desire was to conquer, by means of chemical compounds, all bacterial diseases in the world

Salvarsan was given to the world in 1910. It was soon in use in practically every country of the globe, though neither salvarsan nor an improved version, neosalvarsan, also derived by Ehrlich, proved 100 percent safe in hands less skilled than Ehrlich's. But salvarsan was the first real remedy for one of the worst scourges of man. And it pointed the way toward the age of chemotherapy. Ehrlich, who died in 1915, himself thought that many other chemotherapeutic agents would be found within a few years. Sulfanilamide, the next "wonder drug," though, did not come along until 1935. It took a whole generation for others to follow where this giant had trod.

J. J. Thomson

Discovery of the electron

THE RESEARCH which led to the discovery of the electron began with an attempt to explain the discrepancy between the behavior of cathode rays under magnetic and electric forces. Magnetic forces deflect the rays in just the same ways as they would a negatively electrified particle moving in the direction of the rays. . . .

My first attempt to deflect a beam of cathode rays was to pass it between two parallel metal plates fastened inside the discharge tube, and to produce an electric field between the plates. This failed to produce any lasting deflection. I could, however, detect a slight flicker in the beam when the electric force was first applied. This gave the clue to what I think is the explanation of the absence of the electric deflection of the rays.

If there is any gas between the plates it will be ionized by the cathode rays when they pass through it, and thus produce a supply of both positively and negatively electrified particles.

The positively charged plate will attract to itself negatively electrified particles which will neutralize, in the space between the plates, the effect of its own positive electrification.

Similarly, the effect of the negatively electrified plate will be neutralized by the positively electrified particles it attracts. Thus charging up the plates will not produce an electric force between them; the momentary flicker was due to the neutralization of the plates not being instantaneous.

The absence of deflection on this view is due to the presence of gas—to the pressure being too high—thus the thing to do was to get a much higher vacuum. This was more easily said than done. The technique of producing high vacua in those days was in an elementary stage. The necessity of getting rid of gas condensed on the walls of the discharge tube, and on the metal of the electrodes by prolonged baking was not realized. As this gas was liberated when the discharge passed through the tube, the vacuum deteriorated rapidly during the discharge, and the pumps then available were not fast enough to keep pace with this liberation.

However, after running the discharge through the tube day after day without introducing fresh gas, the gas on the walls and electrodes got driven off and it was possible to get a much better vacuum. The deflection of the cathode rays by electric forces became quite marked, and its direction indicated that the particles forming the cathode rays were negatively electrified.

Thomson's other work included advanced studies on the conduction of electricity through gases, and research in radioactivity

This result removed the discrepancy between the effects of magnetic and electric forces on the cathode particles; it did much more than this: it provided a method of measuring v, the velocity of these particles, and also m/e, when m is the mass of a particle and e its electric charge. . . .

These experiments were of an exploratory nature; the apparatus was of a simple character and not designed to get the most accurate numerical results. It was sufficient, however, to prove that e/m for the cathode-ray particles was of the order 10^7, whereas the smallest value hitherto found was 10^4 for the atom of hydrogen in electrolysis. So that if e were the same as the charge of electricity carried by an atom of hydrogen—as was subsequently proved to be the case—m, the mass of the cathode-ray particle, could not be greater than one thousandth part of the mass of an atom of hydrogen, the smallest mass hitherto recognized. It was also proved that the mass of these particles did not depend upon the kind of gas in the discharge tube.

These results were so surprising that it seemed more important to make a general survey of the subject than to endeavor to improve the determination of the exact value of the ratio of the mass of the particle to the mass of the hydrogen atom. . . .

I next tested electrified particles which had been produced by methods in which no electric force had been applied to their source. It is known that metals when exposed to ultraviolet light give off negative electricity, and that metallic and carbon filaments do so when incandescent.

I measured, by methods based on similar principles to those used for cathode rays, the values of e/m for the carriers of negative electricity in these cases, and found that it was the same as for cathode rays.

After long consideration of the experiments it seemed to me that there was no escape from the following conclusions:

(1) That atoms are not indivisible, for negatively electrified particles can be torn from them by the action of electrical forces, impact of rapidly moving atoms, ultraviolet light or heat.

(2) That these particles are all of the same mass, and carry the same charge of negative electricity from whatever kind of atom they may be derived, and are a constituent of all atoms.

(3) That the mass of these particles is less than one thousandth part of the mass of an atom of hydrogen.

I at first called these particles corpuscles, but they are now called by the more appropriate name "electrons." I made the first announcement of the existence of these corpuscles in a Friday Evening Discourse at the Royal Institution on April 20, 1897, of which an abstract was published in the *Electrican*, May 21, 1897. . . .

At first there were very few who believed in the existence of these bodies smaller than atoms. I was even told long afterward by a distinguished physicist who had been present at my lecture at the Royal Institution that he thought I had been "pulling their legs." I was not surprised at this, as I had myself come to this explanation of my experiments with great reluctance, and it was only after I was convinced that the experiment left no escape from it that I published my belief in the existence of bodies smaller than atoms.

Roentgen, like many eminent authorities, rejected the electron theory—that all matter is electrical in origin—as being purely hypothetical. But it was finally proven that all atoms are built of electrons, and all chemical changes take place because of the existence of these minute bodies

FREUD spent nearly the whole of his adult life in Vienna, studying, writing and practicing as a psychiatrist. The public outrage at his daring to lift the curtain on a side of man that had been passed over for centuries was so great that he received only one appointment in any medical school. In fact, Freud received practically no honors of any kind until 1930 when, at the age of 74, he was awarded the Goethe prize for literature. He was not elected to honorary membership in the American Psychiatric Association until 1936, when he was 80. And he was voted into Britain's august Royal Society only some weeks before he died of cancer, September 23, 1939.

Sigmund Freud

Father of pyschoanalysis
by Leonard Engel

ONE DAY several decades ago, a prominent Viennese physician named Josef Breuer told a young colleague about a remarkable case of his. Under hypnosis, a young woman suffering from hysterical paralysis related a number of unhappy emotional experiences of many years before—experiences which were obviously connected with her symptoms but of which she had no recollection in her waking state. And once she had talked these experiences out, her paralysis completely disappeared.

The two physicians together studied several other hysterical-paralysis patients. In them, too, buried experiences were found to be at the root of their difficulties.

Doctor Breuer soon went back to his regular medical practice; his name is only a footnote in histories of medicine. The other, Sigmund Freud, went on to explore the strange, hidden part of the mind with its burden of "forgotten" memories. It led him to a revolutionary theory of the human mind and a new method of treating mental disorder, which Freud called psychoanalysis. It also made him one of the towering figures of the 20th century and one of the most hotly disputed.

To this day, Freud's discoveries and theories are matters of controversy. Many elements of his theories of human personality are rejected by a good many psychiatrists; and the psychoanalyst's couch has proved no sure panacea for mental ills.

Freud, although often surrounded by contemporaries in the field of psychoanalysis, stands alone—a tribute to his outstanding, inspiring and highly original work

Nevertheless, few men have had a wider influence on our age. Because of Freud and psychoanalysis, we think differently about ourselves, about sex, about slips of the tongue and the forgetting of names. Literature, art, humor and women's magazines have all borrowed ideas and language from Freud. Modern child psychology and education likewise owe much to him.

Finally, modern psychiatry began with Freud. To him are due two great achievements. *First,* he made the world aware that the mind has an Unconscious as well as a Conscious part, and that one is as important as the other in daily life. *Second,* before Freud, psychiatry was concerned only with the "insane"—roughly, those suffering from schizophrenia and other severe mental disorders often requiring hospitalization. Freud turned the attention of psychiatry toward an even larger class of people who need help—the neurotics, the "maladjusted" who are sane but are so unhappy with the world or themselves that they are a burden to themselves and the people around them.

Sigmund Freud was born on May 6, 1856, in Freiberg, a town in what is now Czechoslovakia. His father, a wool merchant, married twice; Sigmund was the oldest son of the second wife. The family moved to Vienna, where he grew up, when Sigmund was four.

The future founder of psychoanalysis was a studious boy. As he grew into manhood, he had an odd confidence that he was going to do something great, though he had no idea in what area of human activity.

Freud took the first step toward the field in which he was to realize his expectations while at the university in Vienna. Ernst von Brucke, a famous 19th-century biologist, took him on as research assistant and set him to work on the anatomy of nerves. The next step came in medical school, where Freud found neurology and psychiatry the only branches of medicine that really interested him. A year with France's Jean Martin Charcot, greatest of the 19th-century psychiatrists, finally set him on his course.

In Charcot's clinic, Freud had watched the master treat certain mental disorders by suggestion while the patients were under hypnosis. Freud was fascinated, though Charcot's procedure produced temporary relief at best and Freud regarded hypnosis as taking unfair advantage of the patient.

He retained his interest in hypnosis when he returned to Vienna and hung out his shingle as a neurologist. Thus his mind was prepared when, not long afterward, Breuer told him about the young lady who revealed her Unconscious under hypnosis. And when Breuer's and Freud's joint studies showed the existence of a submerged part of mind in other patients, Freud was off on the great work of his life.

Between 1893, when Breuer and Freud published a historic report on the "forgotten" experiences of their patients, and his death 46 years later, Freud wrote scores of books and papers setting forth the results of his researches and his views.

Since he was exploring a world—inner psychological life of man —darker than any unknown shore ventured by the boldest of sailors, there were stumbles and twistings and turnings. He changed his theories often, as he came upon new facts; he even changed the meaning of the words he used. Consequently, there has been controversy not only over his ideas, but over what he actually said. His basic ideas, however, can be boiled down as follows:

Freud found, first of all, that the human mind can appropriately be compared to an iceberg. As with an iceberg, most of the mind is out of sight, hidden away in the Unconscious. In other words, mental activity is not confined to conscious levels of the mind. Much goes on below the surface, though we are not ordinarily aware of it.

The Conscious mind is the seat of what Freud called the Ego; and the Unconscious is the site of Id and Superego.

The Id is the seat of the primitive desires and instinctual drives which all of us have (however deeply buried they may be and whatever we may call them) and which hark back to our animal past.

The Ego adjusts desires arising in the Id to reality; that is, the Ego is that part of mind that learns the rules of society and decides whether the Id's desires can be fulfilled.

The Superego is the still small voice of conscience which tells the Ego whether its decisions are morally right; essentially, the Superego represents rules of ideal behavior taught so strongly and so early in life that they have penetrated far below the conscious mind.

Freud, unable to understand why people were interested in his personal life, angrily remarked in his biography, "Psychoanalysis came to be the whole content of my life and (I) rightly assume that no personal experiences of mine are of any interest in comparison to my relations with that science."

247

Freud held that one of the main sources of mental disorder—especially of neurosis rather than "insanity"—is conflict among Id, Ego and Superego. For instance, if the Ego, in response to a desire arising in the Id, makes a decision counter to the conscience or Superego, the Superego exacts punishment in the form of feelings of guilt or worry or the like.

Nearly all psychiatrists today go along with these views of the Viennese pathfinder. They accept also his famous theory—a commonplace now but a startling novelty in 1900—that dreams represent a symbolic acting-out in fantasy of Unconscious desires. Freud's finding that people repress or bury in the Unconscious memories and feelings too painful to be kept in the Conscious part of mind is likewise widely accepted. Also his historic demonstration that experiences even very early in childhood influence us throughout life and that, psychologically, the child makes the man.

His The Interpretation of Dreams, *which was originally published in 1900 in German, is probably the most famous and widely read of Freud's works*

The disputes that have raged around Freud and his ideas have centered mainly about two points. One has been Freud's belief that all of us in the modern world are doomed to frustration and neurosis. According to Freud—who was a strong traditional moralist, for all the charges of immorality hurled at his head—society can never permit people to fulfill their unconscious primitive desires.

Since we all have such desires, eternal frustration must be our lot; at best, we can learn to live in a kind of truce with our "Iddish" desires. Many psychiatrists today do not take such a dim view of man's future; they say that man's unconscious desires are not necessarily antisocial and, in any case, can be changed.

The second, and hotter, controversy has raged about Freud's identification of libido or sexual instinct as the main drive of the Id and the principal force in unconscious mental life. As time went on, Freud broadened what he meant by the term libido; he finally meant it to take in any kind of pleasure-seeking from love of good food to enjoyment of music.

But at first, when Freud said sexual desire, he meant just that, and he always included sex among things meant by libido. He believed that many, if not most, neuroses were the result of unfulfilled or unfulfillable sexual desires.

Most psychiatrists now believe sexual drive and other forms of pleasure-seeking are important forces in life, but so are drives for power, the urge to create, and other psychological forces.

When Breuer and Freud first began digging into the Unconscious back in the early 1890's, they got patients to recall "forgotten" experiences by putting them into a hypnotic state and telling them to talk. Freud found some patients, however, who could not be hypnotized. To get them to talk, he hit upon one of the most famous devices in the history of medicine—the psychoanalyst's couch.

The psychoanalyst's couch is simply a couch in a partly darkened room; the psychoanalyst himself is out of sight behind the head of the couch. The couch and the dim light help the patient to relax. The patient is then asked to talk of anything and everything that comes to mind. In due course and with occasional help from the analyst, the patient on the couch dredges up more and more from his Unconscious.

The sessions on the couch are supposed not only to help the psychoanalyst see the source of the patient's difficulties, but to serve as a means of treatment. As the patient talks himself out, he, too, comes to realize what his difficulties stem from. He takes a more realistic view of himself and, so to speak, makes peace with the forces within him.

When Freud first thought of the couch and the "talking-out" technique, he was confident that they would help nearly all patients. But he himself found that psychoanalysis was no panacea. It has not, so far, been of much help in treating psychotics; it does not help all patients suffering from neuroses. It is extremely expensive as sessions can go on, at the rate of several a week, for two years or even more.

Today, only selected patients get the full couch treatment; psychiatrists use much shorter forms of treatment for most patients. However, the psychoanalyst's couch has proved a remarkable "microscope" for peering into the recesses of the human mind. Without it, and without Freud, we would have little idea of how marvelously complicated the human mind is.

In 1933, the Nazis burned Freud's books because he was a Jew; in 1938 they compelled him to flee from Vienna to London. But his influence on our thinking and our time was so vast that even Hitler resorted to the language of psychoanalysis to excuse his invasion of Poland—the act that started World War II—in 1939. ("These inferior people [the Poles]," Hitler said, "because of their inferiority complexes display all manner of barbaric treatment of others.") Thus, even his bitterest and most foolish enemies, in misusing his ideas, recognized that Sigmund Freud had opened up a great and vital area of knowledge

ROBERT EDWIN PEARY was born at Cresson, Pennsylvania, on May 6, 1856. A few years after he was graduated from Bowdoin College, Peary entered the U.S. Navy as a civil engineer with the rank of lieutenant. Peary's first journey into the North in 1886 was to Greenland. He continued his arctic explorations—and their meteorological and ethnological observations—during his expeditions of 1893-95, 1896, 1897 and 1898-1902. On his expedition of 1905-06, Peary came within 200 miles of the Pole. His next expedition was the successful one. In 1911 Congress, recognizing Peary's feat, retired him with the rank of rear admiral. He died on February 20, 1920.

Robert E. Peary

"We reach the pole"

WE WERE NOW [at ten o'clock on the forenoon of April 6, 1909] at the end of the last long march of the upward journey. Yet with the Pole actually in sight I was too weary to take the last few steps. The accumulated weariness of all those days and nights of forced marches and insufficient sleep, constant peril and anxiety, seemed to roll across me all at once. I was actually too exhausted to realize at the moment that my life's purpose had been achieved. As soon as our igloos had been completed and we had eaten our dinner and double-rationed the dogs, I turned in for a few hours of absolutely necessary sleep, Henson and the Eskimos having unloaded the sledges and got them in readiness for such repairs as were necessary.

But, weary though I was, I could not sleep long. It was, therefore, only a few hours later when I woke. The first thing I did after waking was to write these words in my diary: "The Pole at last. The prize of three centuries. My dream and goal for 20 years. Mine at last! I cannot bring myself to realize it. It seems all so simple and common-place."

Everything was in readiness for an observation at 6 P.M., Columbia meridian time, in case the sky should be clear, but at that hour it was, unfortunately, still overcast. But as there were indications that it would clear before long, two of the Eskimos and myself made ready a light sledge carrying only the instruments, a tin of pemmican, and one or two skins; and drawn by a double team of dogs, we pushed on an estimated distance of ten miles. While we traveled, the sky cleared, and at the end of the journey, I was able to get a satisfactory series of observations at Columbia meridian midnight. These observations indicated that our position was then beyond the Pole.

Nearly everything in the circumstances which then surrounded us seemed too strange to be thoroughly realized; but one of the strangest of those circumstances seemed to me to be the fact that, in a march of only a few hours, I had passed from the western to the eastern hemisphere and had verified my position at the summit of the world.

It was hard to realize that, in the first miles of this brief march, we had been traveling due north, while, on the last few miles of the same march, we had been traveling south, although we had all the time been traveling precisely in the same direction. It would be difficult to imagine a better illustration of the fact that most things are relative. Again, please consider the uncommon circumstance, that in order to return to our camp, it now became necessary to turn and go north again for a few miles and then to go directly south, all the time traveling in the same direction.

As we passed back along that trail which none had ever seen before or would ever see again, certain reflections intruded themselves which, I think, may fairly be called unique. East, west, and north had disappeared for us. Only one direction remained and that was south. Every breeze which could possibly blow upon us, no matter from what point of the horizon, must be a south wind. Where we were, one day and one night constituted a year, a hundred such days and nights constituted a century. Had we stood in that spot during the six months of the arctic winter night, we should have seen every star of the northern hemisphere circling the sky at the same distance from the horizon, with Polaris (the North Star) practically in the zenith.

All during our march back to camp the sun was swinging around in its ever-moving circle. At six o'clock on the morning of April 7, having again arrived at Camp Jesup, I took another series of observa-

Peary learned from previous experience that to succeed at all he would have to split his party into two sections. The first group was the lightly equipped advanced party whose job it was to select the route and break trail while the main party, consisting of sledges with all the necessary provisions, marched one day behind. As food was used up sections of the main party were to turn back, leaving the diminished main group fully equipped for the final assault on the Pole

tions. These indicated our position as being four or five miles from the Pole, towards Bering Strait. Therefore, with a double team of dogs and a light sledge, I traveled directly towards the sun an estimated distance of eight miles. Again I returned to the camp in time for a final and completely satisfactory series of observations on April 7 at noon, Columbia meridian time. These observations gave results essentially the same as those made at the same spot 24 hours before.

I had now taken in all 13 single, or six and one-half double, altitudes of the sun, at two different stations, in three different directions, at four different times. All were under satisfactory conditions, except for the first single altitude on the sixth. The temperature during these observations had been from minus 11° Fahrenheit to minus 30° Fahrenheit, with clear sky and calm weather (except as already noted for the single observation on the sixth). . . .

In traversing the ice in these various directions as I had done, I had allowed approximately ten miles for possible errors in my observations, and at some moment during these marches and countermarches, I had passed over or very near the point where north and south and east and west blend into one.

Peary's attainment of the North Pole came as the climax of more than four centuries of effort to conquer the polar cap made by the boldest explorers of many nations—some of them losing their lives in the attempt

Of course there were some more or less informal ceremonies connected with our arrival at our difficult destination, but they were not of a very elaborate character. We planted five flags at the top of the world. The first one was a silk American flag which Mrs. Peary gave me 15 years ago. That flag has done more traveling in high latitudes than any other ever made. I carried it wrapped about my body on every one of my expeditions northward after it came into my possession, and I left a fragment of it at each of my successive "farthest norths": Cape Morris K. Jesup, the northernmost point of land in the known world; Cape Thomas Hubbard, the northernmost known point of Jesup Land, west of Grant Land; Cape Columbia, the northernmost point of North American lands; and my farthest north in 1906, latitude 87°6′ in the ice of the polar sea. By the time it actually reached the Pole, therefore, it was somewhat worn and discolored.

A broad diagonal section of this ensign would now mark the farthest goal of earth—the place where I and my dusky companions stood.

It was also considered appropriate to raise the colors of the Delta Kappa Epsilon fraternity, in which I was initiated a member while an undergraduate student at Bowdoin College, the "World's

Peary's flag planted at the top of the world. This remarkable yet seldom seen photograph was taken by Robert Peary on the day of his famous discovery of the North Pole—April 6, 1909

Ensign of Liberty and Peace," with its red, white, and blue in a field of white, the Navy League flag, and the Red Cross flag.

After I had planted the American flag in the ice, I told Henson to time the Eskimos for three rousing cheers, which they gave with the greatest enthusiasm. Thereupon, I shook hands with each member of the party—surely a sufficiently unceremonious affair to meet with the approval of the most democratic. The Eskimos were childishly delighted with our success. While, of course, they did not realize its importance fully, or its world-wide significance, they did understand that it meant the final achievement of a task upon which they had seen me engaged for many years.

Then, in a space between the ice blocks of a pressure ridge, I deposited a glass bottle containing a diagonal strip of my flag and records of which the following is a copy:

Peary's original party consisted of 24 men, including 17 Eskimos, 133 dogs and 19 sledges. Out of this party only one man, a member of the last returning section, died. He was drowned while crossing a large lead

90 N. Lat., North Pole,
April 6, 1909.

Arrived here today, 27 marches from C. Columbia.

I have with me 5 men, Matthew Henson, colored, Ootah, Egingwah, Seegloo, and Ookeah, Eskimos; 5 sledges and 38 dogs. My ship, the S.S. *Roosevelt,* is in winter quarters at C. Sheridan, 90 miles east of Columbia.

The expedition under my command which has succeeded in reaching the Pole is under the auspices of the Peary Arctic Club of New York City, and has been fitted out and sent north by the members and friends of the club for the purpose of securing this geographical prize, if possible, for the honor and prestige of the United States of America.

The officers of the club are Thomas H. Hubbard, of New York, President; Zenas Crane, of Mass., Vice-president; Herbert L. Bridgman, of New York, Secretary and Treasurer.

I start back for Cape Columbia tomorrow.

Robert E. Peary,
United States Navy.

90 N. Lat., North Pole,
April 6, 1909

I have today hoisted the national ensign of the United States of America at this place, which my observations indicate to be the North Polar axis of the earth, and have formally taken possession of the entire region, and adjacent, for and in the name of the President of the United States of America.

I leave this record and United States flag in possession.

Robert E. Peary,
United States Navy

If it were possible for a man to arrive at 90° north latitude without being utterly exhausted, body and brain, he would doubtless enjoy a series of unique sensations and reflections. But the attainment of the Pole was the culmination of days and weeks of forced marches, physical discomfort, insufficient sleep, and racking anxiety. It is a wise provision of nature that the human consciousness can grasp only such degree of intense feeling as the brain can endure, and the grim guardians of earth's remotest spot will accept no man as guest until he has been tested by the severest ordeal.

Perhaps it ought not to have been so, but when I knew for a certainty that we had reached the goal, there was not a thing in the world I wanted but sleep. But after I had a few hours of it, there succeeded a condition of mental exaltation which made further rest impossible. For more than a score of years that point on the earth's surface had been the object of my every effort. To its attainment my whole being, physical, mental, and moral, had been dedicated. Many times my own life and the lives of those with me had been risked. My own material and forces and those of my friends had been devoted to this object. This journey was my eighth into the arctic wilderness. In that wilderness I had spent nearly 12 years out of the 23 between my thirtieth and my fifty-third year, and the intervening time spent in civilized communities during that period had been mainly occupied with preparations for returning to the wilderness. The determination to reach the Pole had become so much a part of my being that, strange as it may seem, I long ago ceased to think of myself save as an instru-

One of the original sledges used by Robert Peary on his final dash to the Pole. Peary's thorough acquaintance with both the dogs and Eskimos was the primary factor in his success

Berkshire Museum

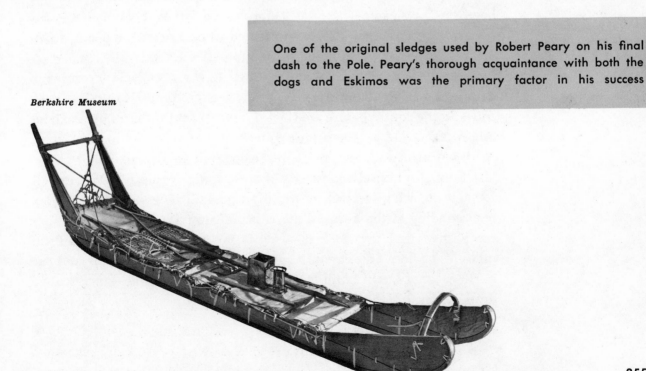

ment for the attainment of that end. To the layman this may seem strange, but an inventor can understand it, or an artist, or anyone who has devoted himself for years upon years to the service of an idea. . . .

But now, while quartering the ice in various directions from our camp I tried to realize that, after 23 years of struggles and discouragement, I had at last succeeded in placing the flag of my country at the goal of the world's desire. It is not easy to write about such a thing, but I knew that we were going back to civilization with the last of the great adventure stories—a story the world had been waiting to hear for nearly 400 years, a story which was to be told at last under the folds of the Stars and Stripes, the flag that during a lonely and isolated life had come to be for me the symbol of home and everything I loved —and might never see again. . . .

In the afternoon of the 7th, after flying our flags and taking our photographs, we went into our igloos and tried to sleep a little, before starting south again.

I could not sleep and my two Eskimos, Seegloo and Egingwah, who occupied the igloo with me, seemed equally restless. They turned from side to side, and when they were quiet I could tell from their uneven breathing that they were not asleep. Though they had not been specially excited the day before when I told them that we had reached the goal, yet they also seemed to be under the same exhilarating influence which made sleep impossible for me.

Finally I rose, and telling my men in the other igloo, who were equally wakeful, that we would try to make our last camp, some 30 miles to the south, before we slept, I gave orders to hitch up the dogs and be off. . . . And about four o'clock on the afternoon of the 7th of April we turned our backs upon the camp at the North Pole.

Though intensely conscious of what I was leaving, I did not wait for any lingering farewell of my life's goal. The event of human beings standing at the hitherto inaccessible summit of the earth was accomplished, and my work now lay to the south, where 413 nautical miles of ice-floes and possibly open leads still lay between us and the north coast of Grant Land. One backward glance I gave—then turned my face toward the south and toward the future.

Peary found the return journey to Cape Columbia fairly easy. The trail, kept open by the various returning sections, was clear and a gale kept the leads closed

RUDOLF DIESEL was born in Paris on March 18, 1858. From his earliest childhood he loved to sketch natural objects and mechanical designs. After a brief schooling in England, Rudolf was sent to the Augsburg Trade School in Germany. There he decided upon an engineering career. He received a two year's scholarship and specialized in mathematics, physics and mechanical drawing. After graduation, he received a scholarship to the Munich Institute of Technology. In 1893 Diesel published his pamphlet, The Theory and Construction of a Rational Heat Motor. During his last years he wrote The Genesis of Diesel Motors.

Rudolf C. Diesel

The diesel engine
by Henry Thomas and Dana Lee Thomas

IT WAS DURING his college days that Rudolf Diesel envisioned his dream of a "more efficient and less expensive power" for the moving of machinery. One of his professors, Karl von Linde, had delivered a number of lectures on the inefficiency of the steam engine, with its "clumsy contraption of furnace, boiler and chimney." As a result of these lectures, Diesel made a complete study of the history of the steam engine, its evident virtues, and its equally evident defects: Too great a waste of effort at too high a cost of fuel.

At about the same time—and again under the inspiration of Prof. Linde—he became interested in an ice-making machine. This machine, a manufacturing project of Prof. Linde's, gave rise to an important train of thought in the mind of Rudolf Diesel. He observed that heat can generate power when it falls from a higher to a lower temperature, just as water can generate power when it falls from a higher to a lower level. A heatfall, a waterfall—and each of them can be harnessed to move machinery in the course of its cascade. A fascinating thought, to be stored away for use as a guide to all sorts of mechanical possibilities.

Rudolf Diesel
The diesel engine

On his graduation from the Munich Institute, Diesel got a job in Paris, at one of the factories where the Linde ice machine was being made. His duties were manifold: he was an engine builder, repair man, inventor, director, adviser, organizer, and purchasing and selling agent. "In this way," his professor-employer advised him, "you will get a postgraduate course in engineering—not only from the technical standpoint, but from the standpoint of the public demand for the better kinds of technique."

One of the first diesel motors built by Rudolf Diesel in 1898. It is now in a museum at Munich

Brown Brothers

Diesel plunged enthusiastically into the complexities of his job. "I work like a dozen slaves, and I am determined to make good."

He had a special reason for making good. He had taken a wife —a German girl who, following their marriage, had gone to live with his parents in Munich while he was trying to establish himself in Paris. He was anxious to "get on his feet" as rapidly as possible.

The burning desire of the French to avenge their defeat of 1870 was making it difficult, even 20 years later, for Germans to live in Paris. Accordingly Diesel sought employment in his own country. He requested Prof. Linde to put him in charge of his ice-making business in Berlin. The professor was only too glad to grant the request —at a substantial increase in salary. But he attached one important condition to the arrangement. "You must refrain from contributing any of your ideas to my invention." It was the haughty teacher dictating to his humble pupil. Diesel resented the implication; but he was so anxious to get away from Paris that he accepted the condition.

"I shall not tinker with your inventions." And Diesel scrupulously held to his bargain. But this understanding didn't prevent him from tinkering with his own inventions. A mechanism for the production of ice directly in a bottle for table use—*carafe frappé*. A motor similar to a steam engine, but propelled by ammonia gas instead of water vapor as a fuel. And—the forerunner of his greatest achievement—an engine working on the principle of internal combustion. That is, an engine *whose power became self-ignited* when fuel was injected into highly compressed air.

This idea of internal combustion, or self-ignition, was Diesel's chief contribution to the mechanics of the world. The idea had come to him as he watched the conversion of heat into a mechanical power that could manufacture ice. Wouldn't it be logical, he asked himself, to assume that the potential power of heat might be utilized in other forms of machinery? A cataract of heat, transformed into power? And ignited through compression?

He got the answer to his questions when he tested out his first engine of compressed air. And the answer almost cost him his life. For the engine exploded in the test. A practical failure, but a theoretical success. "Heated air *can* be sufficiently compressed to be spontaneously set on fire." The machine, in its very explosion, had given a thundering *go ahead* to his inventive quest.

And now, to discover the cause of the explosion and to prevent

Although oil is primarily used as fuel in the diesel engine—it has proven to be the most satisfactory so far—animal greases, glycerin, alcohol and even salad oils have been tried with success

259

its recurrence in the construction of his next machine. The chief trouble, as he learned, was that the walls of the cylinder were not strong enough to sustain the tremendous pressure of the compressed air. He set to work, then—experimenting with cylinders of different shapes and sizes and tensions, measuring the necessary amount of clearance between the top of the piston and the end of the cylinder when the piston had completed the up-stroke in the compression of the air, and trying out different kinds of fuel to discover the one that would produce the maximum of power at a minimum of cost.

And, after five years of patient trial and error, he succeeded (on January 28, 1897) in producing the engine of the "greatest thermal efficiency" in the history of science. "A motor," as he triumphantly pointed out to his wife and his three children, "which has no soot, no vapor, and no smoke . . . an invention which makes me the most powerful man in the world!"

He tried to think of an appropriate name for his engine. The Beta . . . The Delta . . . The Excelsior . . . "Why not," suggested his wife, "call it the Diesel Engine?"

Too slow, too heavy and too complex—only skilled men could build and run the early diesel engines—were the most common complaints received by Rudolf Diesel on his invention. But as improvements were gradually made the engine was adapted to more varied uses

The diesel (the name now is such an accepted part of the language that it need not be capitalized when designating the engine) is based upon the principle of igniting fuel in air at its highest temperature and exhausting it at its lowest temperature. In the first of his models, Diesel drove a small quantity of coal-dust fuel into the cylinder by means of compressed air, and then ignited this fuel by compressing the air in the cylinder until its temperature was higher than that of the ignition point of the fuel. In his later models, he substituted oil for coal dust. The principle, however, remained the same. In the diesel engine the fuel and the air are mixed, and the fuel is ignited, *inside* the cylinder—a process quite different from the gasoline engine in which the fuel and the air are mixed *before they enter* the cylinder.

Thus the diesel engine compressed a charge of air and fuel which is *self-ignited* through the heat of compression, while the gasoline engine compresses a mixture of gas and air which becomes *ignited by an electric spark*. This difference means not only a far greater efficiency, but a far smaller consumption of fuel, in the operation of the diesel engine.

The main idea in the diesel engine is to make the air do as much work as the fuel. A minimum amount of fuel is sprayed into the air, by means of a nozzle with openings so fine—each of them measuring about one-tenth of a thousandth of an inch in diameter—that the fuel comes into the cylinder not as a liquid but as a mist-like vapor. It takes a microscopic measurement of the nozzle in order to produce this fine spray, and of some of the other parts of the cylinder in order to minimize the amount of the fuel in igniting the air and in producing the power. So microscopic indeed, and so meticulously adjusted, that out of every thousand diamonds submitted for the cutting of the dies, only five are accepted as fulfilling the necessary requirements.

The result of this fine manipulation in the harnessing of much air and little fuel is the final word, to date, in the conversion of heat into power. This "supreme mover of our modern machinery" is being put to greater and more extended uses every day—in ocean liners, locomotives, cranes that can lift a building like a toy, power plants, tractors, trucks. And experiments have been made to adapt the diesel motor to the passenger automobile. When a diesel engine can be made small enough and light enough for the modern automobile, a new chapter in transportation will have begun. A few tentative trips in diesel-powered automobiles have been made over large areas of the United States. The fuel cost of one of these trips, all the way from Los Angeles to New York, amounted to somewhat less than $7.75!

On October 10, 1897, Diesel formed a company—Reisinger, Meier and Diesel—for the manufacture of his engine. His income from this company added to the royalties he received from the concessions to other companies—made him a very rich man. "I am now," he said to his wife, "a millionaire!"

The following year, 1898, Diesel gave the first public display of his new engine at the Munich exhibition

On paper. For most of his wealth consisted of stock shares and promissory notes. In actual cash he was still far from the security of a well-feathered nest.

A creature from another world, Diesel was too sensitive perhaps for the grossness of the earth. So many harassments from jealous inventors and unscrupulous business men. "It's amazing," he wrote, "that a man should be compelled to sacrifice time, money and health to counteract the evil fantasies of others whose only object is to steal your ideas and to crush your hopes!" And such terrific headaches—always drugging himself with doses of antipyrin to quiet those stabbing pains. And the constant buffeting of his fragile body between the extremes of anticipation and despair. Those everlasting lawsuits into which he kept pouring away his savings and his energy and his health.

And what would be the outcome of it all? For himself? More especially, for his wife and his three children? Well, he would try to recoup at least *some* of his losses, for *their* sakes, through investments in the stock market. . . .

And then came the day when he was close to financial ruin. He had just returned from a triumphant visit to America. Speeches, adulations, exhibitions of his motor, college degrees—a very pyramid of empty honors built upon a foundation of smoke. He looked over his accounts and checked on his investments during his absence. He found himself a famous and fleeced lamb.

But he kept his troubles to himself. He would still manage to put on a bold front before the world. And before his family. He was too proud to beg for help or to reveal himself as the financial failure that he was.

Diesel hated to see suffering and death. One of his earliest inventions was an ammonia bomb which was calculated "to befuddle the enemy temporarily instead of depriving him of his life." But the world ridiculed this "impractically humane" method of fighting a war

In the summer of 1913 he took a vacation, together with his 24-year-old son, Eugene, in the Bavarian Alps. Towering mountains, puny men. On this trip he partially opened his heart. "How foolish of us to entertain too lofty ambitions!" he remarked to Eugene one day. And, on another occasion, "Better no success at all, than a small measure of success with so many heartaches." Only once did he give a definite hint of the pain that was gnawing at his vitals. "Don't be disappointed, Eugene, when you see my will."

"But why talk about a will, father? You're only fifty-five. . . ."

"Yes, yes, of course. But one can never tell . . ."

When he boarded the *Dresden* for England, on September 29, 1913, he posted a farewell message to his son. *Gruss und Kuss. Im inniger Liebe, dein Vater.* Greetings and a kiss. In fondest love, your father.

Hail, and farewell. . . A few days after his father's disappearance in the English Channel, Eugene stood on the shore and offered—in behalf of the family—a silent requiem to the man who had brought them honor and who had departed in order that he might bring them no disgrace.

When Diesel's safe at Munich was opened after his death, it was found practically empty.

BOTH INVENTORS had shrewd heads in financial matters. Hall consistently added to his stock holdings whenever any pessimistic stockholder wanted to sell. Héroult, equally confident, acquired additional stock whenever he could. Both men became millionaires several times over, received high scientific awards and lived to see their process become known as the Hall-Héroult process. As the two men prospered and grew older their real personalities emerged more clearly. It was almost as if Destiny, anxious to make amends for her whim in matching the lives of these two inventors too closely, was determined to give them utterly different personalities.

Hall and Héroult

Fathers of the aluminum age
by Murray Teigh Bloom

ON THAT SNOWY Friday in January, 1911, the great chemists came from all over to New York to witness the climax of one of science's strangest coincidences. The two multi-millionaire strangers whose fantastically matched lives had produced one of the great discoveries of the modern world were going to meet face to face.

Seated in the center of the dais was thin, spare Charles Martin Hall, the American who was going to receive the prized Perkin Medal for his epoch-making discovery of a cheap method of getting all the aluminum mankind needed out of the earth. Taller, much stockier was the Frenchman seated a few places down the table. His name was Paul Héroult, and he had made the identical discovery independently in the same month of the same year: February, 1886.

A remarkable coincidence in itself, of course, but the eminent scientists present wouldn't have been impressed by that alone. After all, the telegraph, the sewing machine, the microphone, and telephone, photography and chloroform, to name but a few, had been discovered nearly simultaneously by independent investigators. But the discovery of the aluminum reduction process, they knew, was stranger than any of these.

The strange drama had begun in 1863. In that year Charles Martin Hall was born into the large family of a Congregationalist minister in Thompson, a tiny village in northeast Ohio. In a tiny Norman village in France, Paul Louis Toussaint Héroult was born into a leather merchant's family. Both families were about equally well off.

Precocious almost from infancy, both boys were reading by the time they were four. When they were seven each had pounced upon obscure chemistry texts in their fathers' libraries which they read and re-read. By eleven their restless, roving minds were going far beyond the bounds of schoolrooms. At night they filled notebooks with the rough, highly imaginative details of inventions they intended to work on—flying machines, methods of harnessing the tides, of erecting tall buildings.

At fifteen, both came across the book which was to influence their lives profoundly. It was one of the first books devoted to the then rare metal, aluminum, and it was written by Henri Sainte-Claire Deville, a brilliant French chemist who clearly foresaw the tremendous number of uses to which inexpensive aluminum could be put. Deville had succeeded in bringing the price of a pound of the metal down from $545 to $17. Even at that, of course, it was still much too high for any practical commercial application.

The name aluminum was first applied by Sir Humphry Davy, who tried unsuccessfully to isolate the metal. He did, however, prove that aluminum oxide was reducible, thus accomplishing the first step toward wholesale production of aluminum

Somewhere in his book Deville pointed out that every clay bank was a mine of aluminum and that the man who found the process of getting the aluminum out cheaply would, indeed, be one of the great benefactors of mankind.

In Oberlin, Ohio, where Hall's family had moved, he carefully marked the paragraph. In Gentilly, near Paris, where the Héroult family had moved, young Paul also marked the paragraph.

At Oberlin College which Hall attended, there was no specialization in chemistry or the sciences. A similar situation prevailed at St. Barbe College which young Héroult attended.

They both finished college in 1885. It was also the year both decided that the time had come to work on the problem they had both been thinking about since coming across that paragraph in Deville's book.

First they made their own improvised laboratories. Hall converted the old laundry attached to the kitchen of the house his family lived in. Héroult used the small, idle tannery his father had left him.

The basic problem they thus undertook to solve had already daunted hundreds of chemists working with the finest equipment and ample funds at their disposal. Chemists were attracted to the problem because it seemed so simple. They knew that aluminum was the world's most abundant metallic element. They knew that it comprises some eight percent of the earth's crust to a depth of 10 miles. The only trouble was that in nature the metal always is found chemically wedded to other elements. It's so tenacious a marriage that it was considered a great feat when a Danish chemist in 1825 succeeded in separating a few tiny particles of aluminum in its metallic state.

Héroult had a slight advantage. In the small, abandoned tannery was a rusty steam engine. Scraping together some money with the aid of a few young friends he was able to buy a small dynamo so that he could have a steady source of electricity.

Hall really had to start from scratch. With spare-time earnings he was able to purchase minor pieces of chemical apparatus from the laboratory at Oberlin. For a source of electricity he was able to borrow some battery cells, but he had to improvise many more, chopping the wood and casting the zinc plates for his galvanic batteries.

Both young men knew that electric current would break down other compounds into their constituent parts when in molten form or solution. Water solutions of aluminum salts didn't work and easily available alumina (aluminum oxide) had too high a melting point to work with directly. So their first problem was to find some substance that would dissolve the aluminum oxide. Both discovered it in a strange mineral then found only in Greenland and called "ice stone" by the Eskimos because it looked like snow frozen hard. Chemists called it cryolite. Then, as Hall later recalled it:

"I melted some cryolite in a clay crucible and dissolved alumina in it and passed an electric current through the molten mass for about two hours. When I poured out the molten mass I found no aluminum. It then occurred to me that the operation might be interfered with by impurities, principally silica, dissolved from the clay crucible. I next made a carbon crucible and repeated the experiment. After passing the current for about two hours I poured out the material and found a number of small globules of aluminum. I was then quite sure I had the process I was after."

Frederick Woehler in 1826 succeeded in producing aluminum and by 1845 had obtained enough of the metal to discover some of its characteristics

265

Hall and Héroult
Fathers of the aluminum age

Above, first electrolytic cells or furnaces for making aluminum. Right, small aluminum globules made by Hall in 1886. Large one is first aluminum produced commercially. Below, modern furnaces

It was February 23, 1886. That same week in the tannery in Gentilly, France, Héroult had performed almost the identical experiment. At the age of 22 both lads, utterly unknown to one another, had found the goal sought by chemists for decades.

Hall had used up his meager resources on his experiments and now it became necessary for him to find money to pay for his patent filings. In France, Héroult was able to draw upon some friends who had a few francs. He filed his application on April 23, 1886 and found that no one in Europe cared a whit about cheap, pure aluminum.

In America, Hall was having the same difficulties. He drifted from one would-be sponsor to another without finding anyone interested to the point of putting up the necessary capital. Meanwhile, he was improving his process.

For exactly two years neither young man found interested financiers. Then, suddenly, within days of one another, ample financial support was offered them. Hall found it in a group of venturesome Pittsburgh businessmen; Héroult in a Swiss metallurgical combine. In an age when most inventors were treated shabbily if not crookedly, both these young inventors received liberal stock interests in the companies formed to exploit their processes.

And now, for the first time, they discovered to their immense surprise that their discoveries weren't exclusive. When Héroult filed application for an American patent he found that Hall's patent was going to get priority even though, temporarily unable to raise the fee money, Hall had filed later than Héroult did in France. Under American patent law, however, an American citizen was able to ante-date his patent by furnishing proof of previous successful experiments done in the United States.

Their attorneys wrangled across the Atlantic but in the end it was Héroult's process that was largely adopted in Europe and Hall's in America. In Pittsburgh, Hall's backers formed the Pittsburgh Reduction Company, later to become the giant Aluminum Company of America, or Alcoa. Hall and Héroult plunged into the work of improving their processes for the companies that had bought their separate patents.

Only 50 pounds of aluminum a day were produced in Pittsburgh during the early days of the new industry. Even at a comparatively cheap five dollars a pound nobody wanted much aluminum. And even after this price was reduced, with increased production, to two dollars

From 50 pounds a day—on good days—to more than 200 million pounds some 60 years later. And this figure soon will be doubled—for we are on the threshold of an aluminum age

a pound and later to a dollar, demand was still small. But gradually in America and in Europe the new metal began to make headway. Aluminum kettles became popular and aluminum power cables were found to be less expensive.

As demand increased the Pittsburgh plant was expanded and in the 1890's both Hall and Héroult found themselves in charge of huge new plants for the making of aluminum. Hall became the general manager of the Niagara Falls plant and Héroult of the new plant using hydro-electric energy in the French Alps.

The small plant discovered that aluminum in ingot form was of little use to anyone since the metal-working industries refused to develop new methods for working the metal. Consequently Hall's company decided— and did—develop its own processes for working aluminum

Perhaps nothing could better illustrate their very different personalities than the way the two men chose to tell of their discoveries of the aluminum reduction process that night in January, 1911, at the Chemists' Club. Hall, speaking in his soft, precise tone, gave a painstakingly detailed account of his trials and errors in arriving at the successful process.

A few minutes later Héroult got up and told with a grin, in his booming, slightly accented English, how his discovery was due largely to the fact that he and a young friend in Paris for some vacation fun suddenly found themselves broke. Seeking something to pawn so that they could continue their drinking, they came across a souvenir stick of aluminum which Deville had made. A suspicious pawnbroker who had never heard of the metal gave them two francs for it.

"On a hot summer's day in Paris," Héroult told his appreciative audience, "it was better than nothing and we took the money with the firm intention of buying the stick back, which we never did. Maybe that was one of the reasons why, later on, I had to make good and replace it," he added with a broad grin.

In the summer of 1911, after their meeting at the Chemists' Club dinner the two inventors got to know one another at weekend visits. Héroult and his family then were staying at a summer home at Lake Placid. There the two strangely matched inventors exchanged further personal notes and found more coincidences.

Both of them had definite artistic streaks in their makeup. Hall, in fact, at one time had seriously thought of becoming a concert pianist. Héroult, for his part, confessed that at one time he had seriously thought of becoming a professional artist.

As they talked Hall unbent still more. They talked of experiments they were conducting in many different fields of science—experiments, they both readily admitted, that were far-fetched and rather visionary.

Hall told how some of his colleagues had politely tried to dissuade him from pursuing some of the work since it didn't have even the remotest connection with aluminum. Only the fact that he was then the largest single stockholder of the company made it unnecessary for him to stop the work.

Héroult told how the previous winter he had experimented in Chicago with what we can now realize was the amazingly accurate forerunner of the jet aircraft engine. He talked about his experiments with a helicopter, a strange, swift sea glider, of a scheme for getting iodine out of accumulated seaweed in the Sargasso.

Bauxite, the main commercial source of aluminum today, is readily available and contains a high percentage of aluminum oxide

Both men found that they also had in common a passionate love for the sea.

They parted rather good close friends. But not quite close enough to tell each other the disturbing secret each was carrying—the secret that was to carry to its natural conclusion the long and almost unbelievable series of coincidences.

What they had not mentioned was that each man was already under a sentence of death. Hall from an incurable spleen disease; Héroult from a hopeless kidney ailment. Each had been told it might be a matter of months or possibly a few years.

Héroult was the first to go. He died on his yacht in the Mediterranean with the soothing sound of the sea he loved ringing in his ears. Typhoid fever had brought death to him on May 9, 1914. Without the sudden illness he might have lived on a few months longer at best—possibly even until December 27, 1914, when Charles Martin Hall died at Daytona, Florida, also within earshot of the ocean he loved so well. At the comparatively early age of 51 both men were dead, thus ending the full cycle of coincidences.

Had they lived out their normal spans they would have seen how the identical process each discovered in 1886 had made aluminum one of the most versatile metals on earth, having more than 4,000 different uses. They would have lived to hear leading experts predict that before the century was out aluminum would be the most widely used metal, on earth, and would open the Aluminum Age, successor to the Steel Age. It would be an age made possible because a whimsical Destiny chose two amateur chemists to make, simultaneously and apart, one of the fundamental discoveries of the modern world.

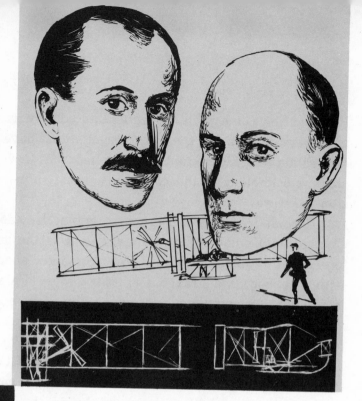

THE WRIGHT BROTHERS, Wilbur, born in 1867, and Orville, born in 1871, were rigorously brought up. Wilbur quit school at 13 or 14, and though Orville went on to high school, both boys went to work at an early age. The bicycle craze of the 1890's prompted the brothers to open a bicycle-repair shop in Dayton, Ohio. About 1892 they formed the Wright Cycle Company, and manufactured their own two-wheelers. Their earliest flight experiments, about 1896, were made with kites and gliders. Within six years they had designed, built and installed a gasoline motor in their most successful glider. In 1903 they made their historic flight.

Wright Brothers

Flight into history
by Elsbeth E. Freundenthal

By TEN O'CLOCK on the morning of December 17, 1903, the Wright brothers had made their decision to try their plane. Three members of the Kill Devil Life Saving Station—John T. Daniels, W. S. Dough, and A. D. Etheridge—and two other neighbors—W. C. Brinkley of Manteo and John Ward of Nag Head—composed the gallery of spectators. Orville made the first attempt—*and succeeded in flying!*

Since the brothers themselves wrote an account of this wonderful achievement, their exact words define what this flight meant:

The first flight lasted only 12 seconds, a flight very modest when compared with that of birds, but it was, nevertheless, the first in the history of the world in which a machine carrying a man had raised itself by its own power into the air in free flight, had sailed forward on a level course without reduction of speed, and had finally landed without being wrecked.

The exhilaration of this successful flight of 12 seconds impelled the Wrights to fly again. Three times more the machine rose, with

After many further experiments and modifications, the Wright brothers made a successful circular—rather than a straight-line— flight of 24½ miles in 38 minutes and 3 seconds at Dayton, on October 5, 1905. On May 22, 1906, they received a U.S. patent for their "flying machine," and in 1908 they made an airplane for the U.S. War Department, which was accepted for army use one year later

the brothers alternating flights, as was their practice. On this notable day, Wilbur had the fourth turn and made the longest distance.

Years would elapse before any other flyer approached this achievement of December 17, 1903, for Wilbur flew for 59 *seconds* and covered a distance of 852 feet.

It adds to the excitement of contemplating these first flights to know that they were not perfect. The effort of being born, of emerging into an actuality, was reflected in the straining of the machine and in its erratic undulations. This handmade craft, carrying its large burden of man's hope and thought, was challenging the hostile elements. The heavy winds increased the problem of controlling the landings, and the fourth flight unfortunately ended in a rough landing which slightly damaged the hard-worked plane.

The brothers paused now to contemplate what they had done, and to assess the damage. Worse followed immediately, for while they were standing around the machine discussing the flights with their spectators, a sudden gust of wind hit it and so damaged the plane that there was no possibility of flying it again.

These flights on December 17, 1903, were the first controlled flights in history. In spite of the many disadvantages and handicaps under which they had worked, the Wrights had made this extraordinary achievement. One of the best results was that all of their calculations, on a preliminary check, seemed to have been absolutely correct.

In the word *controlled* lay their great advance over previous practice and their promise for the future. They had, futhermore, made four consecutive flights. This was not, thus, a chance flight, but a carefully worked out and well-planned feat of the first magnitude.

Enormous elation at achieving one's high goal is inevitably followed by a period during which this success has to be accepted by the mind and absorbed into the emotions. Fortunately, the Wrights had many things to do, and they were kept busy, following the fourth flight on December 17, while their minds and hearts and spirits exulted in their achievement. They sent a happy telegram home to Dayton ending, "Inform Press home Christmas."

Then came the aftermath, which, as always, was a letdown. The brothers now realized the limitations as well as the promise of their first flights. Although elated at their success, they felt also a slight apprehension lest the shortness of their time in the air overshadow the fact that they had gotten into the air. While they happily considered the events of this great day, occasionally they paused to hope that men who really understood the difficulty of flying a new and strange machine would admire the length of their flights rather than wonder at their brevity. So strong was their feeling that it crept into one sentence of the Wrights' subsequent letter to the press, where they mentioned "the difficulties of attempting the first trials of a flying machine in a 25-mile gale."

On the whole, the world was supremely indifferent to what might

Wright airplane showing engine, sprocket, chain drive, chain guides, generator and controls

Smithsonian Institution

be occurring on the sand dunes of North Carolina. Its attention was focused on the many other events of this month of December, 1903: The United States was beginning to stir in preparation for the presidential election of 1904; Russia and Japan were massing troops in preparation for war. Chicago suffered its second greatest fire. The Dreyfus case was getting under way in France. And in New York City, part of the population was completely absorbed by the opening of the new Williamsburg Bridge, while the other part was focused on the opening performance of *Parsifal* (in the afternoon) and the pulsing question of whether or not to wear evening dress for the occasion. . . .

The Wright brothers' statement to the press gave exact descriptions of their flights of December 17, and is therefore included in full below. It is taken from the January 6, 1904, issue of the *Chicago Daily News*:

TELL HOW THEY FLEW

Wright Brothers Give Account of Airship Test in North Carolina

SOARED AGAINST A GALE

Remarkably Fast Time in One Trial in Teeth of Strong December Wind

(By the Associated Press)

Dayton, O., Jan. 6—Wright brothers, inventors of the flying machine which has attracted such widespread attention recently, today gave out the following statement, which they say is the first correct account of the two successful trials:

"On the morning of Dec. 17, between 10:30 and noon four flights were made, two by Orville Wright and two by Wilbur Wright. The starts were all made from a point on the level and about 200 feet west of our camp, which is situated a quarter of a mile north of the Kill Devil sandhill in Dare county, North Carolina.

FLIGHT AGAINST THE WIND

"The wind at the time of the flights had a velocity of 27 miles an hour at 10 o'clock and 24 miles an hour at noon, as recorded by the anemometer at the Kitty Hawk weather bureau station. This ane-

Two propellers instead of one were used for their first airplane so as to exert pressure on a larger area of air. These propellers were driven in different directions to offset torque

mometer is 30 feet from the ground. Our own measurements, made with a hand anemometer at a height of 4 feet from the ground, showed a velocity of about 22 miles when the first flight was made and 22½ when the last flight was made. The flight was made directly against the wind. Each time the machine started from the level ground by its own power, with no aid from gravity or other source whatever.

LAUNCHED FROM ONE RAIL TRACK

"After a run of about 40 feet along a monorail track, which held the machine 8 inches from the ground, it rose from the track and under the direction of the operator, climbed upward on an inclined course, till a height 8 or 10 feet from the ground was reached, after which the course was kept as near horizontal as the wind gusts and the limited skill of the operator would permit.

FAST TIME AGAINST GALE

In 1909 the brothers organized the (American) Wright Company to manufacture airplanes under their own patents. In 1912 Wilbur died of typhoid fever and shortly later Orville sold his interest in the Wright Company and became a member of the U. S. Naval Consulting Board. Later Orville devoted himself to aeronautical consultation. He died at Dayton in January, 1948

"Into the teeth of a December gale the *Flyer* made its way, with a speed of 30 to 35 miles an hour through the air. It had previously been decided that for reasons of personal safety these first trials should be made as close to the ground as possible. The height chosen was scarcely sufficient for maneuvering in so gusty a wind, and with no previous acquaintance with the conduct of the machine and its controlling mechanisms. Consequently the first flight was short.

FLIES HALF MILE, 852 FEET HIGH

"Successful flights rapidly increased in length and at the fourth trial a flight of 59 seconds was made in which the machine flew a little more than a half a mile through the air and a distance of more than 852 feet over the ground. The landing was due to a slight error of judgment on the part of the navigator. After passing over a little hummock of sand in an attempt to bring the machine down to the desired height the operator turned the rudder too far and the machine turned downward more quickly than had been expected. The reverse movement of the rudder was . . . too late to prevent the machine from touching the ground and thus ending the flight. The whole occurrence occupied little if any more than one second of time.

DIFFICULTIES IN STRONG WIND

"Only those who are acquainted with practical aeronautics can appreciate the difficulties of attempting the first trials of a flying machine in a 25-mile gale. As winter was already set in, we should have postponed our trials to a more favorable season but for the fact that we were determined before returning home to know whether the machine possessed sufficient power to fly, sufficient strength to withstand the shock of landings and sufficient capacity of control to make flight safe in boisterous winds as well as in calm air. When these points had been definitely established we at once packed our goods and returned home, knowing that the age of the flying machine had come at last.

NEW PRINCIPLES OF CONTROL

"From the beginning we have employed entirely new principles of control, and as all the experiments have been conducted at our own expense, without assistance from any individual or institution, we do not feel ready at present to give out any pictures or detailed description of the machine."

A blanket of silence enveloped the brothers after their statement to the press, lifted only for an occasional glimpse of their activities. From this time on, they were, actually, pioneering. They were engaged from now on in their real work, for which their flights of December 17 were the first step. The Wright brothers were starting the aviation business.

The engine used by Wilbur and Orville Wright for their first airplane flight at Kitty Hawk

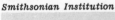
Smithsonian Institution

MARIE SKLODOWSKA CURIE, a professor's daughter, was born in Poland in 1867. Her youthful interest in mathematics and physical science drew her to Paris for university study and research. There she met Pierre Curie, a physicist, whom she married in 1895 and with whom, in spite of poverty and hardships, she discovered radium. After Pierre's accidental death in 1906, Marie continued the work which gave medicine a new weapon against cancer and was one of the keys to the wonderland of radiant energy. A lonely and unassuming woman, she waived the wealth that could have been hers, and, until her death in 1934, was undisturbed by the honors which came to her from all over the world.

Marie Curie

The discovery of radium

I COULD TELL YOU many things about radium and radioactivity and it would take a long time. But as we cannot do that I shall only give you a short account of my early work about radium. Radium is no more a baby; it is [at the time this was written in 1921] more than 20 years old, but the conditions of the discovery were somewhat peculiar, and so it is always of interest to remember them and to explain them.

We must go back to the year 1897. Professor Curie and I worked at that time in the laboratory of the School of Physics and Chemistry where Professor Curie held his lectures. I was engaged in some work on uranium rays which had been discovered two years before by Professor Becquerel.

I shall tell you how these uranium rays may be detected. If you take a photographic plate and wrap it in black paper and then on this plate, protected from ordinary light, put some uranium salt and leave it a day, and the next day the plate is developed, you notice on the plate a black spot at the place where the uranium salt was. This spot has been made by special rays which are given out by the uranium and are able to make an impression on the plate in the same way as ordinary light.

You can also test those rays in another way, by placing them on an electroscope. You know what an electroscope is. If you charge it, you can keep it charged several hours and more, unless uranium salts are placed near it. But if this is the case the electroscope loses its charge and the gold or aluminum leaf falls gradually in a progressive way. The speed with which the leaf moves may be used as a measure of the intensity of the rays; the greater the speed, the greater the intensity.

I spent some time in studying the way of making good measurements of the uranium rays, and then I wanted to know if there were other elements, giving out rays of the same kind. So I took up a work about all known elements, and their compounds and found that uranium compounds are active and also all thorium compounds, but other elements were not found active, nor were their compounds. As for the uranium and thorium compounds, I found that they were active in proportion to their uranium or thorium content. The more uranium or thorium, the greater the activity, the activity being an atomic property of the elements, uranium and thorium.

Then I took up measurements of minerals and found that several of those which contain uranium or thorium or both were active. But then the activity was not what I could expect; it was greater than for uranium or thorium compounds, like the oxides which are almost entirely composed of these elements.

Then I thought that there should be in the minerals some unknown element having a much greater radioactivity than uranium or thorium. And I wanted to find and to separate that element, and I settled to that work with Professor Curie. We thought it would be done in several weeks or months, but it was not so. It took many years of hard work to finish the task. There was not *one* new element; there were several of them. But the most important is radium, which could be separated in a pure state.

All the tests for the separation were done by the method of electrical measurements with some kind of electroscope. We just had to make chemical separations and to examine all products obtained, with respect to their activity. The product which retained the radioactivity was considered as that one which had kept the new element; and, as the radioactivity was more strong in some products, we knew that we

This selection from the works of Madame Curie was, originally, an address delivered by her in the chapel of Vassar College

277

had succeeded in concentrating the new element. The radioactivity was used in the same way as a spectroscopical test.

The difficulty was that there is not much radium in a mineral; this we did not know at the beginning. But we now know that there is not even one part of radium in a million parts of good ore. And, too, to get a small quantity of pure radium salt, one is obliged to work up a huge quantity of ore. And that was very hard in a laboratory.

We had not even a good laboratory at that time. We worked in a hangar where there were no improvements, no good chemical arrangements. We had no help, no money. And because of that, the work could not go on as it would have done under better conditions. I did myself the numerous crystallizations which were wanted to get the radium salt separated from the barium salt, with which it is obtained, out of the ore. And in 1902 I finally succeeded in getting pure radium chloride and determining the atomic weight of the new element, radium, which is 226, while that of barium is only 137.

The Curiegram, a unit for measuring the quantity of radium emanation, has been named after the famous discoverers of the new element

Later I could also separate the metal radium, but that was a very difficult work; and, as it is not necessary for the use of radium to have it in this state, it is not generally prepared that way.

Now, the special interest of radium is in the intensity of its rays, which is several million times greater than the uranium rays. And the effects of the rays make the radium so important. If we take a practical point of view, then the most important property of the rays is the production of physiological effects on the cells of the human organism. These effects may be used for the cure of several diseases. Good results have been obtained in many cases. What is considered particularly important is the treatment of cancer. The medical utilization of radium makes it necessary to get that element in sufficient quantities. And so a factory of radium was started, to begin with, in France, and later in America, where a big quantity of ore named carnotite is available. America does produce many grams of radium every year but the price is still very high because the quantity of radium contained in the ore is so small. The radium is more than a hundred thousand times dearer than gold.

But we must not forget that when radium was discovered no one knew that it would prove useful in hospitals. The work was one of pure science. And this is proof that scientific work must not be considered from the point of view of the direct usefulness of it. It must be done for itself, for the beauty of science, and then there is always the chance that a scientific discovery may become, like radium, a benefit for humanity.

But science is not rich; it does not dispose of important means; it does not generally meet with recognition before the material usefulness of it has been proved. The factories produce many grams of radium every year, but the laboratories have very small quantities. It is the same way for my laboratory, and I am very grateful to the American women who wish me to have more of radium, and give me the opportunity of doing more work with it.

The scientific history of radium is beautiful. The properties of the rays have been studied very closely. We know that particles are expelled from radium with a very great velocity, near to that of light. We know that the atoms of radium are destroyed by expulsion of these particles, some of which are atoms of helium. And in that way it has been proved that the radioactive elements are constantly disintegrating, and that they produce, at the end, ordinary elements, principally helium and lead. That is, as you see, a theory of transformation of atoms, which are not stable, as was believed before, but may undergo spontaneous changes.

Radium is not alone in having these properties. Many having other radioelements are known already: the polonium, the mesothorium, the radiothorium, the actinium. We know also radioactive gases, named emanations. There is a great variety of substances and effects in radioactivity. There is always a vast field left to experimentation and I hope that we may have some beautiful progress in the following years.

It is my earnest desire that some of you should carry on this scientific work, and keep for your ambition the determination to make a permanent contribution to science.

The twin discoveries of radium and polonium, a decomposition product of radium, paved the way for new progress in nuclear physics—along with the discoveries of the X ray and electron

Madame Curie was the recipient of two Nobel awards. The first prize, awarded in 1903 for physics, was shared with her husband and Henri Becquerel, the discoverer of the radioactive properties of uranium. This same year she and Pierre were awarded the Davy medal by the Royal Society of London. The second Nobel award, in 1911, was for her additional work on radium and its compounds.

RUTHERFORD went to no end of trouble for colleagues and students. One of his favorite prescriptions for a sticky problem was a ride in the country. Half a dozen times a year he would tell a student, "What you need is fresh air and scenery," and take him for an all-day ride in his car. He even found time to poke elaborate fun at himself and his most famous foible—his booming voice. In an experiment shortly after the war, Rutherford had to use a tube that was extremely sensitive to noise. He therefore built an electrically lighted sign, TALK SOFTLY PLEASE, for the laboratory. The sign faced his desk, not the lab door.

Ernest Rutherford

Father of the atomic age
by Leonard Engel

IN THE FALL OF 1895, a tall, heavily built young man with a booming voice arrived in England from New Zealand to work in the Cavendish Laboratory, the world-famous Cambridge University center for research in physics. He looked like a farmer's son, as indeed he was —altogether an odd choice for Cambridge's first research student, that is, a student who would be allowed to earn his degree by research alone, without taking any courses.

The farmer's son was Ernest Rutherford, who was, before long, to be hailed as the Newton of the atom, the man who opened the era of nuclear physics, father or grandfather of half of what we know about the subatomic world.

In the next year, as assistant to J. J. Thomson, young Rutherford was to carry out the classic experiments that led to the discovery of the electron. On his own, he would then uncover the nature of the newly discovered radioactive radiations and show their astonishing source—disintegration of the atom. He would work out the complicated changes through which uranium passes as it turns into radium, and the radium into lead. He would discover the "half-life" law.

In 1911, he would demolish the "hard ball" atom of John Dalton and show that the atom consists of a small central nucleus surrounded by dancing electrons. In 1919, he would reach the long-sought goal of the alchemists of old—the artificial transmutation of matter. And, as if this were not enough for one man, he would gather around him and inspire an extraordinary band of talented experimenters who would, among other things, invent the most widely used instrument for detecting radiation, discover isotopes and atomic numbers, find the neutron, and build the first atom-smasher.

Rutherford developed the idea that an atom can be compared to the solar system with the nucleus of the atom as the sun and electrons revolving around it like planets

Ernest Rutherford was born on August 30, 1871, on the South Island of New Zealand. He was the fourth of 12 children, 9 of whom grew to adulthood. His father was a flax farmer of Scottish antecedents who worked out his own process and built his own mill for treating flax; his mother had been a country school teacher. Ernest was "top boy" by a wide margin in every subject at school, and built a first-class camera, clocks, model waterwheels, and a host of other gadgets.

The New Zealander did not disappoint his parents. His father lived to see him Nobel laureate and the successor to Thomson in the Cavendish Professorship, the most famous post in the world of physics, the professorship first held by the immortal James Clerk Maxwell. His mother lived to see him knighted Lord Rutherford of Nelson.

Rutherford's first great discovery was made in 1898. Two years before, the French scientist Henri Becquerel had discovered that uranium gives off a mysterious radiation, about which little was yet known beyond the fact that it would darken photographic plates wrapped in paper impenetrable by ordinary light. Rutherford showed that there were at least two radiations from uranium: a high-energy short-range radiation which he named alpha radiation, and a lower-energy, but longer-range radiation he called beta radiation. (Gamma rays were not discovered until later.)

On the strength of this accomplishment, before Rutherford was 27, he was offered a new professorship of experimental physics at McGill University in Montreal, plus a spanking new research laboratory in which he would have a completely free hand.

There were drawbacks to the offer. For one thing, the professorship had been endowed by a wealthy but personally parsimonious tobacco merchant, Sir William MacDonald, who lived on $1,000 a year and thought $2,000 lavish pay for a professor; this would delay marriage to Mary Newton, the girl Rutherford left behind in New Zealand. For another, Montreal was far from the laboratories where Becquerel, the Curies, Thomson, and others were making scientific history. But Rutherford accepted the post.

It was at McGill that Rutherford discovered that radium gives off a radioactive gas (now called radon). This was the first step toward working out the complicated genealogy of the uranium-radium family, a task Rutherford carried out with Frederick W. Soddy, a young McGill chemist.

Westinghouse Electric Corp.

A "hot cell" built for the purpose of handling and testing radioactive materials. These manipulators, with mechanical, clawlike hands, are operated by remote control outside the cell

Rutherford looked further into the nature of radioactive radiations. He soon showed that beta rays were high-speed electrons. He also got on the track of alpha radiation, though his proof that alpha rays were helium atoms stripped of their outer electrons came after his return to England.

Next, Rutherford uncovered the basic law of radioactive decay. This describes how the radioactivity of a sample of radioactive material declines with time. No matter what amount of radium you start with, half the radium and half the radioactivity will be gone in 1,760 years.

A technician dismantling a radioactive object, by remote control, inside the "hot cell." He views his work, through seven feet of concrete, by means of a specially designed periscope

He calculated the half-life of radium and of several other radioactive elements.

While working on half-lives, Rutherford saw that radioactivity offered a clue to the age of rocks and of the earth. At that time, it was believed that the earth was no more than 100,000,000 years old. Rutherford set geology on its ear by finding samples of pitchblende indisputably 700,000,000 years old.

Lord Kelvin, the inventor of the absolute scale of temperature, had also convinced everyone that the earth was losing heat faster than it was received from the sun. As a result, he contended, the earth would freeze up in no more than a few million years.

But Rutherford, who had measured the heat generated by radioactivity, found that radioactive rocks were generating more than enough heat to make up the difference. Thus life could go on for hundreds of millions of years into the indefinite future. London newspapers headlined his announcement, DOOMSDAY POSTPONED.

From the laboratory at McGill, too, came a conception, commonplace to us now, but revolutionary then. In a historic paper in 1902, Rutherford boldly announced that radioactivity was due to the spontaneous disintegration of atoms. Chemists of the old school, like Sir William Ramsay, were thunderstruck by this flouting of the classic law of the conservation of matter. Rutherford, however, had proof and his revolutionary doctrine stuck.

Rutherford went from McGill to the University of Manchester in England in 1907, and in a few months made it the world's leading center for atomic research.

Soon after he arrived at Manchester, Rutherford tackled the problem of finding a simple means of measuring radioactivity. Up to then, the standard method had been to count the flashes of light when radiation struck a fluorescent screen—a tedious procedure, as the flashes were faint and could be detected only with the aid of a microscope in a darkened room. He suggested to a young German assistant, Hans Geiger, a tube in which an alpha or beta particle would release several thousand ions and generate an easily detected pulse of electricity. This was the origin of the Geiger counter, watchdog of the atomic age.

Rutherford used the new tube to make the first accurate count of the number of disintegrations per second in a gram of radium. The Geiger counter also led to Rutherford's next major discovery.

Ramsay's early work covered many fields but later he specialized in physical and inorganic chemistry. Much of his work was done in the field of gases. He discovered, among others, four inert gases: helium, neon, krypton and xenon. Ramsay also developed the transmutation theory—the transmutation of one metallic element into another

In the course of experiments in which alpha rays were passed through foils of gold before entering the counting tube, Rutherford noticed that an occasional particle bounced back from the foil as though it had collided with something hard, instead of passing through.

The discovery, some ten years before, that alpha and beta particles could pass through supposedly solid matter had been puzzling enough. Now here was something more peculiar still. While most of the particles went through, a few bounced back. Rutherford and Geiger repeated the experiment again and again. The result was always the same. Then one evening in 1911 it came to Rutherford. Most of the alpha particles went through because the atoms in the foil were chiefly open space; a few were hitting a tiny, dense central nucleus containing nearly all of the atom's mass. Rutherford had discovered the atomic nucleus.

During World War I Rutherford's laboratory practically shut down. Rutherford himself left to head the team of British scientists that developed the hydrophone to combat the U-boat menace. Most of his students went into the army or navy.

Rutherford got back to his laboratory a few weeks after the Armistice. Within three months he had scored his greatest triumph. An associate had noticed before the war that hydrogen nuclei could be knocked tremendous distances, atomically speaking, by fast alpha particles. Rutherford now tried the same kind of atomic billiards with alpha particles and nitrogen atoms. He found that nitrogen atoms were likewise knocked about by the high-speed helium nuclei, but that hydrogen nuclei were, strangely, also turning up. The latter could only have come from the nitrogen. In other words, a proton had been knocked out of the nitrogen nucleus, transforming nitrogen into an isotope of oxygen. Rutherford had achieved the transmutation of matter, and opened up an area of physics it would take a whole generation of scientists to explore and which would lead to artificial radioactivity, the man-made elements neptunium and plutonium, and nuclear fission.

Rutherford went back to Cambridge as Cavendish professor in 1919, there to remain to the end of his life. He died on October 19, 1937. Nuclear physics has made enormous strides in the decades since his death, but only because the path toward progress was prepared by a giant.

Rutherford won the Nobel Prize for Chemistry in 1908 for his discovery that alpha rays break down atoms and his studies of radioactive substances

GUGLIELMO MARCONI was born in Bologna, Italy, on April 23, 1874. When only 20 he was excited with the possibility of using electromagnetic waves to carry signals. In 1895, Marconi's homemade combination of a telegraph key and batteries, the Righigap device and an induction coil, Hertz-wave emitter and Branly coherer was powerful enough to chirp across a distance close to one mile. The following year Marconi patented his invention in England, and soon organized a company for its commercial development. Marconi's death in Rome, on July 20, 1937, was announced via the radio to whose development he had contributed so much.

Guglielmo Marconi

Signaler through space
by Edwin Howard Armstrong

IT IS DIFFICULT to find the facts about events of the early days of "wireless," for the pioneers are no longer with us; we cannot ask them why they did what they did do, and not something different. For later stages of radio development we are more fortunate; there are records from which we can reconstruct the history of the wrong roads that were taken, and of how the right roads were found.

Perhaps the most illuminating chapter in this history is Marconi's discovery of the daylight wave—the discovery that created world-wide radio communication as we know it today. It begins with Marconi's much earlier discovery of the grounded wave, which started wireless communication on its course.

When he began his search in 1895 for a practical wireless signaling system, Marconi proceeded at first along conventional lines and, by exercise of great ingenuity, extended the distance over which radio waves could be detected from a few hundred feet to several miles. His expressions of hope for longer distances met adverse criticism from scientists of the day, who recognized kinship between the waves from Marconi's beam and the light waves of a searchlight, and reasoned that the horizon must be the limit of a wireless signal, as of a searchlight's rays.

Had Marconi been more of a scientist and less of a discoverer, he might have concluded that his critics were right, and stopped where he was. But like all the discoverers who have pushed forward the frontiers of human knowledge, he refused to be bound by other men's reasoning.

He went on with his experiments; and he discovered how, by attaching his transmitted waves to the surface of the earth, he could prevent them from traveling in straight lines, and make them slide over the horizon so effectively that in time they joined the continents of the world.

Several years were to pass before agreement was reached on the nature of Marconi's great discovery, though Marconi himself understood very well how to apply it usefully; and it proved to be the foundation upon which the practical art of wireless signaling was built.

The first military use of Marconi's wireless took place during the South African War in 1899

For 20 years the "grounded waves," christened "Marconi waves" by Michael Pupin, were the accepted means of all long distance signaling. But today for long distance communication we no longer use them, save for a few special purposes. They have been replaced by a newer and radically different process of projecting waves into space, free of the earth, to bounce against an electrical ceiling 100 miles or so above the earth's surface, where they are reflected back to ground at some distant point. By a technique acquired through experience and based on the length of wave, the time of day and certain seasonal characteristics, we cause these waves to come back to earth in any desired area.

Surprisingly enough it was Marconi who, more than 25 years after his original discovery, made the second great discovery that was to show that we have been on the wrong track and to set us back on what we are presently pleased to consider the right one.

The story of how radio at the turn of the century went down what turned out to be a dead-end road, and how the right road was ultimately found, is a fascinating one. By 1900, Marconi had carried his experiments to a point where he was ready to make the great test of whether radio waves could be made to span the Atlantic. Accordingly, he built the first "highpower" station in the world at Poldhu, England, and went to St. Johns, Newfoundland, to listen for the signal. There, in December, 1901, his bold project came to a successful conclusion when, with a kite-supported antenna, the agreed signal—the letter "S"—was occasionally detected.

We know all too little about the characteristics of the historic Poldhu transmitter, for the art of measuring wave lengths and antenna power was yet to be developed. The best present-day estimates place the wave length somewhat below 2,000 meters and the power around 10 kilowatts. The experiment evidently showed Marconi that the gap between an occasional signal and regular transoceanic communication would be a large one, and that much more knowledge of the propagation of radio waves would be needed.

In the following year, 1902, experiments conducted between the Poldhu transmitter and receiving equipment on the S.S. *Philadelphia* uncovered a new phenomenon—that Marconi's waves traveled better at night than by day. Various hypotheses, none of them satisfactory, were advanced to explain the loss of signal strength during the day, which came to be known as the "daylight effect." Marconi's reaction was characteristic; he began experimenting to extend the daylight range. His observations led him to try using longer waves; and after much experimenting, he satisfied himself that they gave him an improvement in daytime reception; and he also found it easier with the longer waves to generate high power.

The more he experimented and observed, the more he was led in the direction of longer wave lengths. Other investigators in several countries arrived at the same conclusions, and without further thought, transoceanic communication went down the road of longer and longer wave lengths. Two decades later, the world was to be shown by Marconi that the road to world-wide communication lay in the opposite direction—the direction of short waves.

The goal of the pioneers was transoceanic communication, competitive financially with the solidly established cable system. Toward that end the best technical brains of the art were directed in the development of transmitters of higher and higher power and in the search for more sensitive detectors and more efficient antennas.

During the five or six years following the reception of transatlantic signals at St. Johns, Newfoundland, Marconi carried on ceaseless experiments, of which he has left an all too incomplete account. They culminated in the establishment during 1907 of the first transoceanic radio service, between stations at Glace Bay, Nova Scotia, and Clifden, Ireland.

Seven years later, in 1909, Marconi shared the Nobel Prize in Physics with K. R. Braun

Spark transmitters of about 50 kilowatts power operating on wave lengths of several thousand meters were employed, with receivers using simple rectifying detectors, whose response depended entirely on the energy that could be extracted from the incoming wave. Such a device as a vacuum tube amplifier was then a thing undreamed of. Continuity of service could be described as "somewhat uncertain."

Five more years of experience with the vagaries of the North Atlantic transmission path brought about a gradual lengthening of the waves of the two stations to approximately 5,000 and 6,000 meters respectively, with some improvement in the daytime service.

During these dark ages of transoceanic communication, laborious development work was carried on by a number of organizations to produce a substitute for the imperfect spark system of transmission; and by 1913 several continuous wave generators, giving greater power than the spark system, were in operation. All efforts, as before, were centered on producing waves that were miles in length. The idea of shortening the waves for long distance service, instead of lengthening them, never occurred to anyone.

In 1912, after his wireless system made it possible for the iceberg-torn Titanic to send out its CQD and SOS for help, the peoples of all nations hailed Marconi as a scientific hero

By the end of World War I, the radio communication companies had put a major part of their resources into the development of long wave, high-power transmitters of a variety of types—spark, quenched spark, timed spark, arc, the high frequency alternators of various countries, and the long wave vacuum tube generator. Waves 10,000 meters long were the order of the day. To radiate such waves, costly antenna structures had been erected, some almost 1,000 feet high and a mile long.

The improved receiving means made it possible to operate perfectly, with relatively low power, during the undisturbed periods of the early morning hours. But with the coming of atmospheric disturbances in the afternoon and evening from electrical storms originating in the tropics, reception from even the highest powered transmitters was frequently blotted out.

The idea that there might be a way of working with the forces of nature, rather than against them, seems to have been beyond the imagination of those working in the art. Another basic discovery was required to get off the dead-end road. Marconi was destined to make that discovery, but only after the chance to make it was repeatedly missed—by him and others—for nearly three years.

In a paper presented in New York City in June, 1922, Marconi suggested that radio had perhaps got into a rut by confining practically all its research to the long waves, and that more attention should be given to the shorter waves. He summed up his remarks on the subject with these prophetic words:

"I have brought these results and ideas to your notice as I feel— and perhaps you will agree with me—that the study of short electric waves, although sadly neglected practically all through the history of wireless, is still likely to develop in many unexpected directions, and open up new fields of profitable research."

Upon his return to England, Marconi began a series of classic experiments from the historic Poldhu site, which took him on a cruise in his yacht *Elettra* to the Cape Verde Islands in the South Atlantic during the spring of 1923.

Marconi's Wireless Telegraph Company, in 1921, was the first to bring regular musical broadcasts to the British Isles from stations in England

He had set up a transmitter at Poldhu on the longest "short" wave for which it was then practicable to build a reflecting beam antenna— 97 meters. He listened to the Poldhu signals as he cruised south, and found them to be extraordinarily good. In the Cape Verde Islands, over 2,500 miles from the transmitter they were far better than any signals that had ever been received over a comparable distance from a high power long wave station.

Marconi reported that even when the power at Poldhu had been reduced to one kilowatt, its signals at night were still better than those received from the highest powered transoceanic stations in the British Isles. While the usual disappearance of the signals during daylight hours occurred, Marconi observed that the signals lasted for a time after sunrise at Poldhu and that they became audible again before darkness had set in at the Cape Verde Islands.

That observation led him to suspect that some new phenomenon was present in the short wave band; and after his return to England he laid out a program of further experimentation for the following year, when he would compare the signals at 90 meters with those on a number of shorter wave lengths, down to the region of 30 meters.

In 1924, he cruised through the Mediterranean to the coast of Syria; and in Beyrouth harbor in September of that year he made the astounding observation that the signals on the 32 meter wave from Poldhu, some 2,400 miles away, came in throughout the day—they were in fact as good as the nighttime signals, whereas a longer wave of 92 meters, on the same power, behaved as at the Cape Verde Islands.

What Marconi was observing was transmission by reflection from that ionized layer of the upper atmosphere which later became known as the F_2 layer, after years of observations had laid bare the mechanism by which the effect was produced. But as with Marconi's first discovery, his practical achievement was years ahead of the theory.

Returning to England within a month's time, Marconi sent notification of scheduled transmissions on 32 meters to Argentina, Australia, Brazil, Canada and the United States; and at the appointed times the daylight signals were received in all those countries. From the end of the earth—far-off Australia—came a report of successful reception for 23½ hours out of the 24.

These astonishing results become still more astonishing when it is remembered Marconi used only a small percentage of the power of the transoceanic long wave stations, and was unable to take advantage of his directive beam antenna because of the diversity of the paths of transmission to the various receiving points.

As sometimes happens with radically new discoveries, the significance of Marconi's results was not generally appreciated, at first, outside his own organization. As in the case of his original discovery, what he had done was too far out of line with established teachings to be accepted in advance of a physical demonstration of the result.

But while others hesitated, Marconi moved rapidly, and by the end of 1927 short wave beam transmitters were operating between England and all the principal parts of the Empire—and at speeds (100 words per minute) that no long wave transmitter or cable had ever approached. The long waves were obsolete and the cables had become a secondary means of communication.

In retrospect, no one can regret that it was Marconi who made the great discovery. A reading of his account of his cruises shows that this was no chance discovery, but the result of a careful search by the one man who was able to define the limits of his own knowledge. Marconi set out on a thorough and painstaking exploration of what lay beyond those limits, and his search was rewarded by the success it deserved. To Marconi and those who worked with him goes the credit for the great discovery that put radio in first place in the field of world communication.

It is seldom given to a man to make two great discoveries, as Marconi did. He created the practical art of radio communication; and a generation later, when the limits of its ability to conquer distances seemed to have been reached, he came along with the discovery that made world-wide communication a reality

ALBERT EINSTEIN was born in Germany in 1879. In 1894 the family moved to Italy and Einstein went to school in Switzerland. He later became a Swiss citizen and received his Ph.D degree from the University of Zurich. The same year he published his first works, which were highly thought of and resulted in his appointment to the chair of physics at the University of Prague in 1911. Two years later he became director of the Kaiser Wilhelm Physical Institute in Berlin. His theory of relativity was released, in restricted form, in 1905. Einstein became professor of mathematics at the Institute of Advanced Studies in Princeton, New Jersey, in 1933. He became an American citizen in 1940.

Albert Einstein

The theory of relativity
by Dr. Edwin E. Slosson

A FRIEND OF MINE—I don't know him personally, but any man who buys a book of mine is a friend of mine—writes to me: "If you will put Einstein's theory of relativity in words of one syllable perhaps I can understand it."

Now, that is a foolish notion—even though he is a friend of mine. Short words may be easier to pronounce, but not easier to understand.

But anything to oblige a friend. So here goes:

If you were on a train and saw a train on the side track slip by your pane of glass you could not tell which train moved if yours did not jolt. You might think that your train was at rest, and that one moved back, or that both moved, but not at the same rate or the same way. It would be all the same which way you looked at it.

If now you were in a tight box or chest as big as a room that rests on the ground you would feel a down pull, which we call your weight. It is said to be due to a "force." But if the box is off in space where there is no force from the earth to act on it, and the box is pulled up by a rope at the same rate as a mass falls to the earth, you would feel the floor press up on your feet just the same as when you stood on the ground.

You know how it feels when you are in a lift that goes up with a jerk. If, while you were in this box off in space, you should throw a ball up in the air, it would go up a ways then fall down to the floor. So it looks to you, though to a man not in the box it seems that the floor moves so fast that it must catch up with the slow ball.

If you should fire a shot straight from the right side of the box to the left, its path would seemed curved down at the end as it would on the earth. So, then, a ray of light, which too, we say, moved straight, would seem to you curved when it passed through the box as though it, like the shot, had been pulled down by some force. But there is no down force in this case, for the box is not near the earth. It is due to the fact that the box moves up with more and more speed in the same way as a mass falls to the earth.

Then we must think that a ray of light near a large mass would not move in a straight line but in a curve. It would act just as if there were a force to pull it in. This has been found to be so. As the light from a star goes past the sun its track is bent to the sun as though the sun pulled the ray, as it does the earth, in a curved path. So when the sun is made dark by the moon the stars round about it seem pushed out of place. They do not stand so close as they do on the star map when the sun is not in their midst.

Then, too, the sphere that moves around the sun and is most near to it does not quite close up the ring of its path at the end of a year as it should by the old law. The new law shows why this is so.

A third test of the new law is still to be passed. The light and dark lines that are seen in a beam of light when it is bent out of its course by a wedge of glass should be pushed to the red end of the band if the light comes from large stars like the sun. A long light wave like the red should show more shift than the short waves. This point has not yet been proven for sure. Such a shift has been seen, but does not seem to be of the *right* size.

In the years since Dr. Slosson wrote, the new law was put to this third test and won out

Some strange things must be true if the new law holds good. First, we must say that mass and weight are not fixed, but change when the thing moves, though the change is slight save at high speeds. But near the speed of light the change is great. A thing must weigh more when it moves fast. If a rod goes at great speed in the line of

293

its length it will not seem so long as if it were at rest. No mass can be made to move as swift as light.

A clock in a state of rest does not show the same time as a clock that moves at high speed. As it moves fast through space it seems to slow up. A man would not seem to grow old if he could move with the speed of light.

It is a matter of choice if we say that the earth goes round the sun or that the sun goes round the earth.

If a ring is seen to be one foot through when a rule is laid on it, it will be Pi (3.14159 and so on) times that length round the rim. But if there is a great weight put in the mid point of the ring, then the line round the rim will not be so long as if the space were free. It will be less than Pi times the line that cuts through the ring at its mid point. If a thin steel disk whirls round fast, its rim will seem to shrink like a hot tire on the wheel of a cart.

It seems then that the scheme of points and lines that we got from the Greeks, and that is taught in our schools yet, is not quite true when we come to deal with time and space as a whole. Space would be naught if there were no time. Time would be naught if there were no space. The two must join to form a sort of fixed frame or mesh in which all things are set.

At each point, say the point where you stand, four lines cross and lead out straight in the four ways. One line runs up and down, the next runs right and left, the third runs back and forth, and the fourth runs from time past to time to come. To fix a thing we must know its point on the time line as well as its points on the three space lines. To place an act we must know when as well as where it came to pass.

Mass will wrap this mesh of space and time. A mass as it moves forms a sort of a crease or ridge. A mass that is at rest in space, of course, moves on the time line. A mass, as it moves from this point to that must take the track that is most long through the mesh of space and time.

All this is not just a new and queer way to look at the world. The great thing is that it starts a new path for man's thoughts

Space as a whole may be closed up in the form of a sphere or roll, and in that sense may be said to have no end, though it may not be so large as we used to think. A ray of light that starts out from the sun may not go on straight for all time, but may not round the sphere of space and come back at the end of a long time to the place it set out from.

Irving Langmuir

Scientist of light and weather
by John Pfeiffer

FOR NEARLY 50 of his 70 some years, Dr. Irving Langmuir of the General Electric Research Laboratories in Schenectady, N. Y., has held an eminent and in some ways unique position among leading scientists of the world. His success in research aimed at practical ends and his imaginative use of new ideas have unlocked many a scientific treasure house. While others studied cosmic rays, expanding universes, and atom-smashing, Dr. Langmuir has spent much of his career on more prosaic endeavors, to the great practical benefit of mankind.

One of his outstanding triumphs was an improved electric lamp which led to the gas-filled bulb that saves Americans a half billion dollars each year in electric bills. Inside experimental glass bulbs Dr. Langmuir discovered a new range of physical phenomena, a high-vacuum, miniature universe of sizzling temperatures and splitting molecules. His explorations in this field won him science's highest award, the Nobel Prize, in 1932.

Another project—the latest and most spectacular study of his career—is the production of artificial weather, or rain-making. Dr.

Langmuir has retired as associate director of the Schenectady laboratories, but it is typical of him that the "retirement" merely accelerated his weather studies. As civilian head of Project Cirrus, which is supported by his company, the Army Signal Corps, and the Office of Naval Research, he has been directing the first large-scale scientific study of rain-making.

The basic idea in weather-making, he says, sitting behind his desk at General Electric's new research building near Schenectady, is to select clouds that are "supercooled" to below-zero temperatures and that also contain appreciable amounts of water in the form of droplets too tiny to freeze. If enough of these droplets merge at one place they freeze solid and fall to earth as rain or snow, depending on weather conditions.

To produce this effect, particles of dry ice and silver iodide are used. The particles serve as "seeds" to which water droplets will attach themselves until enough gather to form ice crystals. Theoretically, the crystals will "trigger" an atmospheric chain reaction that will produce legions of other crystals.

It all started during the war. And, like a number of Dr. Langmuir's discoveries, it came about as an accidental by-product of the investigation of another problem. Dr. Langmuir and his assistant, Dr. Vincent Schaefer, were trying to find how static electricity collected on planes that passed through a storm area.

"We set up a station on the top of Mt. Washington in New Hampshire to study the charge and discharge of metal surfaces exposed to blowing rain and snow," Langmuir says. "The experiments didn't work out, but we came across something else. One day, I was climbing the mountain. The temperature was below zero, and I saw a cloud forming. Ice crystals were falling out of it."

He also noticed that ice appeared on metal surfaces even in the absence of rain or snow. Tiny droplets froze from apparently "empty" winds and clouds. Dr. Langmuir went to work with theoretical calculations on crystal formation and evaporation and soon realized that snow and rain might be produced artificially if the droplets in water-filled clouds could be crystallized. How to do this was the problem.

Dr. Schaefer discovered the secret several years later when he was studying experimental clouds in a deep-freeze unit. One hot July afternoon, finding it difficult to keep the open unit at the desired temperature of 10 below zero F., he put a piece of dry ice inside to lower

Recalling one of his most successful rain-making expeditions, Langmuir said: "We started out at 5:30 A.M. using a smoke generator that burned charcoal pellets impregnated with silver iodide. At 10:10 A.M. the first flash of lightning appeared. By the end of the day we had worked 13 hours and used about $13.40 worth of the compound. We produced 320 billion gallons of rain—3 billion in the Pecos River alone."

the temperature and instantly the chamber was filled with falling ice crystals.

There was the answer. The dry ice had chilled the air, causing a few ice nuclei to form, and that was enough to seed the entire cloud. Man's latest effort to make his own weather resulted directly from this test and from Dr. Langmuir's keen eye for the unexpected.

This ability has served him throughout his scientific career. A typical example is his first project at General Electric in 1909. At that time he was a chemistry instructor at the Stevens Institute of Technology in Hoboken and had been invited to spend his summer vacation at the Schenectady laboratories. The 27-year-old chemist chose what seemed to be a promising short-term experiment. Tungsten filaments had just been substituted for carbon in electric lamps, but most of them blew out after several hundred hours of use.

At that time most engineers thought better lamps could be made by producing better vacuums, and were seeking new ways of removing "contaminating" gases. But Langmuir was interested in the little-understood behavior of atoms and molecules at very high temperatures. So he purposely introduced oxygen, carbon monoxide and many other gases into experimental bulbs to see what would happen.

Soon he became fascinated with the peculiar behavior of hydrogen, most of which disappeared from the space inside the bulb 10 to 20 minutes after the lamp was turned on. He finally found out why. The hot tungsten filament was splitting molecular hydrogen into its component atoms. The highly active atoms, unable to recombine with one another, attached themselves to the particles of the glass and covered the surface with a layer only one atom thick.

To check his conclusions, Dr. Langmuir next studied nitrogen molecules which, if theoretical calculations were correct, should not break up in the lamp and would therefore behave in a radically different manner. The nitrogen performed according to expectations, but Dr. Langmuir noticed something he hadn't been looking for—and something which more than repaid his company for two to three years of "aimless" research. The tungsten filaments lasted much longer in nitrogen-containing bulbs than they did in a vacuum, because many evaporating tungsten atoms collided with the gas particles and bounced right back to the metal filament. This accidental discovery was what led to the gas-filled electric lamp, which was first produced in 1912.

This maker of artificial weather bristles a bit when you mention the skepticism of some Weather Bureau scientists. "The weather experts," he says, "are very orthodox. They tend to feel that anyone who hasn't specialized in meteorology isn't in the run. But all of us have to be prepared for the unexpected, for things that don't make sense according to our old ideas. We must continue to experiment with open minds. That's the scientific method."

ALEXANDER FLEMING was born at Lochfield, Scotland, in 1881. He won distinction at Wilmarnoch Academy and at St. Mary's Hospital Medical School. After his graduation he became fascinated by the problem of bacterial action. Following World War I Fleming returned to research work and teaching at St. Mary's. A prelude to his most famous discovery came in 1922 when he discovered lysozyme, a bacteria-destroying substance found in certain animal and vegetable secretions. Fleming was made a fellow of the Royal Society in 1943, knighted in 1944, and received the John Scott Medal in 1945. He shared the 1945 Nobel Prize with Sir Howard Florey and Dr. Ernst B. Chain.

Alexander Fleming

The story of penicillin
by Ruth Fox

THE FALL of 1928 was damp. Damp Septembers were no novelty in London, but this year was outstandingly moist. The basement laboratory of St. Mary's Hospital was ventilated by one slightly open window through which drifted particles of dust, leaves, and other windblown strays calculated to turn a scientist gray before his time.

But Dr. Alexander Fleming, the hospital's bacteriologist, was Scotch by birth and serene by nature, and such small hazards of laboratory life as the contamination of a plate of bacteria by a migratory mold did not upset him overmuch. Molds were an irritating but familiar kind of fungus, always floating in the window onto his purest cultures.

Absently, he moved the plate over to the sink, turned on the water, and then glanced down at the plate. As things turned out, it was a very significant glance.

In the area immediately surrounding the stray mold the flourishing family of murderous staphylococci had simply disappeared. Dr.

Fleming blinked, looked again, and saw that even the colony a few inches from the invader had become transparent. Why?

"When I saw the bacteria fading away," Dr. Fleming said later, "I had no suspicion that I had a clue to the most powerful therapeutic substance yet found to defeat bacterial infection in the human body. But the appearance of that culture plate was such that I thought it should not be neglected."

It was a happy decision for us all. The mold which Fleming grew from that original air-borne particle was a species of the *Penicillium genus*. The substance which it secreted to kill staphylococci the doctor named "penicillin."

Mold culture was a subject on which few bacteriologists were experts. This mold, Dr. Fleming decided, was to be treated with all the affection and understanding which he could muster. With painstaking caution, he transplanted the particle of fuzz from the culture plate and waited for it to grow into a respectably sized community.

Penicillin still cannot be produced artificially and manufacturers must depend on molds

The historic experiments of the next eight months he himself found hard to believe. He could understand why the paper which he published in May of that year met with much skepticism.

Powerful? Fantastically so. Staphylococci, he found, were not the only members of the microbe world which the wandering mold conquered. In dilutions of 1 part to 600, the mold could also prevent the growth of streptococci and pneumococci, two of the most common man-killers known to science. Even the tough bacilli of diphtheria succumbed to it. But the microbe least affected by the broth was the weak, pallid creature which causes influenza. Quite clearly, penicillin did not work according to any set of rules yet recorded.

Dangerous? That, of course, was the question. What good was an antibacterial agent which killed a patient in the process of annihilating his germs? Dr. Fleming injected 20 cubic centimeters of penicillin broth into one rabbit, and 20 cubic centimeters of ordinary broth into another rabbit. If the two had not been labeled, he would have had no way of telling which rabbit had been given which broth. Penicillin was not toxic, at least to rabbits—a slight but promising bit of information.

And then what?

The problem which he now faced would be the plague of penicillin researchers for the next 14 years. His supply of the mold was much too small. He consulted a friend, Dr. Harold Raistrick, a biologist quite capable of coping with the temperament of a cheese mold. Together the two men began an intensive campaign of penicillin-growing. When they had on hand a small, jealously guarded store, they began to think about finding the answer to the most important question they had yet asked themselves.

Penicillin polished off streptococci, staphylococci and pneumococci in the test tube. It had no ill effect on laboratory animals or, as they found, on themselves. What would happen if it were actually tried on a human patient infected with streptococci, staphylococci or pneumococci?

Although penicillin treats many diseases it does not have any effect on conditions where susceptible bacteria are not present, as in the case of cancer

However, there was barely enough penicillin on hand to treat one patient. The doctors could prove nothing about penicillin as long as it existed in such small quantities. If they could interest bacteriologists or mold experts in penicillin, Fleming believed, then someone, somewhere, might come up with a solution to the problem of production. He prepared a report on a series of new laboratory experiments and presented it at a meeting of bacteriologists. But, in the crush of other papers, on less tenuous subjects than floating molds, the report was quietly overlooked.

Years passed quickly, and gradually even the few scientists who had been interested in penicillin abandoned it. The discovery like so many discoveries before it, came dangerously close to being junked. But not quite. For 10 years, Alexander Fleming kept a strain of the original mold growing in a corner of his laboratory. He was a patient man. He could wait.

By 1938 it became clear that England, and possibly the whole world, would soon be at war. Suddenly there was no longer room for apathy on such subjects as antibacterial agents. The new sulfa drugs, heralded a few years before as the cure-all for infectious diseases could do a lot, but they could not begin to do everything that had been claimed for them. Of all the problems which war presented to medical researchers, none was more important than the search for an agent specifically capable of checking wound infection.

At Oxford the professor of pathology, Australian-born Harold Florey, remembered a research paper of 10 years before on the properties of a common mold. He paid a visit to the now white-haired Alexander Fleming. Did the professor have any idea how or where one could locate a mold similar to the one which had drifted into his laboratory in 1928?

Doctor Fleming smiled. He had more than an idea. He had the immediate descendants of the original mold still growing in one corner of his laboratory. A strain of the mold was transferred from St. Mary's Hospital to Oxford and established in the pathology laboratory.

It was not long before Florey and his associates realized that not one word of Dr. Fleming's report on the conduct of his fungi was exaggeration.

Florey isolated eight white mice and proceeded to shoot them full of the most vicious train of staphylococci he could get his hands on. Four of the unlucky eight were left alone; four were given shots of penicillin every three hours, for one day and one night. By morning, four mice were dead and four mice were alive and mending. So far, penicillin was batting a thousand.

"It can save people as well as mice," Florey thought, but he made his first tests with little enthusiasm. There was, undoubtedly, a catch to penicillin.

From their very first animal experiments, the Oxford men had been aware of one unhappy feature about their mold-broth. The body does not retain penicillin. It is thrown out almost as quickly as it can be forced in. "It is like pouring water down a basin with the plug out," Florey said later. The amount necessary to keep four mice alive for 24 hours had almost depleted the laboratory supply. How could they scrape together an amount large enough to treat a man? What, for that matter, did they hope to prove by treating a patient with penicillin? The merits of a substance which existed in quantities just large enough to cure four mice were of questionable value to practical men.

While formerly an injection of penicillin lasted only a few hours, scientific advancements in the preparation of the drug have resulted in an injection lasting as long as 24 hours

In February of 1938 a London policeman cut his face while shaving. It was a common enough accident but, as it developed, a particularly unfortunate one. Two weeks later, the man was dying of blood poisoning, his body invaded by a horde of vicious staphylococci against which sulfa preparations had proved no more effective than a wooden gun against cannon fire.

The case so obviously was made to order for their purposes that Florey and his associates could not let it go by. Every available bit of penicillin in the laboratory was marshaled and moved over to the Radcliffe Infirmary of Oxford. The dying man was given a dose of penicillin injected directly into the blood stream every three hours.

Five days passed—or crawled, as it seemed to Florey. Within

two days a slight drop in temperature was recorded; on the third day, the horrible swellings on the man's face began to subside. The next day his temperature was close to normal, and by the fifth day, his recovery seemed assured. But the last fleck of penicillin was gone.

Back in the laboratory, heartbreaking efforts were being made to scrape together a new supply of the mold. It came too late. Before the treatments could resume, the infection made headway, and the man died.

The telephone rang early one morning. . . ."Florey? This is Fletcher. I have a case here I think you might like to look at. Fifteen-year-old boy—terrific hemolytic strep infection . . . Sulfas? No. Couldn't do a thing for it. I don't give him another 48 hours to live, unless—"

The second time it happened. A patient who should have been dead within 48 hours, by all existing standards, stayed alive. Once again the supply of penicillin was exhausted, but this time it had held out just long enough.

"Now," Florey thought, "we have to stop fooling around. We have to get more of the stuff. . . ." Production, he knew, was a problem for experienced drug manufacturers, not for a pathology laboratory. How did one go about convincing a drug company of so obvious a fact?

It was a vicious circle. Penicillin research had reached a stage at which it demanded large-scale, wholesale experimenting in clinics all over the world. So far, enough of the precious stuff had been produced to treat two patients—one unsuccessfully.

Huge tanks now replace the hundreds of bottles formerly used in the production of penicillin. These tanks are capable of brewing 15,000 gallons of fermented mash, containing impure penicillin

Unless the drug were manufactured by the ton, not by the teaspoon, such experimenting could never be done. Yet what drug manufacturer in his right mind could be expected to say, "Certainly, doctor, I will gladly spend a few million to set up production of this unknown drug which has failed so far in 50 percent of the cases in which it has been tried." No, Florey reasoned, he had to have more figures.

But how? It was a project which would demand the full time, interest, and loyalty of an expert physician. Florey and his associates were barely able to keep the laboratory going, much less take up the practice of medicine. But how could they possibly find a doctor willing and able to drop his heavy wartime burdens simply to hold up the medical end of their project? On the surface it was an impossible order. But Florey's uncommon luck did not desert him.

Ethel Florey was a gentle-faced housewife, the mother of two children, who had recently been evacuated to the United States. But she had been a doctor. Now her husband was asking her to plunge into a field of practice so new that there were not even any established rules to learn. Florey's project was simple enough in outline, he explained. He and his associates would stay in the laboratory and would devote their concerted efforts to the growing of molds and the brewing of penicillin. From there on the responsibility was hers.

It was quite a responsibility. To pick out cases most likely to prove the efficacy of the drug, to watch over every milligram of it as one might guard gold dust on its way to the mint, to bring in reports of undeviating accuracy, calculated to arouse the good will of drug-company stockholders. . . .

Ethel Florey packed the priceless few grams into sterilized cold-cream jars, and set out for the Radcliffe Infirmary. There was a case in residence which interested her—a girl dying of a fatal streptococcus infection. In the same hospital there was a two-months-old baby, its spine twisted, its body aflame with osteomyelitis, one of the most vicious and incurable of all infections.

Although Ethel Florey had hardly dared hope for it, both these patients recovered after being treated with penicillin. So did the empyema, streptococcus meningitis, the bacterial endocarditis and the septicemia patients whom she elected as her test cases. By the end of the year, the cooperative effort of the Florey household had resulted in 187 carefully documented reports of penicillin therapy.

Florey felt that it was time to put penicillin into production on a vast scale. It was a big order, and there was only one possible place to fill it.

In July of 1941, Howard Florey and his colleague, Dr. Norman Heatley, arrived in the United States carrying with them a sample of the mold descended from Dr. Fleming's strain. Penicillin was about to enter the third phase of its career.

Doctors Florey and Heatley were barely off the ship before they found themselves hustled onto a train and headed, of all places, for Peoria, Ill. There the Fermentation Division of the Northern Regional Research Laboratory knew a good mold when it saw one. In no time at all, Florey and Heatley had sold the Laboratory on penicillin. Now they waited to see whether the recalcitrant creature would grow with more enthusiasm in Peoria than it had in Oxford.

The mold from which penicillin is obtained can be most commonly found on decaying lemons

The penicillium growers at Oxford had used as a growing medium a solution containing certain minerals and glucose. The yields from this medium had been discouragingly low, as we have seen. One liter of medium had usually yielded not more than 1,000 units of penicillin. And it took 100,000 units to treat a case of blood poisoning for one day!

The practical Americans came to grips with the problem at once. "We find some new way to grow the stuff, or we forget all about it," they decided. They inaugurated a systematic search for a better medium.

The great organic chemists of the last century and the early years of this one looked for remedies in the man-made molecules of synthetic drugs. They would have been surprised to learn that their followers would devote their energies to such items as soy beans, molds and garlic, searching out the remedies provided by nature herself for curing disease

It was Dr. A. J. Moyer who pulled the much-needed rabbit out of the hat. One day a routine check of his flasks showed that one of them was producing 200 units of penicillin to every cubic centimeter. *Two hundred thousand* to a liter instead of 1,000! The medium which had so intoxicating an effect on the mold? Home-brewed, corn-steeped liquor.

The jinx was broken. With production yields up 200 times almost overnight, the leading firms of the country added the new product to their lists. And all over the country, chemists, bacteriologists, engineers, government officials and medical-research men were sitting up late over their notebooks and test tubes.

In 1943, during the first five months of commercial production, 400,000,000 units of the severely rationed product were turned out. By the end of the year, the figure had jumped to 9,194,000,000 units a month. From that day on, the figures began multiplying themselves in astronomic proportion. In late 1948, eight *million* million units of pure crystalline penicillin came out of the laboratories every month.

While doctors worked out the refinements of penicillin allergies, and pitted their wits against those super-microbes which began learning how to combat the drug, a vast new research enterprise was springing up all over the world.

If nature had concealed so powerful a weapon in a humble wind-blown mold, then it was entirely possible that she had tucked others away in equally unlikely places. The most commonplace bits of matter, easily available in almost any backyard, were suddenly subjected to scrutiny. The results have been making headlines for almost a decade: Aureomycin, bacitracin, chloromycetin, polymyxin, and many others.

ROBERT H. GODDARD was born in 1882. His early school and college work were all obtained at Boston, where he lived until he was 16, and at Worcester, where he was graduated from the Worcester Polytechnic Institute in 1908. His academic career was conventional, rising in the usual steps from fellowship to instructor to assistant professor and finally to full professor at Clark University. In 1924 Goddard married and his wife took an active interest in his work, serving as official photographer of his experiments. Dr. Goddard's death on August 10, 1945, unfortunately brought to an untimely end his plans for further experimentation.

Robert H. Goddard

Rocket pioneer
by G. Edward Pendray

Dr. ROBERT HUTCHINGS GODDARD, a young American physicist of Worcester, Mass., did the pioneer work that established the modern period of rocket research and he was the first man to launch a liquid-fuel rocket—yet to the end he remained almost unknown as a person.

In his school days he was a serious young man, with an odd streak of scientific speculativeness in his nature. He enjoyed mathematics, was fond of figuring out faster ways to travel, and better ways to do things in general. In his freshman year at college one of his professors assigned the topic of "Traveling in 1950" as a theme subject. Goddard produced a bold paper which he read before the class, describing in some detail a railway line in which the cars were supported electromagnetically without any metal-to-metal contact, in a tube from which the air had been exhausted. With such a vacuum railroad he calculated it would be perfectly possible to make enormous velocities safely; for example, a running time of 10 minutes from Boston to New York.

As a young professor of physics, Goddard made contributions of importance on the balancing of airplanes, the production of gases by electrical discharges in vacuum tubes, and other topics. These exploits, however, were merely tune-ups. His real love was rockets and jet propulsion.

It is not known exactly when he made his first experiments with rockets, but he often told friends about carrying on static tests with small rockets (in static tests the rocket is held firmly fixed during firing) in 1908, in the basement of Worcester Tech. He promptly filled the whole place with smoke, and had to talk fast to get out of trouble. It was while he was at Princeton in the season of 1912-1913 that the great excitement of discovery first began to come to him. His calculations showed him that only a little fuel, relatively, would be needed to lift a payload to really great heights by rocket. The theory, in fact, was so promising he could hardly wait to begin transforming his figures into actuality.

Upon returning to Clark in 1914 he began experimenting with ship rockets, which he purchased out of his slender salary as an instructor. Next came tests with steel rockets using smokeless powder, fired both in air and in a vacuum.

Rockets, aside from military use, have been used for astronomical research, exploration of the upper atmosphere, high-altitude photography, and, experimentally in Europe, for carrying mail

In the course of these experiments, Goddard spent some $800 of his own money, and by 1916 had reached the limit of what he thought he could do on his own resources. Being inexperienced in the ways of self-promotion, he could think of no way to obtain a backer except to make out a report of what he had done with rockets, and explain what he thought could finally be accomplished. With characteristic thoroughness, he cast the paper into the best scientific form, rewriting it several times. To complete the job he bound it in a special cover with a neat gold border, and sent it away to one foundation after another, hoping for support.

The Smithsonian Institution was almost the last address on his list. After filing away the collection of polite refusals he had received from the others, it was with some hesitation he sent the document forth once again. This time, after an interval of about three weeks, he received a letter from Dr. Charles D. Walcott, then secretary of the Smithsonian, commending him on his report, and asking how much would be needed to continue the work.

Goddard debated between asking a safe $2,500, which he felt would be inadequate, and $10,000, which perhaps would be enough but might be refused. Finally he compromised on $5,000—and by

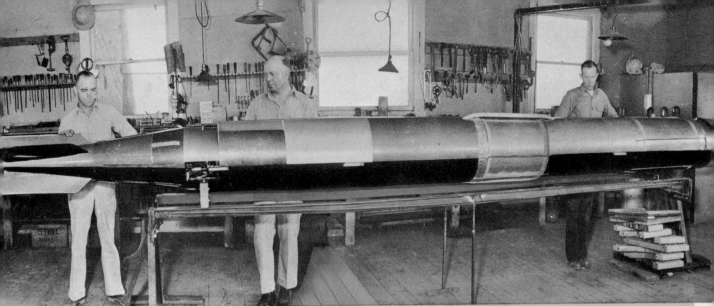

Mrs. Robert H. Goddard

Total length of this rocket, built in 1940, was about 21 feet. It was controlled by movable steering vanes, positioned in the path of the rocket's blast, and by the fixed air vanes, left

return mail received a warm letter granting his request. Folded with the letter was an advance of $1,000: the largest check he had ever seen.

Then began the series of experiments which were to launch modern rocketry and perhaps to change the world's history. Almost nobody except those immediately engaged knew what these experiments were until the first Monday morning in January, 1920, when the Smithsonian Institution issued a news release on the work and simultaneously published the Worcester scientist's first paper on rockets: a modest 69-page monograph bound in brown paper, entitled *A Method of Reaching Extreme Altitudes*.

In his initial paper Goddard disclosed that he had put to rest the old fallacy that a rocket thrusts by "pushing against the air." He had shot rocket motors in partial vacuum, and obtained results equal to or even better than at atmospheric pressure. Likewise, he had tackled the problem of constructing dry-fuel motors separate from the powder charge, and had developed successful intermittent motors in which explosive pellets were inserted by a device working on the general principle of the machine gun. He ended the report with what was, for 1920, a startling conclusion that in theory at least it should be perfectly possible to shoot a rocket at such velocity that it would not return to the earth. With a total launching weight of only 8 or 10 tons, he estimated, a rocket could be constructed capable of carrying enough magnesium powder to create a flash—telescopically visible from the earth—against the dark side of the moon. It was this discussion of a possible moon-rocket, rather than the less spectacular but more practical work reflected by the rest of the book, that most forcefully reached the public. Newspaper readers across the continent were moved to excitement, comment and derision. The rocket came forth out of the history books and military museums and began to have the beginnings of a new world prominence—only this time with an ironic twist.

During the period when for the first time it was really undergoing something like genuine scientific development, the rocket was to become, to many unthinking people, a symbol of impractical ideas and fantastic schemes. Everyone who had to do with rockets during the next two decades was to be branded as "queer"; and rocketors were to inherit the mantle of ridicule previously worn by airplane pioneers.

In the meantime Goddard was going doggedly ahead, making and shooting rockets. After the publication of *A Method of Reaching Extreme Altitudes,* which dealt so optimistically with dry-fuel propellants, Goddard came to the conclusion that despite the convenience of these fuels they could not bring about the results he had in mind. Accordingly he gave them up and turned his attention to the problems of developing liquid-fuel rockets.

While dry-fuel rockets are simple to operate, their inability to travel very far or high makes them impractical for modern use

From 1920 until 1922 he made what are now known as proving-stand tests with liquid-fuel motors, trying liquid oxygen and various liquid fuels, including gasoline, liquefied propane and ether. He presently decided that liquid oxygen and gasoline made the most practical combination; virtually all of his subsequent liquid-fuel experiments were carried out with these liquids.

By 1923 Goddard had reached the point of contemplating an actual shot with a liquid-fuel rocket. But it was not until he had built and discarded two rockets that he constructed one he considered good enough to release for actual flight.

On March 16, 1926, he let it fly. This was the first actual shot of a liquid-fuel rocket anywhere in the world. It occurred at Auburn, Mass., on a cold, clear spring day. There was snow on the ground, a couple of inches or so. The experimenter and his assistants were heavily bundled up: Goddard in a huge double-breasted overcoat and a flat cloth cap. Though his associates wore their gloves, he went barehanded, his gloves crammed into the bulging pocket of his coat.

The only witnesses to that historic flight other than Dr. Goddard himself were Henry Sachs, machinist and instrument maker of the Clark University shop; Dr. P. M. Roope, assistant professor of physics at Clark, and Mrs. Goddard, who came along to take the pictures which later documented the report.

The rocket was an odd and fragile-looking contrivance. The motor, with its metal nozzle nearly as long as the cylindrical blast chamber, was mounted at the forward part of the rocket in a slender frame consisting of the fuel pipes, crossed by a bracing strut. The whole rocket was about 10 feet tall. The motor measured over all about 2 feet, and was separated from the fuel tanks to rearward by an air gap of 4 or 5 feet, bridged by the thin metal tubing that conducted the propellants.

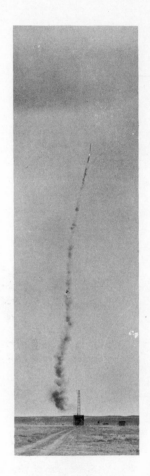

The purpose of this arrangement was to place the motor at the front, where Goddard then believed the thrust should be applied for the best stability in flight. The motor was ignited through a tube at the top, the ignition being supplied by an assistant equipped with a blowtorch on a six-foot pole. In pictures taken before the shot, the assistant is shown posing calmly with the blowtorch held at the ignition point. It is probable he was not quite so collected when the actual shot occurred, for the ignition period is a touchy moment in the launching of the rocket—if it is going to explode, it most likely will do so then.

Goddard's 1926 rocket did not explode. Instead, it took off with a loud roar, rose in a high trajectory, and flew for 2½ seconds, traveling a distance of 184 feet. Timing it with a stop watch, he calculated later that its average speed was 60 miles an hour.

Following this first shot, other short flights with liquid-fuel rockets were made at Auburn; all with such elaborate secrecy that nobody but the experimenter and his immediate circle knew what was going on. But rocket experimentation is hard to keep a secret; the rocket itself is a mighty self-advertiser. On July 17, 1929, Goddard shot a rocket of some size, big enough to carry a small barometer and a camera. It made noise in proportion. Someone who witnessed the flight from a distance mistook the rocket for a burning airplane and notified the police and fire departments.

Goddard was on the front pages of the newspapers again the next day; for the first time, virtually, since the publication of his *A Method of Reaching Extreme Altitudes.* This time the uses of publicity were to be proved to him in a most pleasant and exciting way. Col. Charles A. Lindbergh, then at the height of his popularity, read about Goddard's experiments and became interested. He communicated his interest to Daniel Guggenheim, who promptly made a grant of funds to put Goddard's work on a considerably more adequate financial basis.

When word came of the Guggenheim grant, the first job was to select a suitable site for the experiments. Goddard chose New Mexico, it being a country "of clear air, few storms, moderate winds and level terrain." The final decision fell upon the vicinity of Roswell, in the south, where there were good power and transportation facilities. The actual site was the Mescalero Ranch, where a shop was erected in September, 1930, large enough for himself and four assistants. A small tower 20 feet high was then built near the shop for static tests, equipped with heavy weights to keep the test rockets from rising out of the tower. A 60-foot launching tower previously used at Auburn was put up about 15 miles away from the shop, for the purpose of flight tests.

On December 30, 1930, the first flight of a rocket at the New Mexico site took place. The rocket was 11 feet long, and weighed a little over 33 pounds. It reached an altitude of 2,000 feet, and a maximum speed of 500 miles an hour.

The Wac Corporal was the first high-altitude rocket designed and built by the United States. Although it reached an altitude of 30 miles, use of the Wac Corporal was discontinued because if its inability to carry instruments

It was big, but it set no altitude record, for as Goddard later pointed out, his first objective was to produce a dependable rocket, not to see how high he could shoot. To this end he also began studying the problem of stabilizing the flight.

The first flight of a gyroscopically controlled rocket was made on April 19, 1932. In this rocket the steering vanes were forced into the blast of the rocket motor by gas pressure—the pressure, and therefore the amount of steering, being controlled by a small gyroscope. The scheme showed some signs of working, but was hardly a complete success.

When the original Guggenheim grant was made, it had been agreed to undertake the work in New Mexico for two years; then study the results with a view to a two-year extension.

The committee gravely studied Goddard's reports, and recommended the granting of funds for the two additional years. But the great depression was then on. Goddard went back to Clark University to resume his teaching. The Smithsonian Institution, loath to see the

Above, one of Goddard's early (1926) rockets, a liquid-propellant model with combustion chamber and nozzle at base, gasoline and oxygen tanks above. Below, loading a rocket for test flight

Mrs. Robert H. Goddard

research come to an end, made a small grant to permit some laboratory tests that did not require rocket flights. In the following year the Daniel and Florence Guggenheim Foundation came to the rescue, and work was resumed in New Mexico in 1934.

The job, now, as Goddard saw it, was to develop fully stabilized flight. In the beginning he tried a stabilizer operated by a pendulum.

Goddard's pendulum-controlled rocket rose about 1,000 feet, bellied over, flew horizontally for about 2 miles, and landed 11,000 feet from the launching tower. At one point the speed exceeded 700 miles an hour—or nearly the speed of sound.

Goddard next approached the stabilizer problem by returning to his first idea, a small gyroscope. With his gyro-control, a series of beautiful rocket shots was made, beginning March 8, 1935, when the gyro-rocket reached an altitude of 4,800 feet, flew a horizontal distance of 13,000 feet, and made a maximum speed of 550 miles an hour.

The equipment was gradually improved. A notable gyro-controlled flight was made on October 14, 1935, when the rocket rose 4,000 feet. On May 31, 1935, a gyro-rocket reached an altitude of 7,500 feet, or nearly a mile and a half. As in the previous experiments, Goddard was not attempting to set altitude marks in these shots, but was still concentrating on the complicated task of developing the apparatus to a state of reliable performance. His gyro-rockets weighed from 58 to 85 pounds at starting, and some were 10 to 15 feet in length.

Goddard concluded his last published report, in 1936, with the remark that the next step in the development of liquid-propellant rockets would be the reduction of weight to a minimum, a natural prelude to really high-altitude shots.

The principal disadvantage of modern rockets, which will undoubtedly be overcome in the near future, is that they lack accuracy beyond a certain range

"Some progress along this line," he dryly remarked, "has already been made." The exact nature of this progress was not then disclosed, but it is now known to have included the development of high-speed, high-efficiency, liquid-fuel pumps, in which, as in so many other matters, he anticipated the much more highly advertised accomplishments of the German rocket engineers.

Every single important development made in rockets during the war, including the basic design of long-range rockets such as the V-2, had been worked out before 1940 by Goddard, and was available to military men in this country.